**Oxford University Press 1994**

Oxford University Press, Walton Street, Oxford OX2 6DP

Oxford New York Toronto
Delhi Bombay Calcutta Madras Karachi
Kuala Lumpur Singapore Hong Kong Tokyo
Nairobi Dar es Salaam Cape Town
Melbourne Auckland Madrid

and associated companies in
Berlin Ibadan

Oxford is a trade mark of Oxford University Press

© **W. R. Pickering**

First published 1994

ISBN 0 19 914583 0

Typesetting, design and illustration by Hardlines, Charlbury, Oxford
Printed in Great Britain

# CONTENTS

## GENETICS AND GENETIC ENGINEERING

## INDEX

# Use of the light microscope

## PREPARATION FOR LIGHT MICROSCOPY

**FIXATION** — preserves material in a life-like condition with minimum distortion

**DEHYDRATION** — removes traces of water from the fixed material

**CLEARING** — removes dehydrating alcohol so that material is made transparent

**EMBEDDING** — supports the material so that it is firm enough for sectioning

**SECTIONING** — prepares slices of material which are thin enough to allow light to pass through

**STAINING** — improves contrast between different structures (most biological material is transparent)

**MOUNTING** — embeds and protects material so that it is suitable for viewing over a long period

**Methylene blue**
- nuclei stain blue

**Leishman's stain**
- blood cells stain pink
- white blood cell nuclei stain blue

**Safranin/light green**
- a plant cell stain
- cytoplasm and cellulose stain green
- nuclei and lignin stain red
- chloroplasts stain pink

**Haematoxylin/eosin**
- nuclei stain blue
- cytoplasm stains pink

**Feulgens stain**
- chromosomes during cell division stain purple

**Aniline blue**
- fungal hyphae and spores stain deep blue

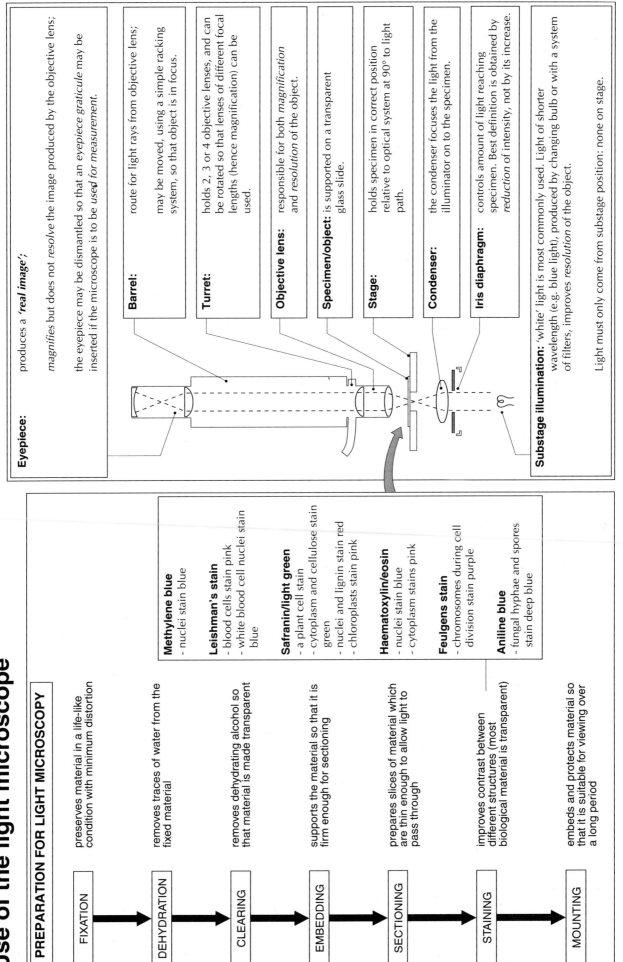

**Eyepiece:** produces a *'real image'*;

*magnifies* but does not *resolve* the image produced by the objective lens;

the eyepiece may be dismantled so that an *eyepiece graticule* may be inserted if the microscope is to be *used for measurement.*

**Barrel:** route for light rays from objective lens;

may be moved, using a simple racking system, so that object is in focus.

**Turret:** holds 2, 3 or 4 objective lenses, and can be rotated so that lenses of different focal lengths (hence magnification) can be used.

**Objective lens:** responsible for both *magnification* and *resolution* of the object.

**Specimen/object:** is supported on a transparent glass slide.

**Stage:** holds specimen in correct position relative to optical system at 90° to light path.

**Condenser:** the condenser focuses the light from the illuminator on to the specimen.

**Iris diaphragm:** controls amount of light reaching specimen. Best definition is obtained by *reduction* of intensity, not by its increase.

**Substage illumination:** 'white' light is most commonly used. Light of shorter wavelength (e.g. blue light), produced by changing bulb or with a system of filters, improves *resolution* of the object.

Light must only come from substage position: none on stage.

# Transmission electron microscope

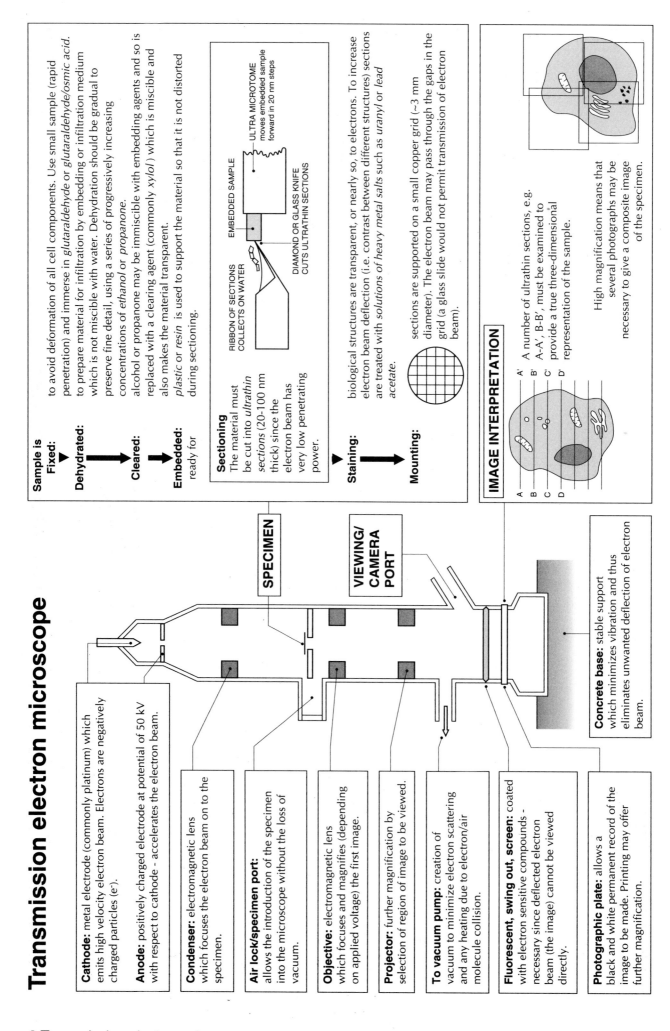

**Sample is Fixed:** to avoid deformation of all cell components. Use small sample (rapid penetration) and immerse in *glutaraldehyde or glutaraldehyde/osmic acid*.

**Dehydrated:** to prepare material for infiltration by embedding or infiltration medium which is not miscible with water. Dehydration should be gradual to preserve fine detail, using a series of progressively increasing concentrations of *ethanol or propanone*.

**Cleared:** alcohol or propanone may be immiscible with embedding agents and so is replaced with a clearing agent (commonly *xylol*) which is miscible and also makes the material transparent.

**Embedded:** ready for *plastic or resin* is used to support the material so that it is not distorted during sectioning.

**Sectioning**
The material must be cut into *ultrathin sections* (20-100 nm thick) since the electron beam has very low penetrating power.

ULTRA MICROTOME moves embedded sample forward in 20 nm steps

EMBEDDED SAMPLE

RIBBON OF SECTIONS COLLECTS ON WATER

DIAMOND OR GLASS KNIFE CUTS ULTRATHIN SECTIONS

**Staining:** biological structures are transparent, or nearly so, to electrons. To increase electron beam deflection (i.e. contrast between different structures) sections are treated with *solutions of heavy metal salts such as uranyl or lead acetate*.

**Mounting:** sections are supported on a small copper grid (~3 mm diameter). The electron beam may pass through the gaps in the grid (a glass slide would not permit transmission of electron beam).

## IMAGE INTERPRETATION

A'  A number of ultrathin sections, e.g.
B'  A-A', B-B', must be examined to
C'  provide a true three-dimensional
D'  representation of the sample.

A
B
C
D

High magnification means that several photographs may be necessary to give a composite image of the specimen.

**SPECIMEN**

**VIEWING/CAMERA PORT**

**Cathode:** metal electrode (commonly platinum) which emits high velocity electron beam. Electrons are negatively charged particles (e⁻).

**Anode:** positively charged electrode at potential of 50 kV with respect to cathode - accelerates the electron beam.

**Condenser:** electromagnetic lens which focuses the electron beam on to the specimen.

**Air lock/specimen port:** allows the introduction of the specimen into the microscope without the loss of vacuum.

**Objective:** electromagnetic lens which focuses and magnifies (depending on applied voltage) the first image.

**Projector:** further magnification by selection of region of image to be viewed.

**To vacuum pump:** creation of vacuum to minimize electron scattering and any heating due to electron/air molecule collision.

**Fluorescent, swing out, screen:** coated with electron sensitive compounds - necessary since deflected electron beam (the image) cannot be viewed directly.

**Photographic plate:** allows a black and white permanent record of the image to be made. Printing may offer further magnification.

**Concrete base:** stable support which minimizes vibration and thus eliminates unwanted deflection of electron beam.

# Physical properties of water

are explained by hydrogen bonding between the individual molecules

**High specific heat capacity** The specific heat capacity of water (the amount of heat, measured in joules, required to raise 1 kg of water through 1 °C) is very high: much of the heat absorbed is used to break the hydrogen bonds which hold the water molecules together.

**High latent heat of vaporization** Hydrogen bonds attract molecules of liquid water to one another and make it difficult for the molecules to escape as vapour: thus a relatively high energy input is necessary to vaporize water and water has a much higher boiling point than other molecules of the same size.

**Molecular mobility** The weakness of individual hydrogen bonds means that individual water molecules continually jostle one another when in the liquid phase.

**Cohesion and surface tension** Hydrogen bonding causes water molecules to 'stick together', and also to stick to other molecules - the phenomenon of *cohesion*. At the surface of a liquid the inwardly-acting cohesive forces produce a 'surface tension' as the molecules are particularly attracted to one another.

**Density and freezing properties** As water cools towards its freezing point the individual molecules slow down sufficiently for each one to form its maximum number of hydrogen bonds. To do this the water molecules in liquid water must move further apart to give enough space for all four hydrogen bonds to fit into. As a result water expands as it freezes, so that ice is less dense than liquid water and therefore floats upon its surface.

**Colloid formation** Some molecules have strong intramolecular forces which prevent their solution in water, but have charged surfaces which attract a covering of water molecules. This covering ensures that the molecules remain dispersed throughout the water, rather than forming large aggregates which could settle out. The dispersed particles and the liquid around them collectively form a *colloid*.

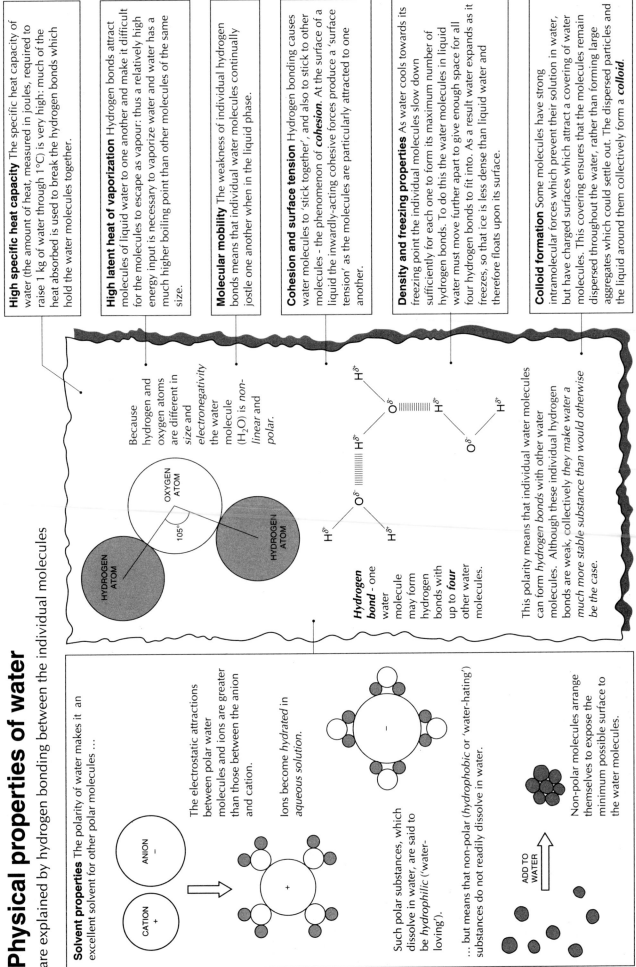

Because hydrogen and oxygen atoms are different in *size* and *electronegativity* the water molecule ($H_2O$) is *non-linear* and *polar*.

OXYGEN ATOM

HYDROGEN ATOM

HYDROGEN ATOM

105°

*Hydrogen bond* - one water molecule may form hydrogen bonds with up to *four* other water molecules.

This polarity means that individual water molecules can form *hydrogen bonds* with other water molecules. Although these individual hydrogen bonds are weak, collectively *they make water a much more stable substance than would otherwise be the case.*

**Solvent properties** The polarity of water makes it an excellent solvent for other polar molecules ...

The electrostatic attractions between polar water molecules and ions are greater than those between the anion and cation.

Ions become *hydrated* in aqueous solution.

CATION +

ANION −

Such polar substances, which dissolve in water, are said to be *hydrophilic* ('water-loving').

... but means that non-polar (*hydrophobic* or 'water-hating') substances do not readily dissolve in water.

ADD TO WATER

Non-polar molecules arrange themselves to expose the minimum possible surface to the water molecules.

# The biological importance of water depends on its physical properties

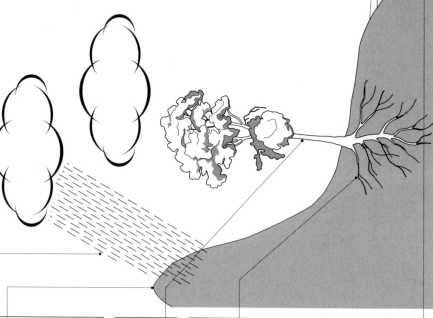

**Lubricant properties:** water's cohesive and adhesive properties mean that it is viscous, making it a useful lubricant in biological systems. For example, *synovial fluid* - lubricates many vertebrate joints; **pleural fluid** - minimizes friction between lungs and thoracic cage (ribs) during breathing; *mucus* - permits easy passage of faeces down the colon, and lubricates the penis and vagina during intercourse.

**Thermoregulation:** the high specific heat capacity of water means that bodies composed largely of water (cells are typically 70-80% water) are very thermostable, and thus less prone to heat damage by changes in environmental temperatures.

The high latent heat of vaporization of water means that a body can be considerably cooled with a minimal loss of water - this phenomenon is used extensively by mammals (sweating) and reptiles (gaping) and may be important in cooling transpiring leaves.

**Transparency:** water permits the passage of visible light. This means that photosynthesis (and associated food chains) is possible in relatively shallow aquatic environments.

**Volatility/stability:** is balanced at Earth's temperatures so that a water cycle of evaporation, transpiration and precipitation is maintained.

**Solvent properties:**
allow water to act as a transport medium for polar solutes. For example,
  movements of minerals to lakes and seas;
  transport via blood and lymph in multicellular animals;
  removal of metabolic wastes such as urea and ammonia in urine.

**Transpiration stream:** the continuous column of water is able to move up the xylem because of cohesion between water molecules and adhesion between water and the walls of the xylem vessels.

**Molecular mobility:** the rather weak nature of individual hydrogen bonds means that water molecules can move easily relative to one another - this allows *osmosis* (vital for uptake and movement of water) to take place.

**Expansion on freezing:** since ice floats it forms at the surface of ponds and lakes - it therefore insulates organisms in the water below it, and allows the ice to thaw rapidly when temperatures rise. Changes in density also maintain circulation in large bodies of water, thus helping nutrient cycling. Floating ice also means that penguins and polar bears have somewhere to stand!

**Supporting role:** the cohesive forces between water molecules mean that it is not easily compressed, and thus it is an excellent medium for support. Important biological examples include the *hydrostatic skeleton* (e.g. earthworm), *turgor pressure* (in herbaceous parts of plants), *amniotic fluid* (which supports and protects the mammalian foetus) and as a *general supporting medium* (particularly for large aquatic mammals such as whales).

**Metabolic functions**
Water is used directly ...
1. as a reagent (source of reducing power) in photosynthesis
2. to hydrolyse macromolecules to their subunits, in digestion for example.
... and is also the medium in which all biochemical reactions take place.

# Osmosis

Water molecules, like other molecules, are mobile. In pure water, or in solutions containing very few solute molecules, the water molecules can move very freely (they have a high **free kinetic energy**). As a result, many of the water molecules may cross the membrane, which is freely permeable to water.

**Partially permeable membrane** allows the free passage of some particles but is not freely permeable to others. Biological membranes are **freely permeable to water** but have **restricted permeability to solutes** such as sodium ions and glucose molecules, i.e. they are **selectively permeable.**

In a solution with many solute molecules the movement of the water molecules is restricted because of solute-water interactions. Fewer of the water molecules have a **free kinetic energy** which is great enough to enable them to cross the membrane.

Solute molecules cannot cross the membrane as freely or as rapidly as water molecules can.

MANY WATER MOLECULES CAN MOVE IN THIS DIRECTION

FEW WATER MOLECULES CAN MOVE IN THIS DIRECTION

THERE IS A NET MOVEMENT OF WATER MOLECULES IN THIS DIRECTION * .

➤ This movement of water depends on how many water molecules have sufficient free kinetic energy to 'escape from' the system

➤ so that any system in which the water molecules have a **high** average kinetic energy will have a greater tendency to lose water than will a system in which the water molecules have a **low** average kinetic energy

➤ and when describing water movements scientists replace the term **free kinetic energy** with the term **water potential**, so that

Water molecules **in a dilute solution** have a **high water potential**

Water molecules **in a concentrated solution** have a **low water potential**

\* Water moves down a **water potential gradient**

\* In the absence of a partially permeable membrane all water molecules would quickly attain the same free kinetic energy and there would be no water potential gradient.

**Osmosis is**
* **the movement of water**
* **down a water potential gradient**
* **across a partially permeable membrane**
* **to a solution with a more negative water potential.**

# Structural components of

## membranes permit fluidity, selective transport and recognition, integrity and compartmentalization.

Because of the different solubility properties of the two ends of phospholipid molecules …

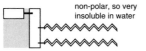

polar, so very soluble in water

non-polar, so very insoluble in water

… such molecules form a layer at a water surface

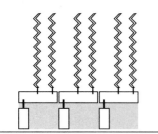

and a **phospholipid bilayer** can act as a barrier between two aqueous environments.

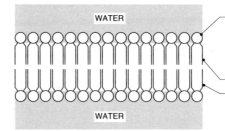

**Hydrophilic heads** point outwards: form hydrogen bonds with water

**Hydrophobic tails** point towards one another: this maximizes hydrophobic attractions and excludes water

**Lipid composition** influences membrane fluidity: unsaturated fatty acid tails are 'kinked', limit close packing of the hydrophobic tails and so **increase** fluidity, but cholesterol may interfere with lateral movement of hydrophobic tails and thus **reduce** membrane fluidity.

**Surface carbohydrates** (collectively the **glycocalyx)** are usually oligosaccharides which are positioned to aid in cell recognition functions.

**Diffusion across the lipid bilayer** is responsible for the movement of **small, uncharged molecules.**

Thus $O_2$, $H_2O$, $CO_2$, urea and ethanol cross rapidly (they 'squeeze between') the polar phospholipid heads then dissolve in the lipid on one side of the membrane and emerge on the other.

**Large** or **charged molecules** cannot cross the lipid bilayer.

Thus $Na^+$, $K^+$, $Cl^-$, $HCO_3^-$ and glucose do not cross in this way.

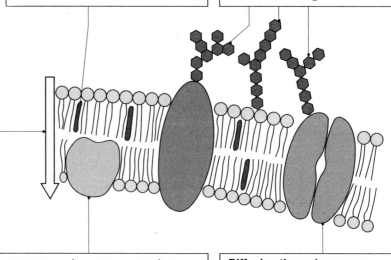

**Active transport** uses a **carrier protein** to transport a solute across a membrane but **energy is required** since transport may be **against a concentration gradient.** Typically ATP is hydrolysed and the binding of the phosphate group to the carrier changes the protein's conformation in such a way that the solute molecule is moved across the membrane.

**Facilitated diffusion** uses a **carrier protein** to transfer a molecule across a membrane **along** its electrochemical gradient. The binding of the solute alters the conformation of the carrier so that its position in the membrane changes and the solute molecule is discharged on the other side of the membrane. Glucose uptake by erythrocytes occurs in this way.
   N.B. There is **no requirement for ATP,** as there is **no energy consumption.**

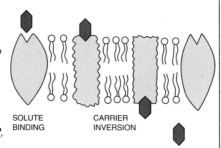

SOLUTE BINDING

CARRIER INVERSION

SOLUTE RELEASE AND CARRIER RETURN

**Diffusion through aqueous channels in pore proteins:** transmembrane proteins may have aqueous channels through which charged molecules may pass and thus avoid the hydrophobic tails of the phospholipid molecules.

$Na^+$

Some channels are open all of the time, but others are **gated** (they open and close only in response to a stimulus, such as a change in the membrane's electrical potential). Such **gated channels** are vital to the operation of nerve and muscle, where movements of $Na^+$, $K^+$ and $Ca^{2+}$ initiate information transfer.

# Animal cell ultrastructure

**Peroxisome** is one of the group of vesicles known as *microbodies*. Each of them contains oxidative enzymes such as *catalase*, and they are particularly important in delaying cell ageing.

**Centrioles** are a pair of structures, held at right angles to one another, which act as organizers of the nuclear spindle in preparation for the separation of chromosomes or chromatids during nuclear division.

**Secretory vesicle** undergoing exocytosis. May be carrying a synthetic product of the cell (such as a protein packaged at the Golgi body) or the products of degradation by lysosomes. Secretory vesicles are abundant in cells with a high synthetic activity, such as the cells of the *Islets of Langerhans*.

**Smooth endoplasmic reticulum** is a series of flattened sacs and sheets that are the sites of synthesis of steroids and lipids.

**Rough endoplasmic reticulum** is so-called because of the many ribosomes attached to its surface. This intracellular membrane system aids cell compartmentalization and transports proteins synthesized at the ribosomes towards the Golgi bodies for secretory packaging.

**Golgi apparatus** consists of a stack of sacs called *cisternae*. It modifies a number of cell products delivered to it, often enclosing them in vesicles to be secreted. Such products include trypsinogen (from *pancreatic acinar cells*), insulin (from *beta-cells of the Islets of Langerhans*) and mucin (from **goblet cells in the trachea**). The Golgi is also involved in lipid modification in cells of the ileum, and plays a part in the formation of lysosomes.

**Plasmalemma (plasmamembrane)** is the surface of the cell and represents its contact with its environment. It is differentially permeable and regulates the movement of solutes between the cell and its environment. There are many specializations of the membrane, often concerning its protein content.

**Microfilaments** are threads of the protein *actin*. They are usually situated in bundles just beneath the cell surface and play a role in endo- and exocytosis, and possibly in cell motility.

**Cytoplasm** is principally water, with many solutes including glucose, proteins and ions. It is permeated by the *cytoskeleton*, which is the main architectural support of the cell.

**Microvilli** are extensions of the plasmamembrane which increase the cell surface area. They are commonly abundant in cells with a high absorptive capacity, such as *hepatocytes* or cells of the *first coiled tubule of the nephron*. Collectively the microvilli represent a *brush border* to the cell.

**Lysosomes** are sacs that contain high concentrations of hydrolytic (digestive) enzymes. These enzymes are kept apart from the cell contents which they would otherwise destroy, and they are kept inactive by an alkaline environment within the lysosome. They are especially abundant in cells with a high phagocytic activity, such as some *leukocytes*.

**Free ribosomes** are the sites of protein synthesis, principally for proteins destined for intracellular use. There may be 50 000 or more in a typical eukaryote cell.

**Endocytic vesicle** may contain molecules or structures too large to cross the membrane by active transport or diffusion.

**Microtubules** are hollow tubes of the protein *tubulin*, about 25 nm in diameter. They are involved in intracellular transport (e.g. the movement of mitochondria), have a structural role as part of the cytoskeleton and are components of other specialized structures such as the centrioles and the basal bodies of cilia and flagella.

**Nucleus** is the centre of the regulation of cell activities since it contains the hereditary material, DNA, carrying the information for protein synthesis. The DNA is bound up with histone protein to form chromatin. The nucleus contains one or more nucleoli in which ribosome subunits, ribosomal RNA, and transfer RNA are manufactured. The nucleus is surrounded by a double nuclear membrane, crossed by a number of nuclear pores. The nucleus is continuous with the endoplasmic reticulum. There is usually only one nucleus per cell, although there may be many in very large cells such as those of striated (skeletal) muscle. Such multinucleate cells are called coenocytes.

**Mitochondrion** (pl. mitochondria) is the site of aerobic respiration. Mitochondria have a highly folded inner membrane which supports the proteins of the electron transport chain responsible for the synthesis of ATP by oxidative phosphorylation. The mitochondrial matrix contains the enzymes of the TCA cycle, an important metabolic 'hub'. These organelles are abundant in cells which are physically (*skeletal muscle*) and metabolically (*hepatocytes*) active.

# Typical plant cell
**contains chloroplasts and a permanent vacuole, and is surrounded by a cellulose cell wall.**

**Plasmodesmata** are minute strands of cytoplasm which pass through pores in the cell wall and connect the protoplasts of adjacent cells. This represents the *symplast* pathway for the movement of water and solutes throughout the plant body. These cell-cell cytoplasm connections are important in cell survival during periods of drought. The E.R. of adjacent cells is also in contact through these strands.

**Cell wall** is composed of long cellulose molecules grouped in bundles called *microfibrils* which, in turn, are twisted into rope-like *macrofibrils*. The macrofibrils are embedded in a matrix of *pectins* (which are very adhesive) and *hemicelluloses* (which are quite fluid). There may be a *secondary cell wall*, in which case the outer covering of the cell is arranged as:

Plasmalemma

Secondary cell wall: laid down on inside of primary wall. Often impregnated with *lignin* (gives mechanical strength to xylem) or *suberin* (waterproofs endodermis).

Primary cell wall: laid down first, by plasmamembrane.

Middle lamella: contains gums and calcium pectate to cement cells together.

The function of the cell wall is a mechanical one - pressure from the cell protoplast maintains cell turgidity. The wall is freely permeable to water and most solutes so that the cell wall represents an important transport route - the *apoplast system* - throughout the plant body.

**Rough endoplasmic reticulum** is the site of protein synthesis (on the attached ribosomes), storage and preparation for secretion. The endoplasmic reticulum (E.R.) also plays a part in the compartmentalization of the cell.

**Nucleus** is surrounded by the nuclear envelope and contains the genetic material, DNA, associated with histone protein to form chromatin. The nucleus thus controls the activity of the cell through its regulation of protein synthesis. The nucleolus is the site of synthesis of transfer RNA, ribosomal RNA, and ribosomal subunits.

**Mitochondrion** contains the enzyme systems for ATP synthesis by oxidative phosphorylation. May be abundant in sieve tube companion cells, root epidermal cells and dividing meristematic cells.

**Golgi body (dictyosome)** synthesizes polysaccharides and packages them in vesicles which migrate to the plasmamembrane for eventual incorporation in the cell wall.

**Smooth endoplasmic reticulum** is the site of lipid synthesis and secretion.

**Chloroplast** is the site of photosynthesis. It is one of a number of plastids, all of which develop from *proplastids* which are small, pale green or colourless organelles.

Other typical plastids of complex cells are *chromoplasts* which may develop from chloroplasts by internal rearrangements. Chromoplasts are coloured due to the presence of carotenoid pigments and are most abundant in cells of flower petals or fruit skins.

**Leucoplasts** are a third type of plastid common in cells of higher plants - they include *amyloplasts* which synthesize and store starches and *elaioplasts* which synthesize oils.

**Vacuole** may occupy 90% of the volume of a mature plant cell. It is filled with cell sap (a solution of salts, sugars and organic acids) and helps to maintain turgor pressure inside the cell. The vacuole also contains anthocyanins, pigments responsible for many of the red, blue and purple colours of flowers. Vacuoles also contains enzymes involved in recycling of cell components such as chloroplasts. The vacuolar membrane is called the *tonoplast*.

**Microtubules** are hollow structures (about 25 nm in diameter) composed of the protein tubulin. They occur just below the plasmamembrane where they may aid the addition of cellulose to the cell wall. They are also involved in the cytoplasmic streaming of organelles such as Golgi bodies and chloroplasts, and they form the spindles and cell plates of dividing cells.

**Plasmamembrane (plasmalemma, cell surface membrane)** is the differentially-permeable cell surface, responsible for the control of solute movements between the cell and its environment. It is flexible enough to move close to or away from the cell wall as the water content of the cytoplasm changes. The membrane is also responsible for the synthesis and assembly of cell wall components.

# Cell membrane systems are important in intracellular division of labour. They allow compartmentalization and therefore efficiency through locations of multi-enzyme pathways.

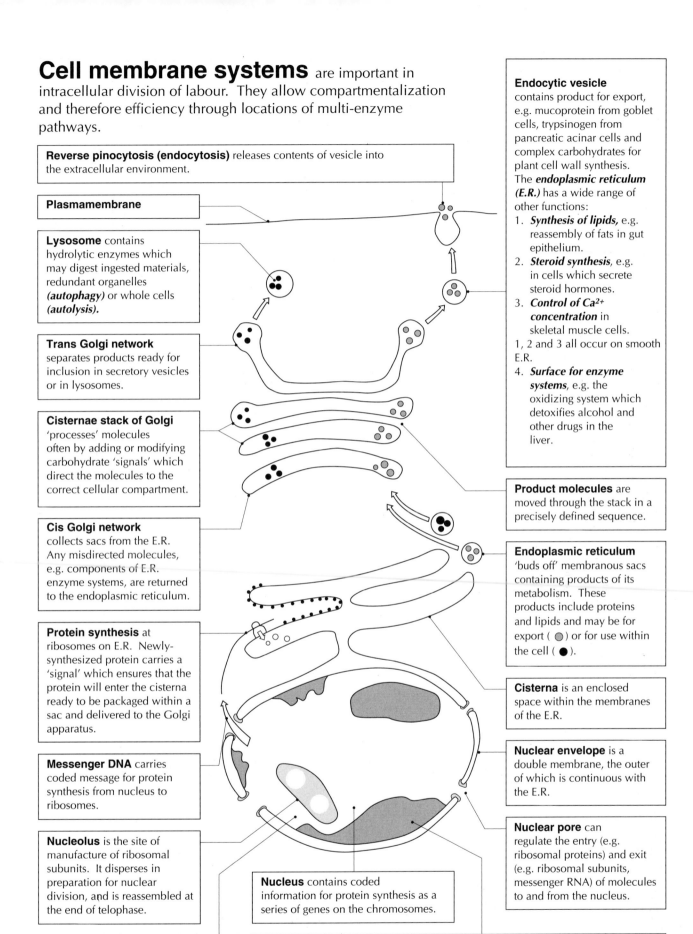

**Reverse pinocytosis (endocytosis)** releases contents of vesicle into the extracellular environment.

**Plasmamembrane**

**Lysosome** contains hydrolytic enzymes which may digest ingested materials, redundant organelles *(autophagy)* or whole cells *(autolysis).*

**Trans Golgi network** separates products ready for inclusion in secretory vesicles or in lysosomes.

**Cisternae stack of Golgi** 'processes' molecules often by adding or modifying carbohydrate 'signals' which direct the molecules to the correct cellular compartment.

**Cis Golgi network** collects sacs from the E.R. Any misdirected molecules, e.g. components of E.R. enzyme systems, are returned to the endoplasmic reticulum.

**Protein synthesis** at ribosomes on E.R. Newly-synthesized protein carries a 'signal' which ensures that the protein will enter the cisterna ready to be packaged within a sac and delivered to the Golgi apparatus.

**Messenger DNA** carries coded message for protein synthesis from nucleus to ribosomes.

**Nucleolus** is the site of manufacture of ribosomal subunits. It disperses in preparation for nuclear division, and is reassembled at the end of telophase.

**Nucleoplasm** contains a variety of solutes, including nucleoside triphosphates for DNA synthesis, and the enzyme complex (DNA polymerase) which regulates DNA replication and repair.

**Endocytic vesicle** contains product for export, e.g. mucoprotein from goblet cells, trypsinogen from pancreatic acinar cells and complex carbohydrates for plant cell wall synthesis. The *endoplasmic reticulum (E.R.)* has a wide range of other functions:
1. *Synthesis of lipids,* e.g. reassembly of fats in gut epithelium.
2. *Steroid synthesis*, e.g. in cells which secrete steroid hormones.
3. *Control of $Ca^{2+}$ concentration* in skeletal muscle cells.
1, 2 and 3 all occur on smooth E.R.
4. *Surface for enzyme systems*, e.g. the oxidizing system which detoxifies alcohol and other drugs in the liver.

**Product molecules** are moved through the stack in a precisely defined sequence.

**Endoplasmic reticulum** 'buds off' membranous sacs containing products of its metabolism. These products include proteins and lipids and may be for export ( ◎ ) or for use within the cell ( ● ).

**Cisterna** is an enclosed space within the membranes of the E.R.

**Nuclear envelope** is a double membrane, the outer of which is continuous with the E.R.

**Nuclear pore** can regulate the entry (e.g. ribosomal proteins) and exit (e.g. ribosomal subunits, messenger RNA) of molecules to and from the nucleus.

**Nucleus** contains coded information for protein synthesis as a series of genes on the chromosomes.

**Chromatin** is the genetic material, containing the coded information for protein synthesis in the cell. It is composed of DNA bound to basic proteins called *histones.* The DNA and histone are organized into *nucleosomes.* During nuclear division the chromatin condenses to form the *chromosomes,* and the chromatin containing DNA which is being 'expressed' (transcribed into mRNA) becomes visible as more loosely-coiled threads called *euchromatin.*

# A prokaryotic cell (e.g. a bacterium) has no true organelles.

**Genetic material** is composed of a circle of double-stranded DNA *which is not enclosed within a nuclear membrane.* There are typically about 2000 genes, about 0.2% of the number found in a eukaryotic cell.

**Ribosomes** smaller than those in eukaryotes. They are scattered throughout the cytoplasm, not supported on an endoplasmic reticulum.

**Plasmamembrane** is a typical phospholipid bilayer.

**Food stores** are typically lipid globules or glycogen granules.

**Flagellum** is responsible for motility of many bacteria. It is much simpler than the flagellum of a eukaryotic cell, being composed of a single cylinder of protein subunits (flagellin). The flagellum does not 'beat' but instead rotates about a 'bearing' anchored in the cell wall to produce a corkscrew motion which drives the cell along.

ROTOR   BEARING   PLASMA MEMBRANE   CELL WALL   FLAGELLAR FILAMENT

**Mesosomes** are infoldings of the plasma membrane on which the enzymes associated with respiration are located. A proton gradient generated across these membranes is used to drive the synthesis of ATP.

SCALE |—| 0.1μm

**Photosynthetic membranes** are surfaces for light-absorbing pigments, principally *bacteriochlorophyll*, in green (e.g. *Chlorobium*) and purple (e.g. *Chromatium*) bacteria. N.B. Bacterial photosynthesis does not evolve oxygen.

**Capsule** is a gummy layer of mucilage which may unite bacteria into colonies (e.g. *Bacillus anthracis*) or confer protection (e.g. rough strain of *D. pneumoniae*).

**Plasmids** are short pieces of circular DNA which replicate independently of the cell genome. They have been widely exploited in recombinant DNA technology.

**Pili (or fimbriae)** are protein rods concerned with cell-cell attachment. The *sex pilus* is involved in DNA transfer during sexual reproduction.

**Cell wall** has a rigid framework of *murein*, a polysaccharide cross-linked by peptide chains. In *gram-positive* bacteria the wall is thickened with further polysaccharide and protein deposits, whilst in *gram-negative* bacteria the wall is thinner but coated with a lipid layer which provides protection against *lysozyme* and *penicillin*. The rigidity of the cell wall prevents osmotic damage (penicillin interferes with this in susceptible gram-positive bacteria) and confers shape on the cell. The three most common shapes are:

COCCUS   BACILLUS (ROD)   SPIRILLUM (HELICAL)

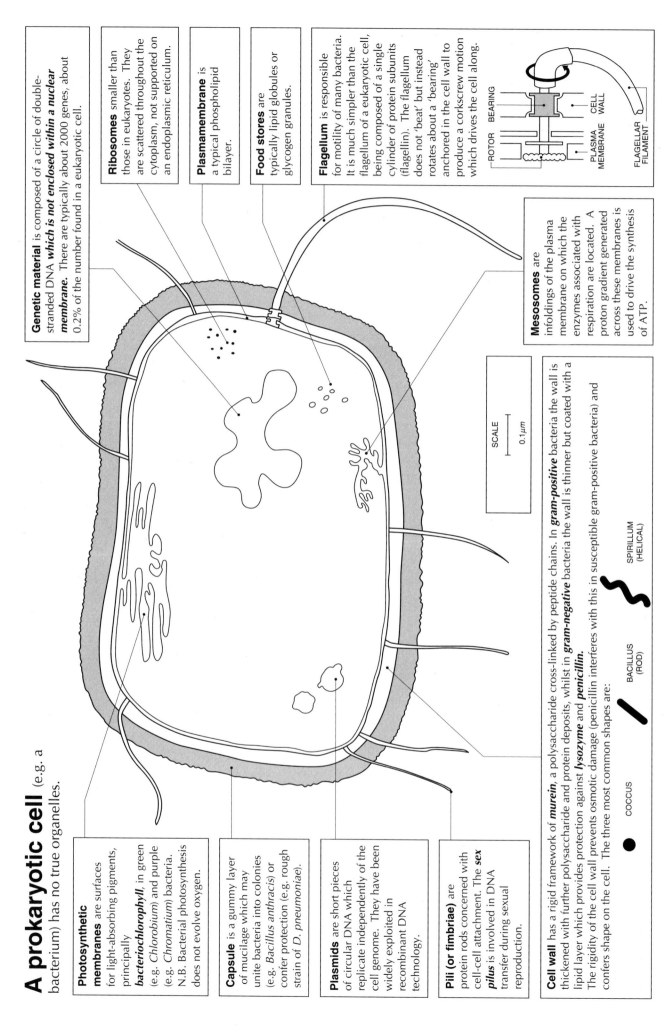

# Lipid structure and function

**TRUE LIPIDS** are esters of fatty acids and alcohols, formed by condensation reactions. Many of their properties result from their insolubility in water.

Since the hydrocarbon chains are long (19 C in arachidonic acid) most of the weight of the triglyceride is fatty acid.

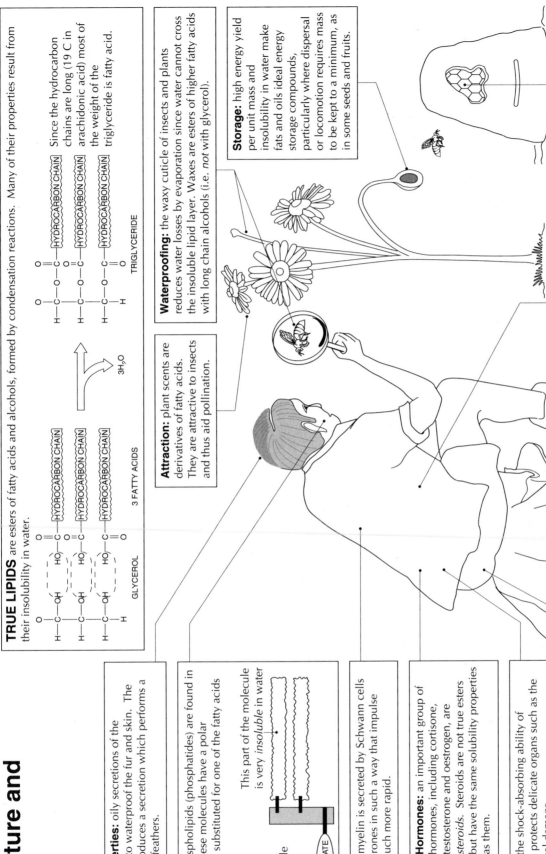

GLYCEROL    3 FATTY ACIDS

TRIGLYCERIDE

$3H_2O$

**Attraction:** plant scents are derivatives of fatty acids. They are attractive to insects and thus aid pollination.

**Waterproofing:** the waxy cuticle of insects and plants reduces water losses by evaporation since water cannot cross the insoluble lipid layer. Waxes are esters of higher fatty acids with long chain alcohols (i.e. *not* with glycerol).

**Storage:** high energy yield per unit mass and insolubility in water make fats and oils ideal energy storage compounds, particularly where dispersal or locomotion requires mass to be kept to a minimum, as in some seeds and fruits.

**Honeycomb:** bees use wax in constructing their larval chambers.

**Nutrition:** both bile acids and vitamin D (involved in fat digestion and $Ca^{2+}$ absorption respectively) are manufactured from steroids.

**Water-repellent properties:** oily secretions of the sebaceous glands help to waterproof the fur and skin. The preen gland of birds produces a secretion which performs a similar function on the feathers.

**Cell membranes:** phospholipids (phosphatides) are found in all cell membranes. These molecules have a polar 'phosphate-base' group substituted for one of the fatty acids in a triglyceride.

This part of the molecule is very *insoluble* in water

This part of the molecule is very *soluble* in water

ORGANIC BASE    PHOSPHATE

**Electrical insulation:** myelin is secreted by Schwann cells and insulates some neurones in such a way that impulse transmission is made much more rapid.

**Hormones:** an important group of hormones, including cortisone, testosterone and oestrogen, are *steroids*. Steroids are not true esters but have the same solubility properties as them.

BASIC STEROID NUCLEUS

**Physical protection:** the shock-absorbing ability of subcutaneous fat stores protects delicate organs such as the kidneys from mechanical damage.

**Thermal insulation:** fats conduct heat very poorly - subcutaneous fat stores help heat retention in endothermic animals. Incompressible blubber is an important insulator in diving mammals.

# Functions of soluble carbohydrates include transport, protection, recognition and energy release.

In naturally occurring **disaccharides** monosaccharide rings are joined together by *glycosidic bonds*.

$H_2O$

This most usually occurs between *aldehyde or keto group* (i.e. the reducing group) of one monosaccharide and an *hydroxyl group* of another monosaccharide.

e.g. *lactose*

LACTOSE IS A REDUCING DISACCHARIDE

Reducing group of glucose = carbonyl group (C=O)

GALACTOSE — GLUCOSE

Hydroxyl group on $C_4$ of glucose

Reducing group of galactose

(*Maltose* is a reducing disaccharide formed from two molecules of adjacent monosaccharides,

or, more rarely, between *reducing groups of adjacent monosaccharides*,

e.g. *sucrose*

SUCROSE IS A NON-REDUCING DISACCHARIDE

GLUCOSE — FRUCTOSE

Reducing groups are joined

**Sucrose** (*glucose-fructose*) is the main transport compound in plants. Commonly extracted from sugar cane and sugar beet and used as a sweetener.

TATE & LYLE

SEMI SKIM

**Lactose** (*glucose-galactose*) is the carbohydrate source for suckling mammals - milk is about 5% lactose.

**Maltose** (*glucose-glucose*) is a respiratory substrate in germinating seeds.

---

**Glucose** is the most common substrate for respiration (energy release).
**Fructose** is a constituent of nectar and sweetens fruits to attract animals and aid seed dispersal.

**Glucose and fructose** are both *monosaccharides* (single sugar units) with the typical formula $C_nH_{2n}O_n$. They each have *six carbon atoms* and are thus called *hexoses* (*pentoses* have 5 carbon atoms and *trioses* have 3). *Glucose* and *fructose* are isomers of $C_6H_{12}O_6$.

α-FRUCTOSE

α-GLUCOSE

---

**Sugar derivatives** include *sugar alcohols*, e.g. glycerol, *sugar acids*, e.g. ascorbic acid, and *mucopolysaccharides*, which are important components of connective tissues, synovial fluid, cartilage and bone. Heparin (anticoagulant in blood) is derived from mucopolysaccharides and has a protective function.

BATS LIKE IT RUNNY!

**Oligosaccharides** are short (often 6-12 units) condensation products which combine with protein (*glycoprotein*) or lipid (*glycolipid*) and form the outer coat (*glycocalyx*) of animal cells. They are important in cell-cell recognition and the *immune response*.

INVADER

---

Other important roles are in the *electron carriers* NAD, FAD and NADP and as the 'energy currency'.

ATP

ADENINE

P P P

**Ribose** and **deoxyribose** are constituents of *nucleotides*

ORGANIC BASE

P

CHAIN OF NUCLEOTIDES

which are the subunits of *nucleic acids* (e.g. DNA).

**Ribulose bis phosphate** is the *acceptor of $CO_2$ in the Calvin Cycle.*

$CO_2$

RuBP

CALVIN CYCLE 'FIXES' $CO_2$

TRIOSE SUGAR

# Polysaccharides

are polymers formed by glycosidic bonding of monosaccharide subunits

**Cellulose** is a polymer of glucose linked by β 1,4 glycosidic bonds. The β-conformation inverts successive monosaccharide units so that a straight chain polymer is formed.

β 1,4 GLYCOSIDIC BONDS

The parallel polysaccharide chains are then cross-linked by *hydrogen bonds*.

Hydrogen bonds

This cross-linking prevents access by water, so that cellulose is very resistant to hydrolysis and is therefore an excellent *structural molecule* (cellulose cell walls): ideal in plants which can readily synthesize excess carbohydrate.

**Chitin** is another β 1,4 *polymer* - the subunits in this case are amino derivatives of β-glucose called *N-acetylglucosamine*. It is another *structural molecule* abundant in arthropod exoskeletons and in fungal cell walls.

α-GLUCOSE

**Glycogen** is an α-glucose polymer, very similar to amylopectin but with very many more cross-links and shorter α 1,4 chains. This is appropriate to animal cells which may need to hydrolyse food reserves more rapidly than plant cells would do.

**Starch** is a mixture of two polymers of α-glucose: *amylose* typically contains about 300 glucose units joined by α 1,4 *glycosidic bonds*

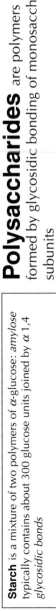

The bulky –CH₂OH side chains cause the molecule to adopt a helical shape (excellent for packing many subunits into a limited space).

Amylose helix (6 glucose units in each turn)

α-glucose molecules

**Amylopectin** is a branched chain, containing up to 1500 glucose subunits, in which α 1,4 chains are cross-linked by α 1,6 *glycosidic bonds*.

α 1,6 GLYCOSIDIC BOND

Because there are so few 'ends' within the starch molecule there are few points to begin hydrolysis by the enzyme *amylase*. Starch is therefore an excellent long-term *storage compound*.

# Levels of protein structure

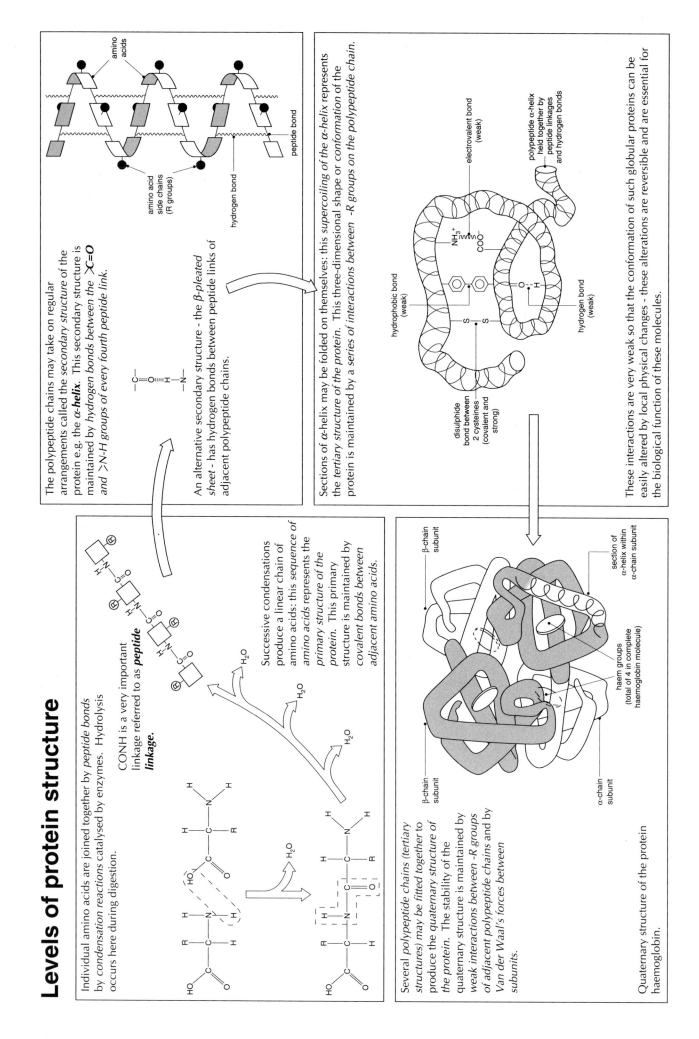

The polypeptide chains may take on regular arrangements called the *secondary structure* of the protein e.g. the *α-helix*. This secondary structure is maintained by *hydrogen bonds between the >C=O and >N-H groups of every fourth peptide link.*

An alternative secondary structure - the *β-pleated sheet* - has hydrogen bonds between peptide links of adjacent polypeptide chains.

amino acids

amino acid side chains (R groups)

hydrogen bond

peptide bond

Sections of α-helix may be folded on themselves: this *supercoiling of the α-helix represents the tertiary structure of the protein.* This three-dimensional shape or *conformation* of the protein is maintained by *a series of interactions between -R groups on the polypeptide chain.*

electrovalent bond (weak)

hydrophobic bond (weak)

disulphide bond between 2 cysteines (covalent and strong)

hydrogen bond (weak)

polypeptide α-helix held together by peptide linkages and hydrogen bonds

These interactions are very weak so that the conformation of such globular proteins can be easily altered by local physical changes - these alterations are reversible and are essential for the biological function of these molecules.

Individual amino acids are joined together by *peptide bonds* by *condensation* reactions catalysed by enzymes. Hydrolysis occurs here during digestion.

CONH is a very important linkage referred to as **peptide linkage.**

Successive condensations produce a linear chain of amino acids: this *sequence of amino acids represents the primary structure of the protein.* This primary structure is maintained by *covalent bonds between adjacent amino acids.*

Several *polypeptide chains (tertiary structures) may be fitted together to produce the quaternary structure of the protein.* The stability of the quaternary structure is maintained by *weak interactions between -R groups of adjacent polypeptide chains and by Van der Waal's forces between subunits.*

β-chain subunit

α-chain subunit

haem groups (total of 4 in complete haemoglobin molecule)

section of α-helix within α-chain subunit

Quaternary structure of the protein haemoglobin.

# Functions of proteins

include transport, catalysis, protection, storage, sensitivity, structure and co-ordination.

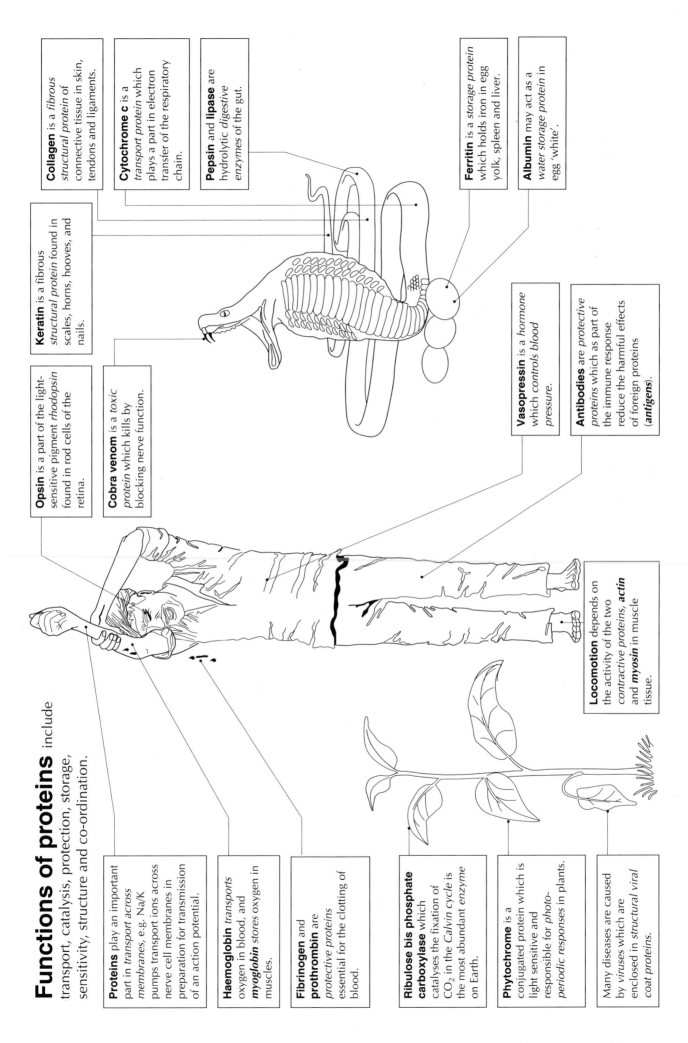

**Collagen** is a *fibrous structural protein* of connective tissue in skin, tendons and ligaments.

**Cytochrome c** is a *transport protein* which plays a part in electron transfer of the respiratory chain.

**Pepsin** and **lipase** are hydrolytic *digestive enzymes* of the gut.

**Ferritin** is a *storage protein* which holds iron in egg yolk, spleen and liver.

**Albumin** may act as a *water storage protein* in egg 'white'.

**Keratin** is a fibrous *structural protein* found in scales, horns, hooves, and nails.

**Opsin** is a part of the light-sensitive pigment *rhodopsin* found in rod cells of the retina.

**Cobra venom** is a *toxic protein* which kills by blocking nerve function.

**Vasopressin** is a *hormone* which *controls blood pressure*.

**Antibodies** are *protective proteins* which as part of the immune response reduce the harmful effects of foreign proteins (**antigens**).

**Proteins** play an important part in *transport across membranes*, e.g. Na/K pumps transport ions across nerve cell membranes in preparation for transmission of an action potential.

**Haemoglobin** *transports oxygen in blood*, and **myoglobin** *stores oxygen in muscles*.

**Fibrinogen** and **prothrombin** are *protective proteins* essential for the clotting of blood.

**Ribulose bis phosphate carboxylase** which catalyses the fixation of $CO_2$ in the *Calvin cycle* is the most abundant enzyme on Earth.

**Phytochrome** is a conjugated protein which is light sensitive and responsible for *photo-periodic responses* in plants.

Many diseases are caused by *viruses* which are enclosed in *structural viral coat proteins*.

**Locomotion** depends on the activity of the two *contractive proteins*, **actin** and **myosin** in muscle tissue.

# Testing for biochemicals

**Aqueous solution, suspension or extract of test substance**

Remove a 2 cm³ sample

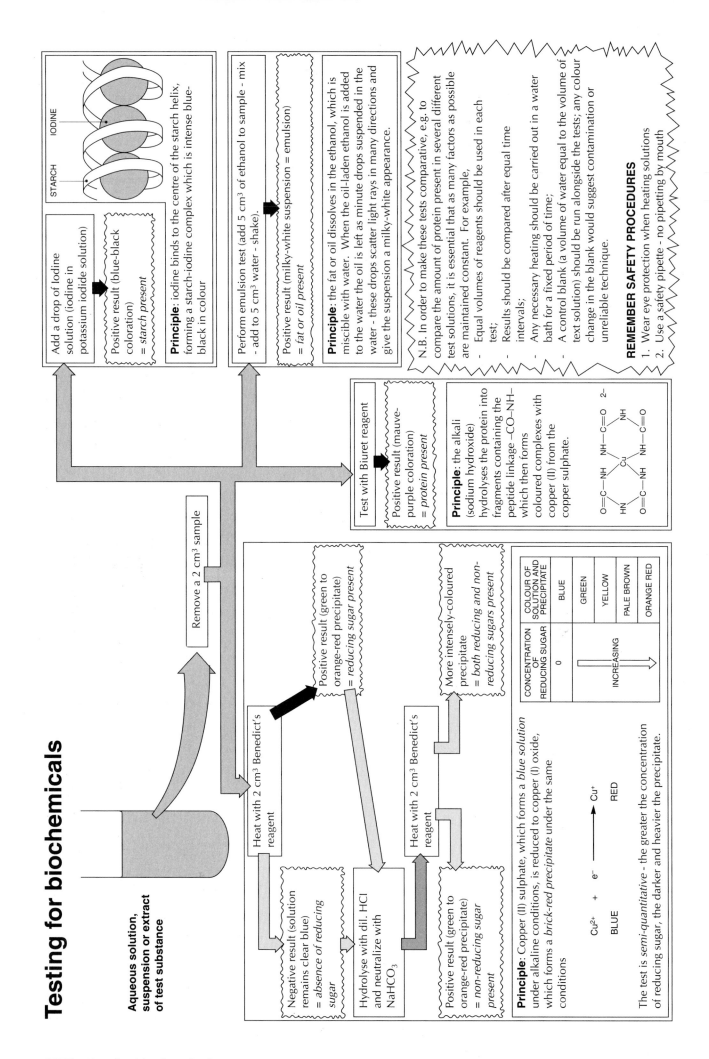

Add a drop of Iodine solution (iodine in potassium iodide solution)

Positive result (blue-black coloration) = *starch present*

**Principle**: iodine binds to the centre of the starch helix, forming a starch-iodine complex which is intense blue-black in colour

Perform emulsion test (add 5 cm³ of ethanol to sample - mix - add to 5 cm³ water - shake).

Positive result (milky-white suspension = emulsion) = *fat or oil present*

**Principle**: the fat or oil dissolves in the ethanol, which is miscible with water. When the oil-laden ethanol is added to the water the oil is left as minute drops suspended in the water - these drops scatter light rays in many directions and give the suspension a milky-white appearance.

N.B. In order to make these tests comparative, e.g. to compare the amount of protein present in several different test solutions, it is essential that as many factors as possible are maintained constant. For example,
- Equal volumes of reagents should be used in each test;
- Results should be compared after equal time intervals;
- Any necessary heating should be carried out in a water bath for a fixed period of time;
- A control blank (a volume of water equal to the volume of test solution) should be run alongside the tests; any colour change in the blank would suggest contamination or unreliable technique.

**REMEMBER SAFETY PROCEDURES**
1. Wear eye protection when heating solutions
2. Use a safety pipette - no pipetting by mouth

Test with Biuret reagent

Positive result (mauve-purple coloration) = *protein present*

**Principle**: the alkali (sodium hydroxide) hydrolyses the protein into fragments containing the peptide linkage –CO–NH– which then forms coloured complexes with copper (II) from the copper sulphate.

Heat with 2 cm³ Benedict's reagent

Positive result (green to orange-red precipitate) = *reducing sugar present*

Negative result (solution remains clear blue) = *absence of reducing sugar*

Hydrolyse with dil. HCl and neutralize with NaHCO₃

Positive result (green to orange-red precipitate) = *non-reducing sugar present*

Heat with 2 cm³ Benedict's reagent

More intensely-coloured precipitate = *both reducing and non-reducing sugars present*

**Principle**: Copper (II) sulphate, which forms a *blue solution* under alkaline conditions, is reduced to copper (I) oxide, which forms a *brick-red precipitate* under the same conditions

$$Cu^{2+} + e^- \longrightarrow Cu^+$$
BLUE          RED

The test is *semi-quantitative* - the greater the concentration of reducing sugar, the darker and heavier the precipitate.

| CONCENTRATION OF REDUCING SUGAR | COLOUR OF SOLUTION AND PRECIPITATE |
|---|---|
| 0 | BLUE |
| INCREASING | GREEN |
| | YELLOW |
| | PALE BROWN |
| | ORANGE RED |

# Catalysis by enzymes

An important step in enzyme catalysis is substrate binding to the active sites.

Enzymes form *enzyme-substrate complexes which reduce the activation energy for reactions which they catalyse.*

Consider the reaction: SUBSTRATE (S) $\longrightarrow$ PRODUCT (P)

which can be illustrated by a *reaction profile.*

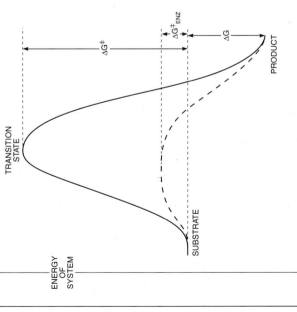

TRANSITION STATE

$\Delta G^{\ddagger}$

$\Delta G^{\ddagger}_{ENZ}$

$\Delta G$

ENERGY OF SYSTEM

SUBSTRATE

PRODUCT

PROGRESS OF REACTION

## Effect of enzyme on activation energy

For a reaction S⇌P the rate of the forward reaction depends on temperature and activation energy (difference in free energy between substrate and transition state, $\Delta G^{\ddagger}$). The reaction rate is proportional to the number of molecules which have an energy $\geq \Delta G^{\ddagger}$. *Enzymes act as catalysts by providing alternative reaction pathways in which $\Delta G^{\ddagger}$'s lower than it otherwise would be.* Heat cannot be used by cells to increase rates of reaction because of possible denaturation.

$$E + S \rightleftharpoons E\overline{\cdot}S \rightleftharpoons E + P$$

ENZYME-SUBSTRATE COMPLEX

---

## Stereospecificity: relationship of substrate(s) to active site

*Emil Fischer's lock and key hypothesis suggested that the active site and the substrate were exactly complementary*

SUBSTRATE

ENZYME

ENZYME-SUBSTRATE COMPLEX

*but more recent work allowed Koshland to propose the induced fit hypothesis which suggests that active site and substrate are only fully complementary after the substrate is bound.*

SUBSTRATE

ENZYME

ENZYME-SUBSTRATE COMPLEX

This latter process of *dynamic recognition* is now the more widely accepted hypothesis.

---

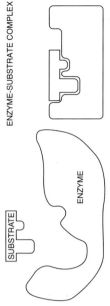

ENZYME

---

## Cofactors are essential for enzyme activity

Some, such as $Zn^{2+}$ or $Mg^{2+}$, or porphyrin groups such as the *haem* in catalase, may form part of the active site and cannot easily be separated from the enzyme protein: these are commonly called *prosthetic groups.*

Some, such as NAD (nicotinamide adenine dinucleotide), bind temporarily to the active site and actually take part in the reaction.

e.g. lactate + NAD $\xrightarrow[\text{DEHYDROGENASE}]{\text{LACTATE}}$ pyruvate + $NADH_2$

Such *coenzymes* shuttle between one enzyme system and another - most are formed from dietary components called *vitamins* (e.g. NAD is formed from niacin, one of the B vitamin complex).

# Factors affecting enzyme activity

exert their effects by altering the ease with which an enzyme-substrate complex is formed.

**Any factor which alters the conformation (dependent on tertiary structure) of the enzyme will alter the shape of the active site, affect the frequency of enzyme-substrate complex formation and thus influence the rate of the enzyme-catalysed reaction.**

**Competitive inhibitors** compete for the active site with the normal substrate. These inhibitors therefore must have a similar structure to the natural substrate.

The success of the binding of I to the active site depends on the relative concentrations of I and S, and such inhibition is therefore *reversible by an increase in substrate concentration*, e.g. malonate competes with succinate for the active site on the enzyme *succinate dehydrogenase*.

*Irreversible inhibition* occurs if the enzyme-inhibitor binding is covalent and the distortion of the active site may be permanent, e.g. cyanide (CN⁻) binds irreversibly to the active site of the enzyme *cytochrome oxidase.*

**Non-competitive inhibitors** reduce enzyme activity by distortion of enzyme conformation caused by binding to some site *other than the active site*. If the binding is non-covalent the inhibition may be *reversible if the inhibitor concentration is diminished*. Many such inhibitors are natural *allosteric regulators* of metabolism, e.g. ATP controls the rate of respiration by inhibition of the enzyme *phosphofructokinase*.

**Activators** may be necessary to complete the structural relationship between active site and substrate, e.g. chloride ions (Cl⁻) are required for activity of the enzyme *salivary amylase.*

There are also *allosteric activators* which enhance enzyme-substrate binding by alteration of enzyme conformation when binding to another ('allosteric') site on the enzyme.

## EFFECT OF TEMPERATURE

RATE OF ENZYME ACTIVITY

OPTIMUM TEMPERATURE

TEMPERATURE /°C

Enzymes have an *optimum temperature* which represents a compromise between *activation* due to increased rate of collision between E and S and *loss of activity* due to denaturation of E molecules and consequent distortion of the active site.

## EFFECT OF pH

RATE OF ENZYME ACTIVITY

OPTIMUM pH

pH

An enzyme has an *optimum pH* which results from the effects of hydrogen ion concentration on the 3-dimensional shape of the enzyme in the active site region.

# Metabolic pathways help to organize metabolism: each pathway is a series of reactions organized such that the products of one reaction become substrates for the next.

**Metabolism** – the sum of the chemical reactions within the cell.

**Catabolism** – degradation reactions, some of which release energy and raw materials.

**Anabolism** – synthesis in which large complex molecules are assembled from subunits.

DRIVE

**Reactants/precursors** are the initial substrates for the metabolic pathway.

**Enzymes** catalyse the individual steps in a metabolic pathway. These enzymes are highly specific, the first in a metabolic pathway is often subject to allosteric control by an end product.

**End products** are compounds which the cell can use, store or secrete. These compounds must not be allowed to accumulate, and their concentration commonly regulates the rate of the initial reaction in the pathway which leads to their synthesis by *allosteric control or end product inhibition*.

**Common intermediates** are compounds which occur at cross-over or branching points in metabolic pathways.

At a **branching point** an intermediate may proceed down one of several alternative pathways, depending on the cell's needs. The 'selection' of a pathway is made by alteration of activity of the enzymes at the branch point. Some branching points may represent *key junctions* in metabolism.

**Metabolic cycles** are *metabolic hubs* which allow the use and re-use of relatively small numbers of molecules in the acceptance of products of one metabolic pathway and their transfer to another metabolic pathway. Important examples are the *Krebs TCA cycle, the urea cycle and the Calvin cycle*.

**Metabolites** are compounds involved in metabolic pathways; often they are *intermediates between reactants and end products*.

## Advantages of metabolic pathways

1. Biochemical reactions may be made to proceed since *equilibrium* is never attained as products become substrates of subsequent reactions.
2. Reactants may be modified in a series of small steps – thus energy is released in controlled amounts or minor adjustments can be made to the structure of molecules.
3. Each step is catalysed by a specific enzyme, and each enzyme represents a *point for control* of the overall pathway.
4. The steps in the pathway may be spatially arranged so that the product of one reaction is ideally located to become the substrate of the next enzyme. This permits the build up of high local concentrations of substrate molecules and biochemical reactions proceed rapidly. A pathway arranged in this way may be catalysed by a *multienzyme complex*.

**Glucose oxidase**
The reaction catalysed by glucose oxidase is

$$\beta - D - glucose + O_2 \longrightarrow gluconic\ acid\ +\ H_2O_2$$

The quick and accurate measurement of glucose is of great importance both medically (in sufferers from diabetes, for example) and industrially (in fermentation reactions, for example). A simple quantitative procedure can be devised by coupling the production of hydrogen peroxide to the activity of the enzyme *peroxidase.*

$$DH_2\ +\ H_2O_2\ \xrightarrow{\text{peroxidase}}\ 2H_2O\ +\ D$$

chromagen
a hydrogen donor
(colourless)

coloured
compound
(colour)

**Peroxidase** can oxidize an organic chromagen (DH$_2$) to a coloured compound (D) utilizing the hydrogen peroxide – the amount of the coloured compound D produced is a direct measure of the amount of glucose which has reacted. It can be measured quantitatively using a colorimeter or, more subjectively, by comparison with a colour reference card.

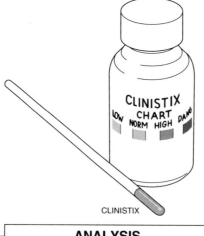

CLINISTIX

This method of glucose analysis is **highly specific** and has the enormous advantage over chemical methods in that this specificity allows glucose to be assayed **in the presence of other sugars**, e.g. in a biological fluid such as blood or urine, without the need for an initial separation.

Both of the enzymes glucose oxidase and peroxidase, and the chromagen DH$_2$, can be immobilized on a cellulose fibre pad. This forms the basis of the glucose dipsticks ('Clinistix') which were developed to enable diabetics to monitor their own blood or urine glucose levels.

**ANALYSIS**

# Commercial applications of enzymes

**PHARMACEUTICALS** *Papain* (protein → peptides) is used to remove stains from false teeth.

**TEXTILES** *Lipase* (fats → fatty acids) is used in biological washing powders.

There are many applications of enzyme technology to industry. Enzyme technology has several advantages over 'whole-organism' technology.

a. **No loss of substrate due to increased biomass.** For example, when whole yeast is used to ferment sugar to alcohol it always 'wastes' some of the sugar by converting it into cell wall material and protoplasm for its own growth.

b. **Elimination of wasteful side reactions.** Whole organisms may convert some of the substrate into irrelevant compounds or even contain enzymes for degrading the desired product into something else.

c. **Optimum conditions for a particular enzyme may be used.** These conditions may not be optimal for the whole organism – in some organisms particular enzymes might be working at less than maximum efficiency.

d. **Purification of the product is easier.** This is especially true using immobilized enzymes.

**MEDICINE**

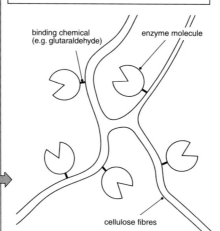

binding chemical
(e.g. glutaraldehyde)

enzyme molecule

cellulose fibres

**Enzyme immobilization**
**Immobilization** means physically or chemically trapping enzymes or cells onto surfaces or inside fibres. The benefits can be considerable:

a. the same enzyme molecules can be used again and again, since they are not lost;

b. the enzyme does not contaminate the end product;

c. the enzymes may be considerably more stable in immobilized form – for example, glucose isomerase is stable at 65 °C when immobilized.

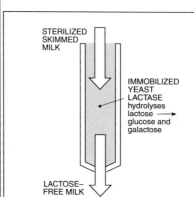

STERILIZED
SKIMMED
MILK

IMMOBILIZED
YEAST
LACTASE
hydrolyses
lactose →
glucose and
galactose

LACTOSE–
FREE MILK

**An important medical application of an immobilized enzyme**

Some adults are **lactose-intolerant** since they lack an intestinal lactase, and undigested lactose in the gut is metabolized by bacteria causing severe abdominal pain and diarrhoea.

Milk is an important dietary component and can be made **lactose-free** by passage down a column packed with **yeast lactase** immobilized on fibres of cellulose acetate.

# Glycolysis generates ATP, reduced electron carriers and pyruvate.

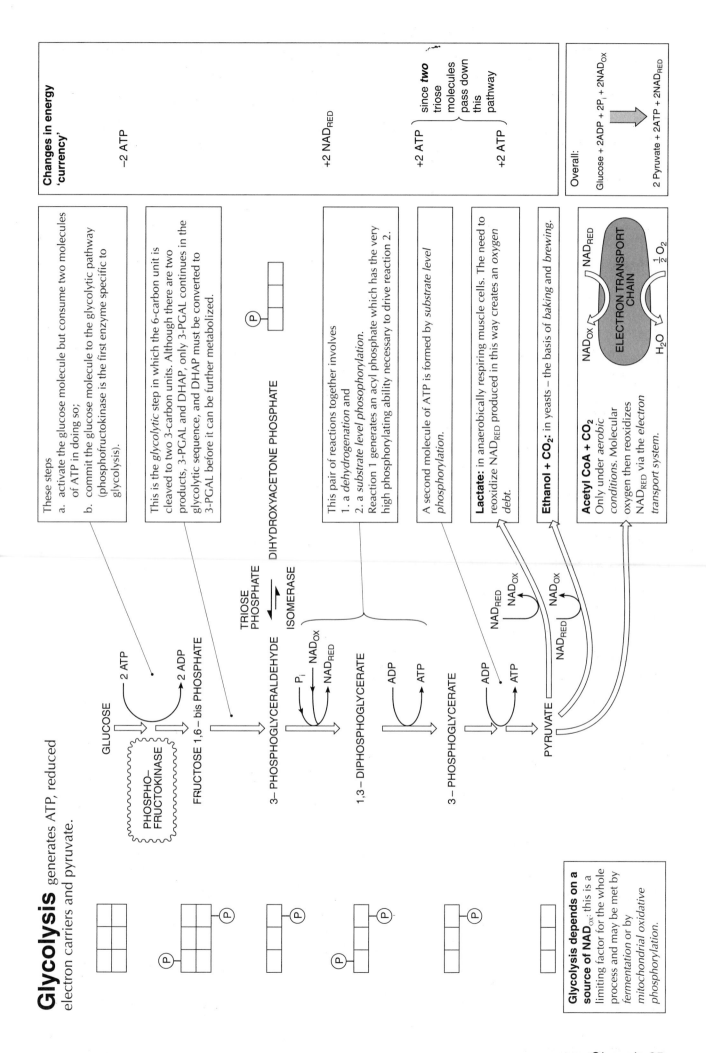

**Changes in energy 'currency'**

−2 ATP

+2 NAD$_{RED}$

+2 ATP
since *two* triose molecules pass down this pathway
+2 ATP

Overall:

Glucose + 2ADP + 2P$_i$ + 2NAD$_{OX}$ → 2 Pyruvate + 2ATP + 2NAD$_{RED}$

These steps
a. activate the glucose molecule but consume two molecules of ATP in doing so;
b. commit the glucose molecule to the glycolytic pathway (phosphofructokinase is the first enzyme specific to glycolysis).

This is the *glycolytic* step in which the 6-carbon unit is cleaved to two 3-carbon units. Although there are two products, 3-PGAL and DHAP, only 3-PGAL continues in the glycolytic sequence, and DHAP must be converted to 3-PGAL before it can be further metabolized.

DIHYDROXYACETONE PHOSPHATE

This pair of reactions together involves
1. a *dehydrogenation* and
2. a *substrate level phosophorylation*.
Reaction 1 generates an acyl phosphate which has the very high phosphorylating ability necessary to drive reaction 2.

A second molecule of ATP is formed by *substrate level phosphorylation*.

**Lactate:** in anaerobically respiring muscle cells. The need to reoxidize NAD$_{RED}$ produced in this way creates an *oxygen debt*.

**Ethanol + CO$_2$:** in yeasts – the basis of *baking* and *brewing*.

**Acetyl CoA + CO$_2$** Only under *aerobic conditions*. Molecular oxygen then reoxidizes NAD$_{RED}$ via the *electron transport system*.

GLUCOSE
2 ATP
2 ADP

PHOSPHO-FRUCTOKINASE

FRUCTOSE 1,6 – bis PHOSPHATE

TRIOSE PHOSPHATE ISOMERASE

3 – PHOSPHOGLYCERALDEHYDE
P$_i$  NAD$_{OX}$  NAD$_{RED}$

1,3 – DIPHOSPHOGLYCERATE
ADP  ATP

3 – PHOSPHOGLYCERATE
ADP  ATP

PYRUVATE
NAD$_{RED}$  NAD$_{OX}$
NAD$_{RED}$  NAD$_{OX}$
NAD$_{RED}$

ELECTRON TRANSPORT CHAIN
NAD$_{OX}$
$\frac{1}{2}$O$_2$
H$_2$O

**Glycolysis depends on a source of NAD$_{OX}$:** this is a limiting factor for the whole process and may be met by *fermentation* or by mitochondrial oxidative *phosphorylation*.

# The TCA (Krebs) cycle is
essential for energy release from, and interconversion of, a variety of nutrients.

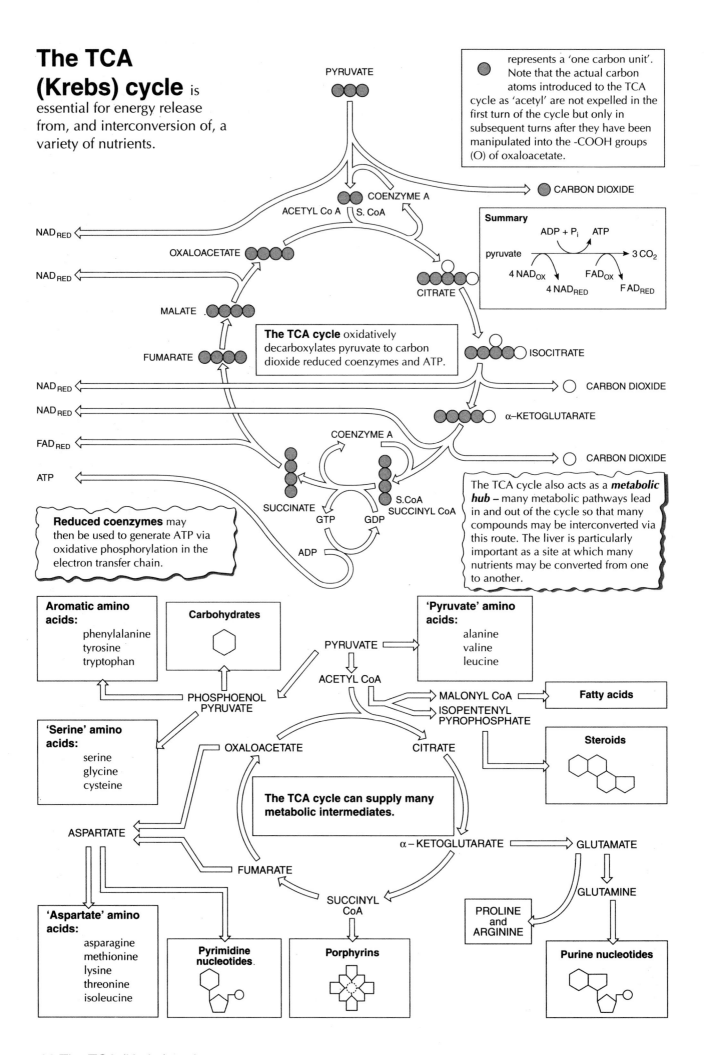

represents a 'one carbon unit'. Note that the actual carbon atoms introduced to the TCA cycle as 'acetyl' are not expelled in the first turn of the cycle but only in subsequent turns after they have been manipulated into the -COOH groups (O) of oxaloacetate.

PYRUVATE

CARBON DIOXIDE

COENZYME A

ACETYL Co A    S. CoA

**Summary**

$$\text{pyruvate} \xrightarrow[\substack{4\,NAD_{OX} \\ \searrow \\ 4\,NAD_{RED}}]{\substack{ADP + P_i \quad ATP \\ \searrow \quad \nearrow}} 3\,CO_2$$

FAD_{OX}  →  FAD_{RED}

NAD_{RED}

NAD_{RED}

OXALOACETATE

CITRATE

MALATE

ISOCITRATE

FUMARATE

**The TCA cycle** oxidatively decarboxylates pyruvate to carbon dioxide reduced coenzymes and ATP.

CARBON DIOXIDE

NAD_{RED}

NAD_{RED}

α–KETOGLUTARATE

FAD_{RED}

COENZYME A

CARBON DIOXIDE

ATP

SUCCINATE      S.CoA
                SUCCINYL CoA

GTP    GDP

**Reduced coenzymes** may then be used to generate ATP via oxidative phosphorylation in the electron transfer chain.

ADP

The TCA cycle also acts as a **metabolic hub** – many metabolic pathways lead in and out of the cycle so that many compounds may be interconverted via this route. The liver is particularly important as a site at which many nutrients may be converted from one to another.

**Aromatic amino acids:**
phenylalanine
tyrosine
tryptophan

**Carbohydrates**

**'Pyruvate' amino acids:**
alanine
valine
leucine

PYRUVATE

ACETYL CoA

PHOSPHOENOL PYRUVATE

MALONYL CoA → **Fatty acids**

ISOPENTENYL PYROPHOSPHATE

**'Serine' amino acids:**
serine
glycine
cysteine

OXALOACETATE

CITRATE

**Steroids**

**The TCA cycle can supply many metabolic intermediates.**

ASPARTATE

α–KETOGLUTARATE → GLUTAMATE

FUMARATE

GLUTAMINE

SUCCINYL CoA

PROLINE and ARGININE

**'Aspartate' amino acids:**
asparagine
methionine
lysine
threonine
isoleucine

**Pyrimidine nucleotides**

**Porphyrins**

**Purine nucleotides**

# Cellular respiration

occurs in a series of localized stages.

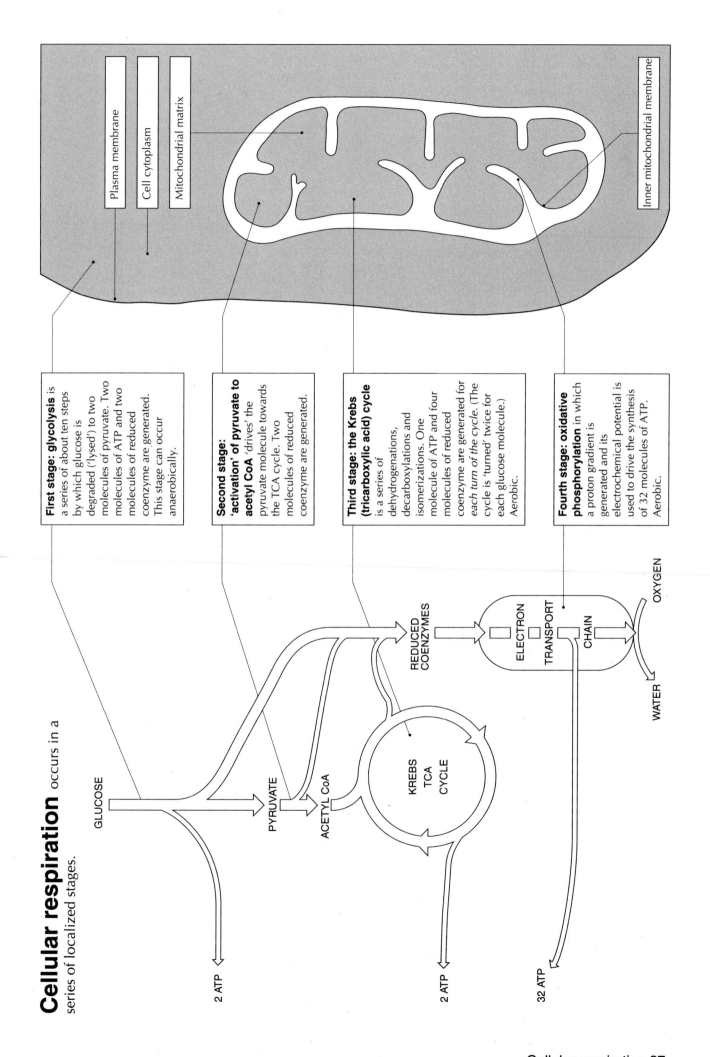

Plasma membrane

Cell cytoplasm

Mitochondrial matrix

Inner mitochondrial membrane

**First stage: glycolysis** is a series of about ten steps by which glucose is degraded ('lysed') to two molecules of pyruvate. Two molecules of ATP and two molecules of reduced coenzyme are generated. This stage can occur anaerobically.

**Second stage: 'activation' of pyruvate to acetyl CoA** 'drives' the pyruvate molecule towards the TCA cycle. Two molecules of reduced coenzyme are generated.

**Third stage: the Krebs (tricarboxylic acid) cycle** is a series of dehydrogenations, decarboxylations and isomerizations. One molecule of ATP and four molecules of reduced coenzyme are generated for *each turn of the cycle*. (The cycle is 'turned' twice for each glucose molecule.) Aerobic.

**Fourth stage: oxidative phosphorylation** in which a proton gradient is generated and its electrochemical potential is used to drive the synthesis of 32 molecules of ATP. Aerobic.

GLUCOSE

PYRUVATE

ACETYL CoA

KREBS TCA CYCLE

REDUCED COENZYMES

ELECTRON TRANSPORT CHAIN

OXYGEN

WATER

2 ATP

2 ATP

32 ATP

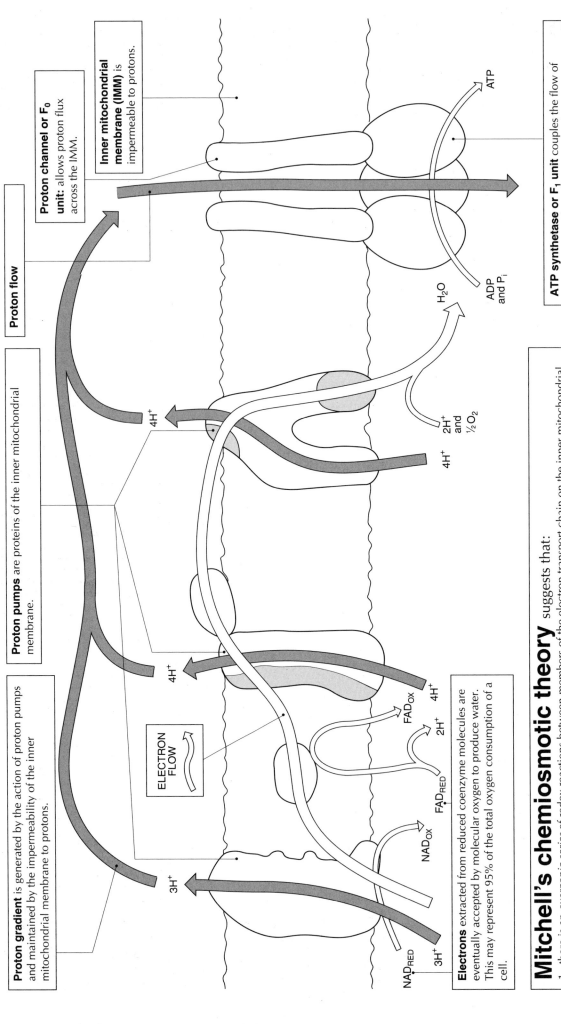

**Inner mitochondrial membrane (IMM)** is impermeable to protons.

**Proton channel or F$_0$ unit:** allows proton flux across the IMM.

**Proton flow**

**Proton pumps** are proteins of the inner mitochondrial membrane.

**Proton gradient** is generated by the action of proton pumps and maintained by the impermeability of the inner mitochondrial membrane to protons.

ATP

ADP and P$_i$

**ATP synthetase or F$_1$ unit** couples the flow of protons down the proton concentration gradient to the phosphorylation of ADP. It has been suggested that the proton flux through the enzyme alters the nucleotide-binding properties of the active site, promoting ATP synthesis.

4H$^+$

H$_2$O

2H$^+$ and ½O$_2$

4H$^+$

4H$^+$

ELECTRON FLOW

FAD$_{OX}$

2H$^+$

4H$^+$

FAD$_{RED}$

NAD$_{OX}$

3H$^+$

3H$^+$

NAD$_{RED}$

**Electrons** extracted from reduced coenzyme molecules are eventually accepted by molecular oxygen to produce water. This may represent 95% of the total oxygen consumption of a cell.

## Mitchell's chemiosmotic theory suggests that:

1. there is an *exergonic series* of redox reactions between members of the electron transport chain on the inner mitochondrial membrane;
2. these exergonic redox reactions can drive three proton pumps which transport H$^+$ from the mitochondrial matrix to the inter-membrane space, thus generating a *proton gradient* across the IMM;
3. dissipation of proton gradient can be coupled to the phosphorylation of ADP to ATP.

# ATP: the energy currency of the cell

## ATP hydrolysis is favoured

$ATP^{4-} + H_2O \rightleftharpoons ADP^{3-} + P^{2-} + H^+ + 30.5 \text{ kJ mol}^{-1}$

i.e. ATP has a strong tendency to transfer its terminal phosphoryl group, a reaction associated with the release of 30.5 kJ mol$^{-1}$ of ATP, because

1. the repulsion between the four negative charges in ATP$^{4-}$ is reduced when ATP is hydrolysed because two negative charges are removed with phosphate.
2. the H$^+$ ion which is released when ATP is hydrolysed reacts with OH$^-$ ions to form water – this is a highly favoured reaction.
3. the charge distribution on ADP + P is more stable than that on ATP.

This part of the molecule acts like a 'handle' – it has a shape which can be recognized by highly specific enzymes.

This part of the molecule contains anhydride bonds (O-P) which can be hydrolysed in reactions which are **exergonic** (energy-yielding) and can be coupled to **endergonic** (energy-demanding) reactions.

NH$_2$

ADENINE

RIBOSE

OH   OH

$CH_2 - O - P - O - P - O - P - O^-$

ADENOSINE

ADENOSINE TRIPHOSPHATE

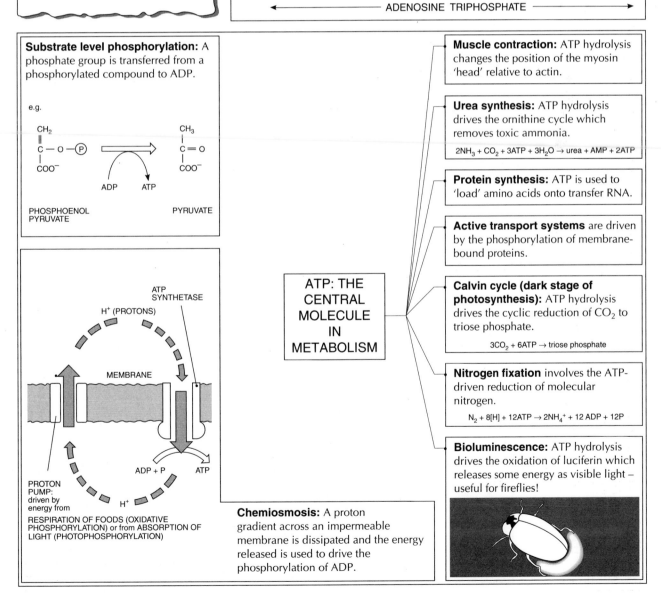

**Substrate level phosphorylation:** A phosphate group is transferred from a phosphorylated compound to ADP.

e.g.

PHOSPHOENOL PYRUVATE

ADP   ATP

PYRUVATE

ATP SYNTHETASE

H$^+$ (PROTONS)

MEMBRANE

ADP + P   ATP

PROTON PUMP: driven by energy from RESPIRATION OF FOODS (OXIDATIVE PHOSPHORYLATION) or from ABSORPTION OF LIGHT (PHOTOPHOSPHORYLATION)

H$^+$

**ATP: THE CENTRAL MOLECULE IN METABOLISM**

**Muscle contraction:** ATP hydrolysis changes the position of the myosin 'head' relative to actin.

**Urea synthesis:** ATP hydrolysis drives the ornithine cycle which removes toxic ammonia.

$2NH_3 + CO_2 + 3ATP + 3H_2O \rightarrow$ urea $+ AMP + 2ATP$

**Protein synthesis:** ATP is used to 'load' amino acids onto transfer RNA.

**Active transport systems** are driven by the phosphorylation of membrane-bound proteins.

**Calvin cycle (dark stage of photosynthesis):** ATP hydrolysis drives the cyclic reduction of CO$_2$ to triose phosphate.

$3CO_2 + 6ATP \rightarrow$ triose phosphate

**Nitrogen fixation** involves the ATP-driven reduction of molecular nitrogen.

$N_2 + 8[H] + 12ATP \rightarrow 2NH_4^+ + 12 ADP + 12P$

**Bioluminescence:** ATP hydrolysis drives the oxidation of luciferin which releases some energy as visible light – useful for fireflies!

**Chemiosmosis:** A proton gradient across an impermeable membrane is dissipated and the energy released is used to drive the phosphorylation of ADP.

# Nucleic acids I: DNA

*The Watson–Crick model for DNA* suggests that the molecule is a double helix of two complementary, anti-parallel polynucleotide chains

This is the *5′ end of the chain* since the terminal phosphate group is only bonded to the $C_5$ of the sugar molecule.

**Base pairing in DNA** was proposed to explain how two polynucleotide chains could be held together by hydrogen bonds. To accommodate the measured dimensions of the molecule each base pair comprises *one purine - one pyrimidine*.

The double helix is most stable, that is the greatest number of hydrogen bonds is formed, when the base pairs

A ┈┈┈┈┈ T     (two hydrogen bonds)

and   G ┈┈┈┈┈┈ C     (three hydrogen bonds)

are formed. These are *complementary base pairs*.

Note that in order to form and maintain this number of hydrogen bonds the nucleotides are inverted with respect to one another so that the phosphate groups (here shown as (P)) *face in opposite directions*.

The chains are *anti-parallel*, that is one chain runs from $5′ \rightarrow 3′$ whilst the other runs from $3′ \rightarrow 5′$.

The chains are *complementary*: because of base pairing, the base sequence on one of the chains automatically dictates the base sequence on the other.

There are *ten base pairs* for each pitch of the double helix.

**Nucleotides** are the subunits of nucleic acids, including DNA. Each of these subunits is made up of:

AN ORGANIC
(NITROGENOUS) BASE
+
A PENTOSE SUGAR
+
A PHOSPHATE GROUP

Note that the phosphate group is bonded to the $C_5$ atom of the pentose sugar.

There are *four different nucleotides* in a DNA molecule; they differ only in the organic (nitrogen) base present.

There are two different *pyrimidine (single ring) bases*, called *cytosine (C)* and *thymine (T)*

and

two different *purine (double ring) bases* called *adenine (A)* and *guanine (G)*.

The different dimensions of the purine and pyrimidine bases is extremely important in the formation of the double-stranded DNA molecule.

Nucleotides are linked to form a *polynucleotide* by the formation of *3′ 5′ phosphodiester links* in which a phosphate group forms a bridge between the $C_3$ of one sugar molecule and the $C_5$ of the next sugar molecule.

This is the 3′ *end of the chain* since the $C_3$ atom of the sugar molecule of the final nucleotide has a 'free' -OH group which is not part of a phosphodiester link.

# Nucleic acids II: RNA *Ribonucleic acid* has a number of functions in protein synthesis.

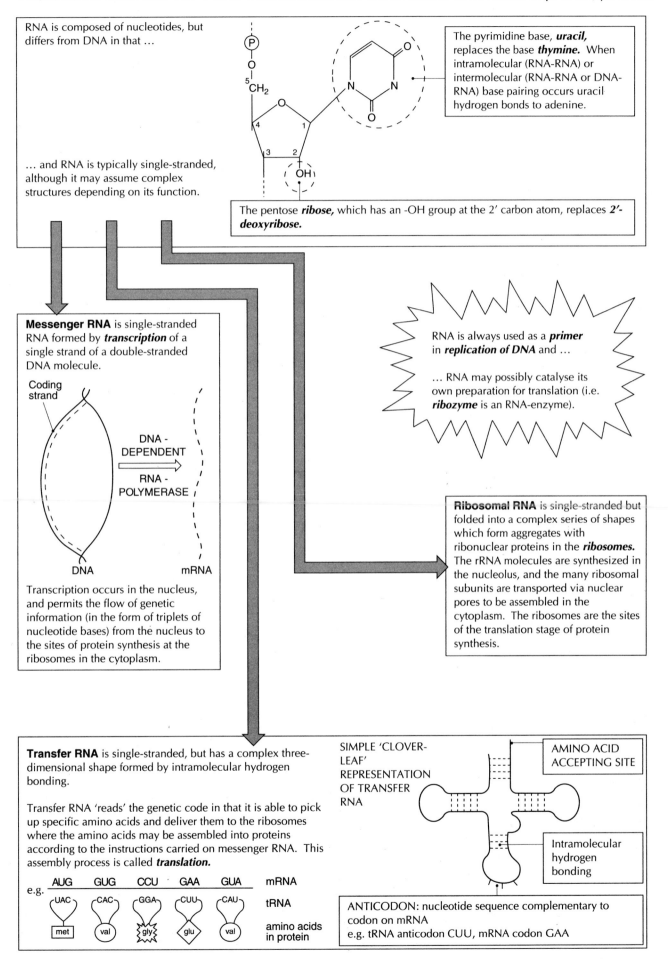

RNA is composed of nucleotides, but differs from DNA in that …

… and RNA is typically single-stranded, although it may assume complex structures depending on its function.

The pyrimidine base, **uracil,** replaces the base **thymine.** When intramolecular (RNA-RNA) or intermolecular (RNA-RNA or DNA-RNA) base pairing occurs uracil hydrogen bonds to adenine.

The pentose **ribose,** which has an -OH group at the 2' carbon atom, replaces **2'-deoxyribose.**

**Messenger RNA** is single-stranded RNA formed by **transcription** of a single strand of a double-stranded DNA molecule.

Coding strand

DNA - DEPENDENT

RNA - POLYMERASE

DNA          mRNA

Transcription occurs in the nucleus, and permits the flow of genetic information (in the form of triplets of nucleotide bases) from the nucleus to the sites of protein synthesis at the ribosomes in the cytoplasm.

RNA is always used as a **primer** in **replication of DNA** and …

… RNA may possibly catalyse its own preparation for translation (i.e. **ribozyme** is an RNA-enzyme).

**Ribosomal RNA** is single-stranded but folded into a complex series of shapes which form aggregates with ribonuclear proteins in the **ribosomes.** The rRNA molecules are synthesized in the nucleolus, and the many ribosomal subunits are transported via nuclear pores to be assembled in the cytoplasm. The ribosomes are the sites of the translation stage of protein synthesis.

**Transfer RNA** is single-stranded, but has a complex three-dimensional shape formed by intramolecular hydrogen bonding.

Transfer RNA 'reads' the genetic code in that it is able to pick up specific amino acids and deliver them to the ribosomes where the amino acids may be assembled into proteins according to the instructions carried on messenger RNA. This assembly process is called **translation.**

e.g.

| AUG | GUG | CCU | GAA | GUA | mRNA |
| UAC | CAC | GGA | CUU | CAU | tRNA |
| met | val | gly | glu | val | amino acids in protein |

SIMPLE 'CLOVER-LEAF' REPRESENTATION OF TRANSFER RNA

AMINO ACID ACCEPTING SITE

Intramolecular hydrogen bonding

ANTICODON: nucleotide sequence complementary to codon on mRNA
e.g. tRNA anticodon CUU, mRNA codon GAA

# Leaf structure is adapted for photosynthesis and for gas exchange.

**Phototropism** is a growth response which allows shoots to grow towards the light to allow optimum illumination of the leaves.

**Large leaf surface area** is held perpendicular to the light source (and kept there by a 'tracking' system).

**Leaves are thin** so that there are few cell layers to absorb light before it is received by the photosynthetic cells.

**Leaf mosaic** is the arrangement of leaves in a pattern which minimizes overlapping/shading but maximizes leaf exposure to light.

**Shoot system** holds leaves in optimum position for illumination and $CO_2$ uptake.

**Etiolation** causes rapid elongation of internodes kept in darkness to extend shoot.

**Cuticle:** is composed of a waxy compound called *cutin* and is secreted by the epidermis. It is the cuticle which reduces water loss by evaporation, not the epidermis itself. May be considerably thickened in xerophytes.

**Upper epidermis:** is one or two cells thick – protects against *water loss* (either by cuticle – see left – or by epidermal hairs which trap moisture and reflect light) and against *invasion by pathogens* so that the moist inner leaf is quite sterile. Transparent to visible light.

**Palisade mesophyll:** is the major site of photosynthesis – cells packed vertically with many chloroplasts which may move by cytoplasmic streaming to optimum position within the cell for light absorption and subsequent photosynthesis.

**Xylem vessel:** transports water and mineral salts to the leaves. Heavily lignified cell walls help to maintain extension of the leaf blade.

**Phloem sieve tube:** removes products of photosynthesis (principally sucrose) and may import other organic solutes such as amino acids/amides and help to redistribute ions such as phosphate.

**Spongy mesophyll:** irregularly shaped cells which fit together loosely to leave large air spaces which permit diffusion of gases through leaves. There is much evaporative water loss from the surface of these cells.

**Lower epidermis:** similar protective functions to upper epidermis. Cuticle much thinner than that of upper epidermis.

**Guard cell:** has chloroplasts and membrane proteins to permit pumping of $K^+$ ions to drive osmotic movement of water. Uneven thickening of cellulose cell wall permits opening/closure of stomatal pore as turgidity changes.

**Stomatal pore** can be opened (to allow diffusion of $O_2$ and $CO_2$ down concentration gradients) or closed (to limit water losses by evaporation to a drier atmosphere).

LEAF INTERNAL STRUCTURE IS ADAPTED

GAS EXCHANGE IN STEMS IS MADE POSSIBLE BY LENTICELS

**Loosely packed cork cells** with moist covering permit exchange of gases between tissues and environment.

**Epidermis with waterproof cuticle** prevents gas exchange between stem and environment.

**Intercellular air spaces** permit free movement of gases through plant body.

$CO_2$ $O_2$

# Autotrophic nutrition in plants: note the role of Krebs and Calvin cycles as metabolic centres.

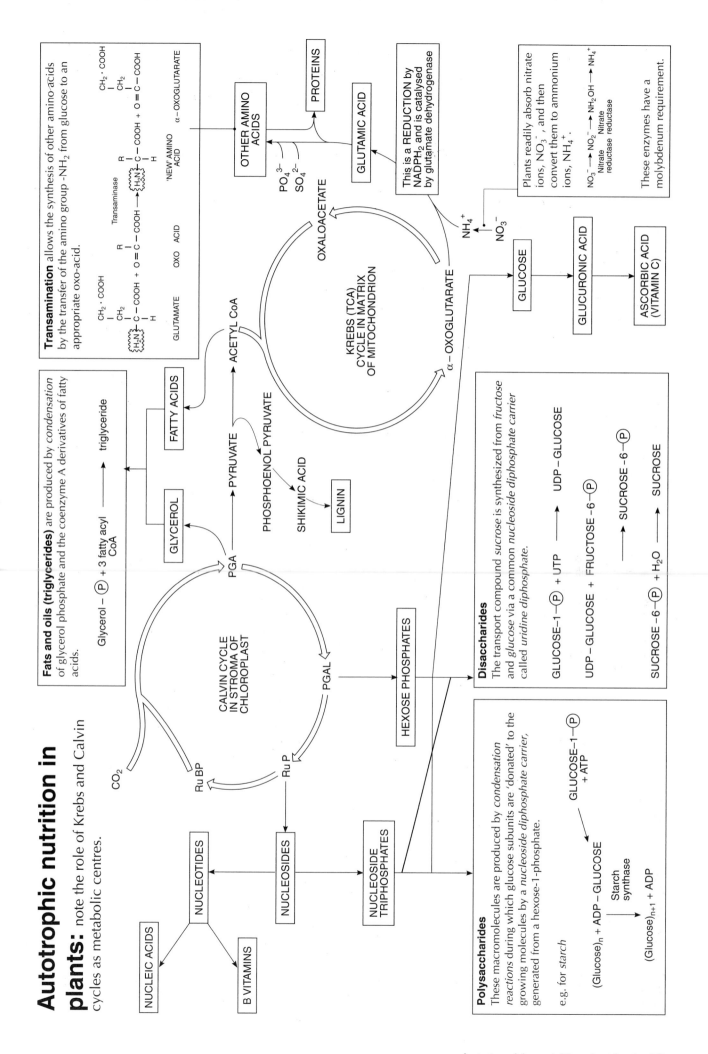

**Transamination** allows the synthesis of other amino-acids by the transfer of the amino group -NH₂ from glucose to an appropriate oxo-acid.

**Fats and oils (triglycerides)** are produced by *condensation* of glycerol phosphate and the coenzyme A derivatives of fatty acids.

Glycerol – (P) + 3 fatty acyl CoA ⟶ triglyceride

This is a REDUCTION by NADPH₂ and is catalysed by glutamate dehydrogenase

Plants readily absorb nitrate ions, $NO_3^-$, and then convert them to ammonium ions, $NH_4^+$.

$NO_3^- \rightarrow NO_2^- \rightarrow NH_2OH \rightarrow NH_4^+$
Nitrate Nitrite
reductase reductase

These enzymes have a molybdenum requirement.

**Disaccharides**
The transport compound *sucrose* is synthesized from *fructose* and *glucose* via a common *nucleoside diphosphate carrier* called *uridine diphosphate*.

GLUCOSE-1–(P) + UTP ⟶ UDP – GLUCOSE

UDP – GLUCOSE + FRUCTOSE-6–(P) ⟶ SUCROSE-6–(P)

SUCROSE-6–(P) + H₂O ⟶ SUCROSE

**Polysaccharides**
These macromolecules are produced by *condensation reactions* during which glucose subunits are 'donated' to the growing molecules by a *nucleoside diphosphate carrier*, generated from a hexose-1-phosphate.

e.g. for *starch*

GLUCOSE-1–(P) + ATP ⟶ ADP – GLUCOSE

(Glucose)ₙ + ADP – GLUCOSE ⟶ (Glucose)ₙ₊₁ + ADP
Starch synthase

# Law of limiting factors

Blackman stated: 'when a process is affected by more than one factor its rate is limited by the factor which is nearest its minimum value: it is that *limiting factor* which directly affects a process if its magnitude is changed.'

Photosynthesis is a multi-stage process – for example the Calvin cycle is dependent on the supply of ATP and reducing power from the light reactions – and the principle of limiting factors can be applied.

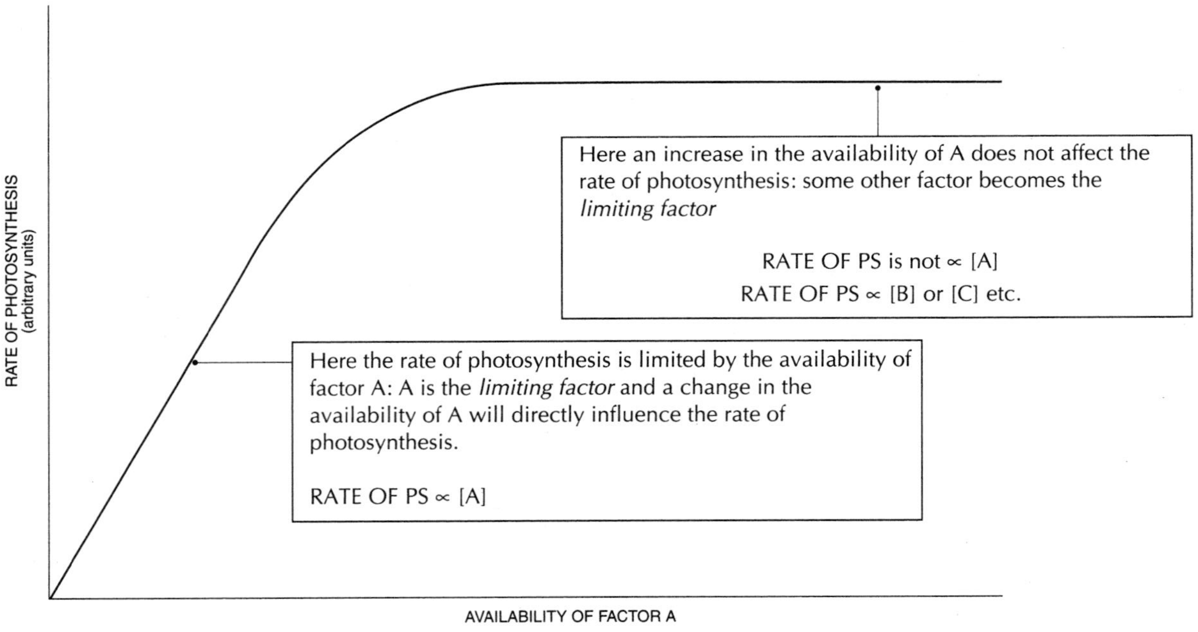

The rate of a multi-stage process may be subject to different limiting factors at different times. Photosynthesis may be limited by *temperature* during the early part of a summer's day, by *light intensity* during cloudy or overcast conditions or by *carbon dioxide concentration* at other times. The principal limiting factor in Britain during the summer is *carbon dioxide concentration*: the atmospheric [$CO_2$] is typically only 0.04%. Increased $CO_2$ emissions from combustion of fossil fuels may stimulate photosynthesis.

The *mechanism of photosynthesis* is made clearer by studies of limiting factors – the fact that *light* is a limiting factor indicates a *light-dependent stage*, the effect of *temperature* suggests that there are *enzyme-catalysed reactions*, the *interaction of [$CO_2$]* and *temperature* suggests an enzyme catalysed *fixation of carbon dioxide*. The existence of more than one limiting factor suggests that *photosynthesis is a multi-stage process*.

The study of limiting factors has *commercial and horticultural applications*. Since [$CO_2$] is a limiting factor, crop production in greenhouses is readily stimulated by raising local carbon dioxide concentrations (from gas cylinders or by burning fossil fuels). It is also clear to horticulturalists that expensive increases in energy consumption for lighting and heating are not economically justified if neither of these is the limiting factor applying under any particular set of conditions.

Here the rate of photosynthesis is limited by the availability of factor A: A is the *limiting factor* and a change in the availability of A will directly influence the rate of photosynthesis.

RATE OF PS ∝ [A]

Here an increase in the availability of A does not affect the rate of photosynthesis: some other factor becomes the *limiting factor*

RATE OF PS is not ∝ [A]

RATE OF PS ∝ [B] or [C] etc.

RATE OF PHOTOSYNTHESIS (arbitrary units)

AVAILABILITY OF FACTOR A

The *limiting factors* which affect *photosynthesis* are:

**Light intensity:** light energy is necessary to generate ATP and NADPH$_2$ during the light dependent stages of photosynthesis.

**Carbon dioxide concentration:** $CO_2$ is 'fixed' by reaction with ribulose bisphosphate in the initial reaction of the Calvin cycle.

**Temperature:** the enzymes catalysing the reactions of the Calvin cycle and some of the light-dependent stages are affected by temperature.

**Water availability** and **chlorophyll concentration** are not normally limiting factors in photosynthesis.

# Light reaction: non-cyclic photophosphorylation

Light energy excites electrons, resulting in the splitting of water and the synthesis of ATP and NADPH$_2$.

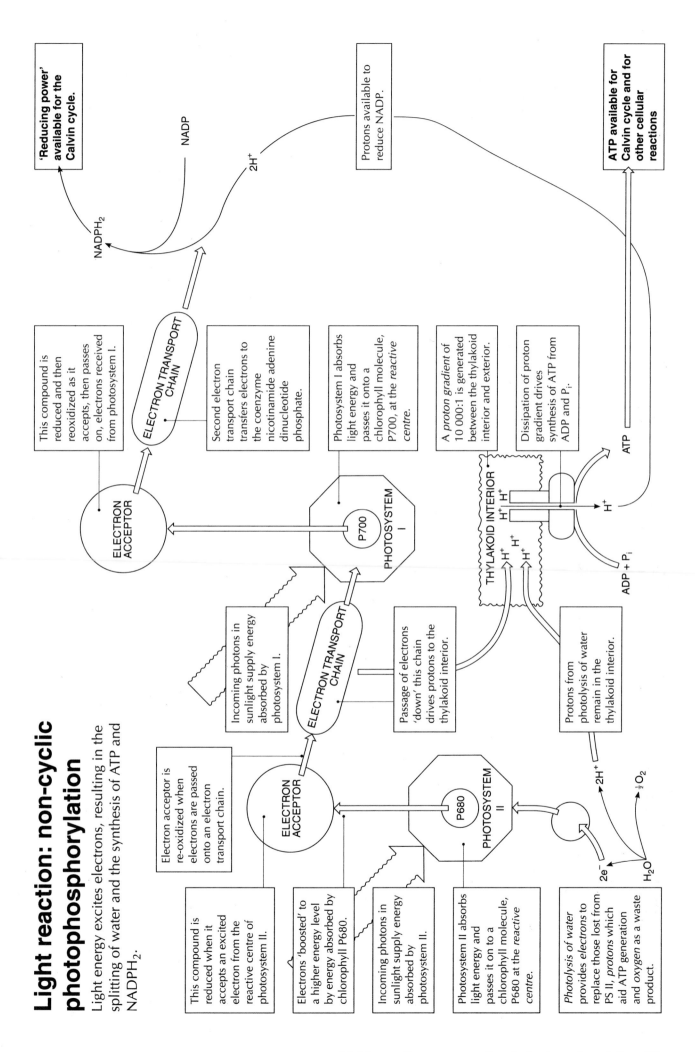

**'Reducing power' available for the Calvin cycle.**

NADP

NADPH$_2$

2H$^+$

Protons available to reduce NADP.

This compound is reduced and then reoxidized as it accepts, then passes on, electrons received from photosystem I.

ELECTRON TRANSPORT CHAIN

Second electron transport chain transfers electrons to the coenzyme nicotinamide adenine dinucleotide phosphate.

ELECTRON ACCEPTOR

Photosystem I absorbs light energy and passes it onto a chlorophyll molecule, P700, at the *reactive centre*.

A *proton gradient* of 10 000:1 is generated between the thylakoid interior and exterior.

Dissipation of proton gradient drives synthesis of ATP from ADP and P$_i$.

**ATP available for Calvin cycle and for other cellular reactions**

ATP

P700

PHOTOSYSTEM I

THYLAKOID INTERIOR

H$^+$ H$^+$

H$^+$

ADP + P$_i$

H$^+$ H$^+$

H$^+$ H$^+$

Incoming photons in sunlight supply energy absorbed by photosystem I.

ELECTRON TRANSPORT CHAIN

Passage of electrons 'down' this chain drives protons to the thylakoid interior.

Protons from photolysis of water remain in the thylakoid interior.

Electron acceptor is re-oxidized when electrons are passed onto an electron transport chain.

ELECTRON ACCEPTOR

P680

PHOTOSYSTEM II

2H$^+$

$\frac{1}{2}$O$_2$

This compound is reduced when it accepts an excited electron from the reactive centre of photosystem II.

Electrons 'boosted' to a higher energy level by energy absorbed by chlorophyll P680.

Incoming photons in sunlight supply energy absorbed by photosystem II.

Photosystem II absorbs light energy and passes it on to a chlorophyll molecule, P680 at the *reactive centre*.

*Photolysis of water* provides *electrons* to replace those lost from PS II, *protons* which aid ATP generation and *oxygen* as a waste product.

H$_2$O

2e$^-$

# Dark reaction: the Calvin cycle

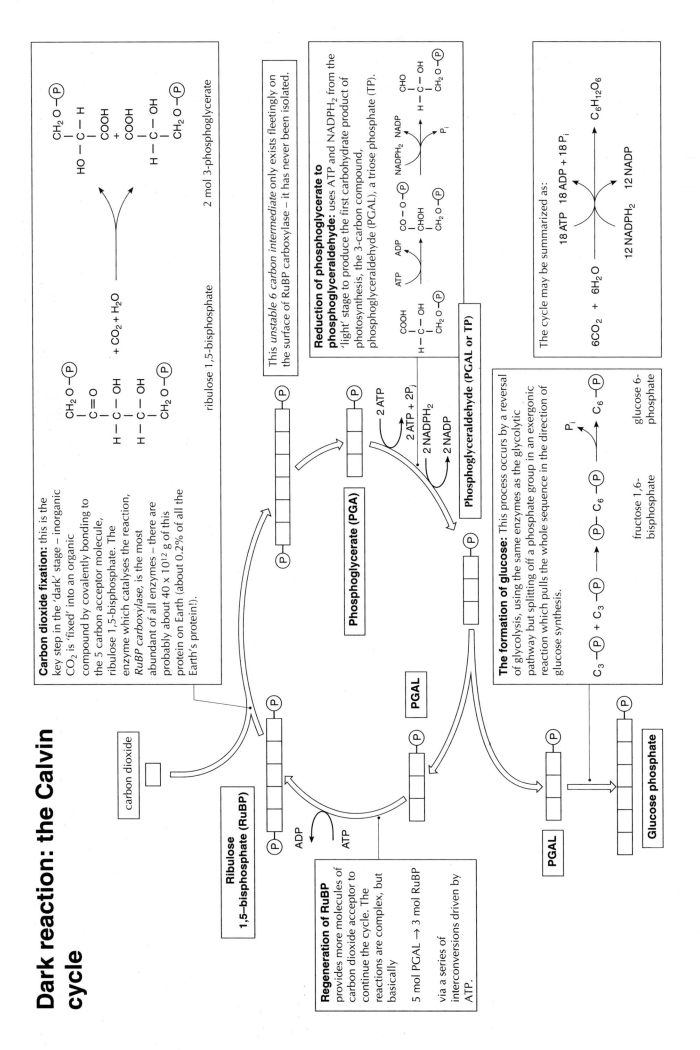

**Carbon dioxide fixation:** this is the key step in the 'dark' stage – inorganic $CO_2$ is 'fixed' into an organic compound by covalently bonding to the 5 carbon acceptor molecule, ribulose 1,5-bisphosphate. The enzyme which catalyses the reaction, *RuBP carboxylase*, is the most abundant of all enzymes – there are probably about $40 \times 10^{12}$ g of this protein on Earth (about 0.2% of all the Earth's protein!).

ribulose 1,5-bisphosphate

2 mol 3-phosphoglycerate

This *unstable 6 carbon intermediate* only exists fleetingly on the surface of RuBP carboxylase – it has never been isolated.

**Reduction of phosphoglycerate to phosphoglyceraldehyde:** uses ATP and $NADPH_2$ from the 'light' stage to produce the first carbohydrate product of photosynthesis, the 3-carbon compound, phosphoglyceraldehyde (PGAL), a triose phosphate (TP).

The cycle may be summarized as:

$$6CO_2 + 6H_2O \xrightarrow[\substack{12\,NADPH_2 \quad 12\,NADP}]{18\,ATP \quad 18\,ADP + 18\,P_i} C_6H_{12}O_6$$

**Phosphoglycerate (PGA)**

**Phosphoglyceraldehyde (PGAL or TP)**

PGAL

2 ATP

2 ATP + 2P$_i$

2 NADPH$_2$

2 NADP

**The formation of glucose:** This process occurs by a reversal of glycolysis, using the same enzymes as the glycolytic pathway but splitting off a phosphate group in an exergonic reaction which pulls the whole sequence in the direction of glucose synthesis.

$$C_3\!-\!\text{P} + C_3\!-\!\text{P} \longrightarrow \text{P}\!-\!C_6\!-\!\text{P} \xrightarrow{P_i} C_6\!-\!\text{P}$$

fructose 1,6-bisphosphate

glucose 6-phosphate

carbon dioxide

**Ribulose 1,5–bisphosphate (RuBP)**

ADP

ATP

PGAL

**Glucose phosphate**

**Regeneration of RuBP** provides more molecules of carbon dioxide acceptor to continue the cycle. The reactions are complex, but basically

5 mol PGAL → 3 mol RuBP

via a series of interconversions driven by ATP.

# Chloroplasts: absorption and action spectra of chlorophyll

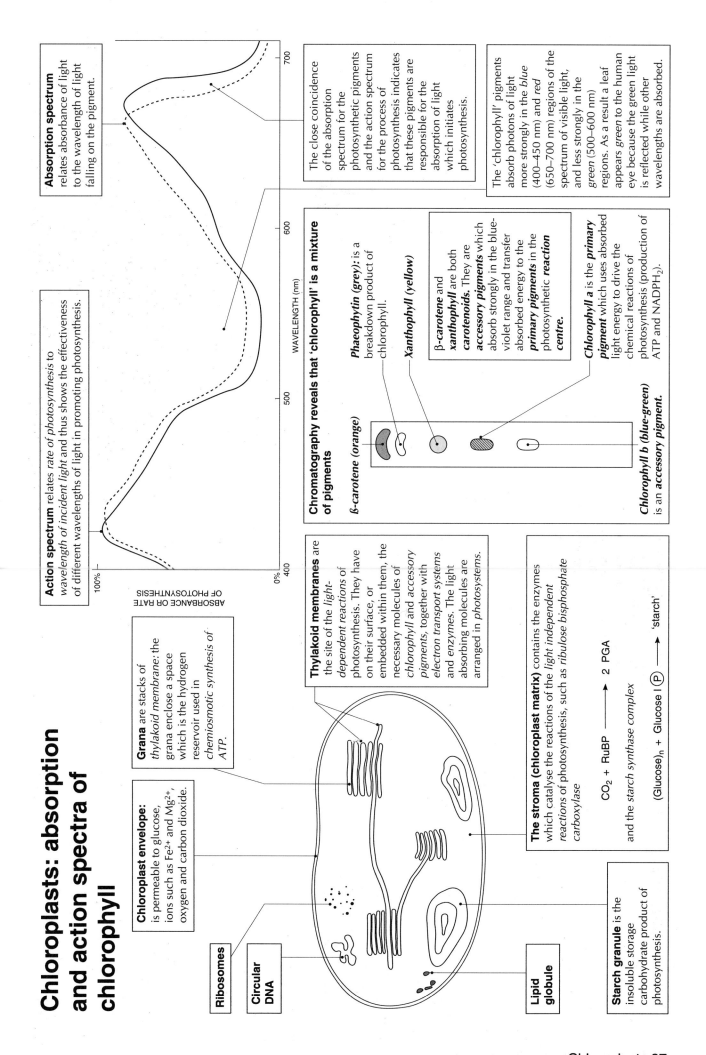

**Absorption spectrum** relates absorbance of light to the wavelength of light falling on the pigment.

**Action spectrum** relates *rate of photosynthesis* to *wavelength of incident light* and thus shows the effectiveness of different wavelengths of light in promoting photosynthesis.

ABSORBANCE OR RATE OF PHOTOSYNTHESIS

100%

0%

400    500    600    700

WAVELENGTH (nm)

The close coincidence of the absorption spectrum for the photosynthetic pigments and the action spectrum for the process of photosynthesis indicates that these pigments are responsible for the absorption of light which initiates photosynthesis.

The 'chlorophyll' pigments absorb photons of light more strongly in the *blue* (400–450 nm) and *red* (650–700 nm) regions of the spectrum of visible light, and less strongly in the *green* (500–600 nm) regions. As a result a leaf appears *green* to the human eye because the green light is reflected while other wavelengths are absorbed.

**Chromatography reveals that 'chlorophyll' is a mixture of pigments**

*β-carotene (orange)*

*Phaeophytin (grey):* is a breakdown product of chlorophyll.

*Xanthophyll (yellow)*

β-carotene and xanthophyll are both accessory pigments which absorb strongly in the blue-violet range and transfer absorbed energy to the *primary pigments* in the photosynthetic *reaction centre.*

*Chlorophyll a* is the *primary pigment* which uses absorbed light energy to drive the chemical reactions of photosynthesis (production of ATP and NADPH₂).

*Chlorophyll b (blue-green)* is an *accessory pigment.*

**Chloroplast envelope:** is permeable to glucose, ions such as $Fe^{2+}$ and $Mg^{2+}$, oxygen and carbon dioxide.

**Grana** are stacks of *thylakoid membrane*: the grana enclose a space which is the hydrogen reservoir used in *chemiosmotic synthesis of ATP.*

**Thylakoid membranes** are the site of the *light-dependent reactions* of photosynthesis. They have on their surface, or embedded within them, the necessary molecules of chlorophyll and accessory pigments, together with electron transport systems and enzymes. The light absorbing molecules are arranged in *photosystems.*

**The stroma (chloroplast matrix)** contains the enzymes which catalyse the reactions of the *light independent reactions* of photosynthesis, such as *ribulose bisphosphate carboxylase*

$$CO_2 + RuBP \longrightarrow 2 \; PGA$$

and the *starch synthase complex*

$$(Glucose)_n + Glucose \; I \; \text{(P)} \longrightarrow \text{'starch'}$$

**Ribosomes**

**Circular DNA**

**Lipid globule**

**Starch granule** is the insoluble storage carbohydrate product of photosynthesis.

# Mineral requirements of plants

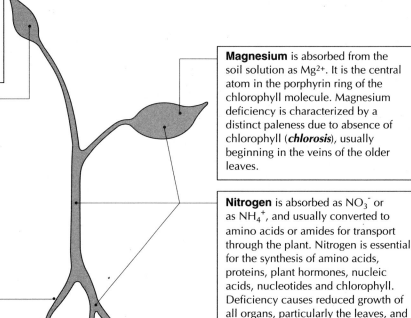

**Calcium** is absorbed as $Ca^{2+}$. It forms junctions between the molecules of pectate in the middle lamella, strengthening the binding of adjacent cells to one another. Deficiency leads to die-back of shoots due to death of apical buds.

**Phosphorus** is absorbed from the soil solution as $H_2PO_4^-$ (a type of phosphate). Its availability is probably *the major limiting factor* in plant growth in *uncultivated soils.* It is a component of nucleic acids, phospholipids and ATP. Lack of phosphorus usually affects processes which consume ATP, particularly the active uptake of minerals by roots.

**Magnesium** is absorbed from the soil solution as $Mg^{2+}$. It is the central atom in the porphyrin ring of the chlorophyll molecule. Magnesium deficiency is characterized by a distinct paleness due to absence of chlorophyll (***chlorosis***), usually beginning in the veins of the older leaves.

**Nitrogen** is absorbed as $NO_3^-$ or as $NH_4^+$, and usually converted to amino acids or amides for transport through the plant. Nitrogen is essential for the synthesis of amino acids, proteins, plant hormones, nucleic acids, nucleotides and chlorophyll. Deficiency causes reduced growth of all organs, particularly the leaves, and a marked chlorosis. Nitrogen availability is probably the ***major limiting factor*** in plant growth in ***cultivated soils.***

**HYDROPONICS** ('growing in water') permits study of plant deficiency symptoms in controlled conditions which eliminate the many variables associated with soil as a growth medium.

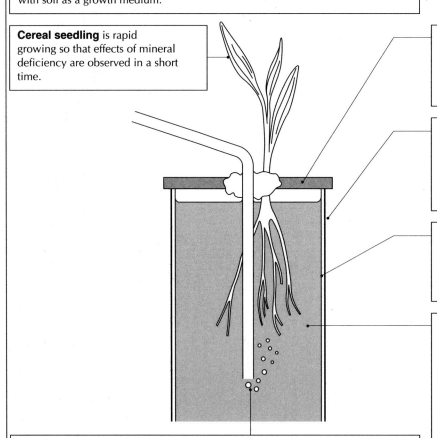

**Cereal seedling** is rapid growing so that effects of mineral deficiency are observed in a short time.

**Lightproof cover**
1. prevents entry of airborne contaminants and
2. supports seedling in growing position.

**Black card** or ***foil cover*** prevents entry of light so that no aquatic photoautotrophs can compete with seedling roots for mineral ions. Cover can be easily removed to examine the growth of the seedling roots.

**Glass container** can be thoroughly cleaned (using acid) so that no minute traces of mineral remain where they might lead to erroneous results.

**Growth/nutrient solution** contains mineral ions in previously determined optimum concentrations. Complete (control) solution contains ***all*** ions, test solutions have a single ion omitted. N.B. to eliminate ***one*** ion, a salt is omitted but its 'second' ion is replaced.
e.g. for nitrogen-free solution omit calcium nitrate but increase concentration of another calcium salt.
The complete solution is often called ***Knop's solution.***

**Aeration**
has two functions:
1. mixing of solution so that no stagnation occurs;
2. oxygenation so that aerobic (root) respiration may provide energy for active uptake of ions from solution by roots.

# Tissue distribution in an herbaceous stem

The tissue location provides *mechanical support* and *transport.*

**Phloem:** transport of organic solutes such as sucrose, amino acids. Some redistribution of ions.

Phloem parenchyma: packing

Companion cell: dense cytoplasm, many mitochondria. Loading/unloading/maintenance of sieve tube.

Sieve plate: may be a defence system to protect damaged phloem in 'wounded' plants.

**Cambium:** a lateral meristem. Simple, non-specialized cells divide and then differentiate into phloem (to outside) and xylem (to inside).

**Xylem:** transport of water and ions. Lignified cells offer support.

**Protoxylem:** incomplete lignification – may have cytoplasm

**Metaxylem:** heavily lignified secondary cell wall – no living contents

| Phloem | together comprise a |
| Intra-fascicular cambium | *vascular bundle* |
| Xylem | |

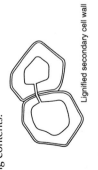

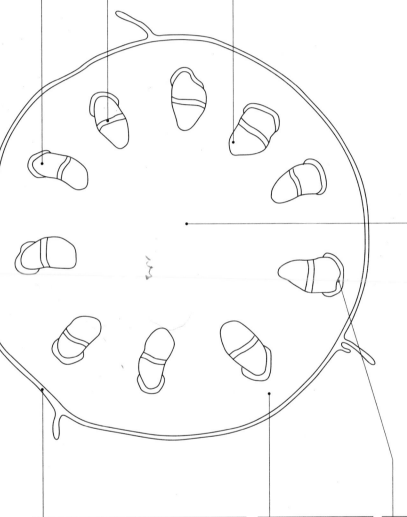

**Epidermis:** protects the moist inner tissues of the stem against desiccation and invasion by pathogens. Epidermis also contributes to support by holding in the turgid parenchyma cells of the cortex.

Waxy cuticle secreted by epidermal cells

The epidermis is typically one cell thick but may have extended unicellular or multicellular hairs which (a) reduce air movements and water loss and (b) reflect light and prevent overheating.

**Collenchyma:** provide support, especially in young stems as they are living cells and thus can expand as the stem grows.

Cellulose thickening at corners of cells

**Sclerenchyma:** are elongated into supporting fibres. Have heavily lignified secondary cell walls and thus have no living contents.

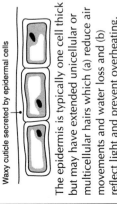

Lignified secondary cell wall

**Parenchyma:** is the basic unspecialized packing tissue of the plant body. Cells may store food (commonly starch) and may provide support when turgid. Intracellular air spaces aid diffusion of gases through plant body. Forms the *pith (inner cortex).*

# Tissue distribution in a dicotyledonous root

**Piliferous layer** is an epidermis modified to produce root hairs. The root hairs are outgrowths of a *single cell*. Layer is only one cell thick, has no protective function (hence no cuticle) and is soon lost by abrasion – hence root hairs only present on youngest part of root. Root hairs provide increased surface area for uptake of water and ions in solution.

**Exodermis:** protection against desiccation and invasion by pathogens. May replace epidermis in older roots, may become suberized and thus restrict water uptake to younger regions of root. Layer may be several cells thick.

Suberized cell walls

**Cortex:** composed of parenchyma. May store starch and can be infected by *Rhizobium* species to form root nodules in leguminous plants.

Intercellular air space allows diffusion of gases through the root

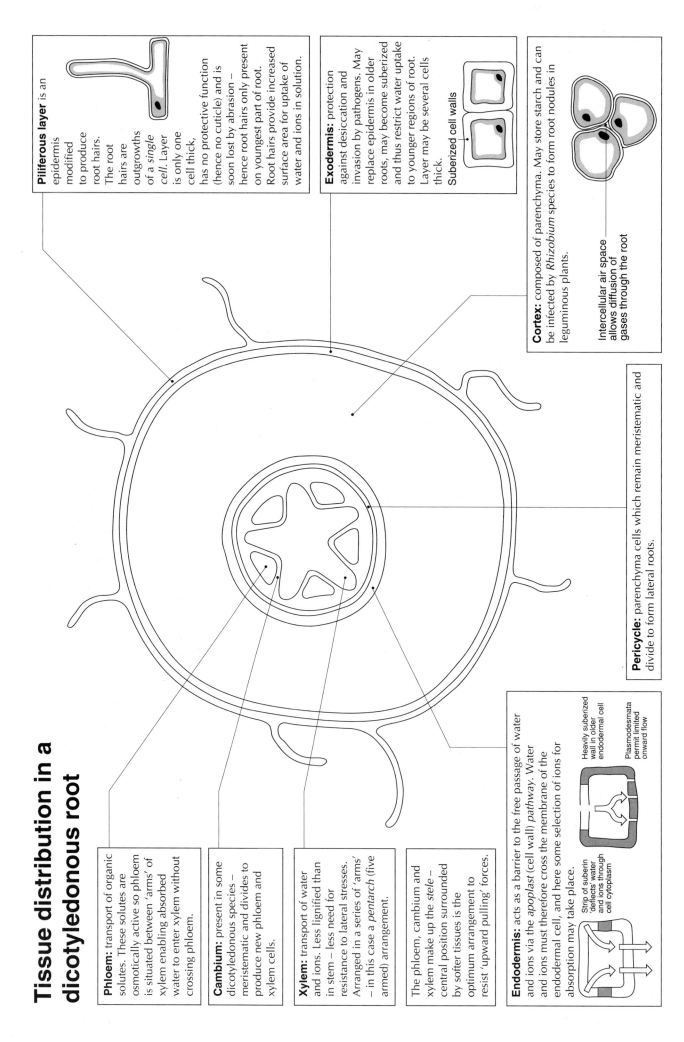

**Pericycle:** parenchyma cells which remain meristematic and divide to form lateral roots.

**Phloem:** transport of organic solutes. These solutes are osmotically active so phloem is situated between 'arms' of xylem enabling absorbed water to enter xylem without crossing phloem.

**Cambium:** present in some dicotyledonous species – meristematic and divides to produce new phloem and xylem cells.

**Xylem:** transport of water and ions. Less lignified than in stem – less need for resistance to lateral stresses. Arranged in a series of 'arms' – in this case a *pentarch* (five armed) arrangement.

The phloem, cambium and xylem make up the *stele* – central position surrounded by softer tissues is the optimum arrangement to resist 'upward pulling' forces.

**Endodermis:** acts as a barrier to the free passage of water and ions via the *apoplast* (cell wall) *pathway*. Water and ions must therefore cross the membrane of the endodermal cell, and here some selection of ions for absorption may take place.

Strip of suberin 'deflects' water and ions through cell cytoplasm

Heavily suberized wall in older endodermal cell

Plasmodesmata permit limited onward flow

# Evidence for phloem as the tissue for translocation

comes from the use of radioactive tracers, aphids and metabolic poisons.

The pattern of movement of these solutes within the plant body has also been investigated using radioisotopes, and it has been shown that the pattern of movement may be modified as the plant ages. Up to maturity the lower leaves of an actively photosynthesizing plant may pass their products to the roots for consumption and storage, but once fruit formation begins, ever-increasing numbers of leaves pass their products up to the fruits and eventually even the lower leaves are doing so. Minerals are often remobilized – having been delivered to the photosynthetic leaves via the xylem they may be re-exported through the phloem as the leaves age prior to abscission. The direction of solute movement is under the control of plant growth substances, particularly IAA and the cytokinins.

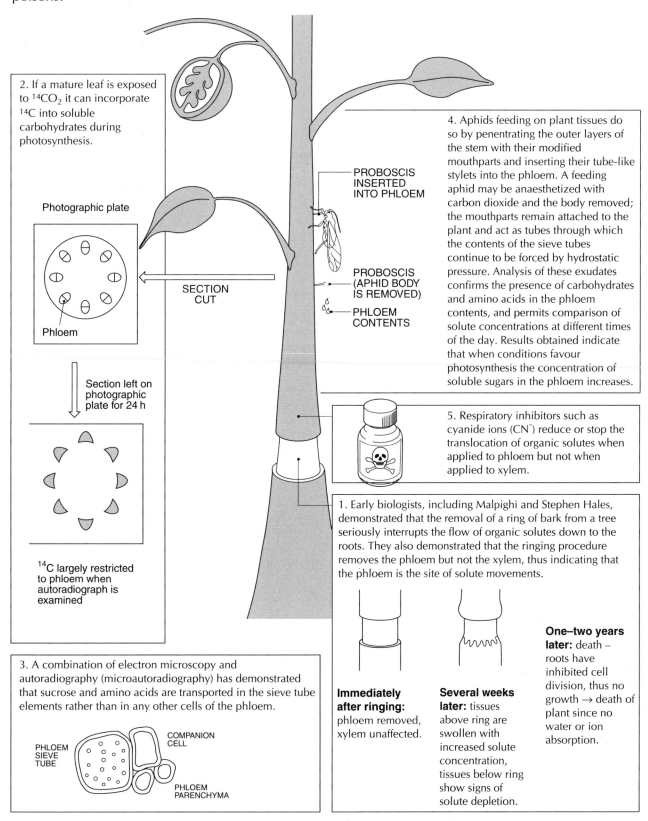

2. If a mature leaf is exposed to $^{14}CO_2$ it can incorporate $^{14}C$ into soluble carbohydrates during photosynthesis.

Photographic plate

Phloem

SECTION CUT

Section left on photographic plate for 24 h

$^{14}C$ largely restricted to phloem when autoradiograph is examined

PROBOSCIS INSERTED INTO PHLOEM

PROBOSCIS (APHID BODY IS REMOVED)

PHLOEM CONTENTS

4. Aphids feeding on plant tissues do so by penentrating the outer layers of the stem with their modified mouthparts and inserting their tube-like stylets into the phloem. A feeding aphid may be anaesthetized with carbon dioxide and the body removed; the mouthparts remain attached to the plant and act as tubes through which the contents of the sieve tubes continue to be forced by hydrostatic pressure. Analysis of these exudates confirms the presence of carbohydrates and amino acids in the phloem contents, and permits comparison of solute concentrations at different times of the day. Results obtained indicate that when conditions favour photosynthesis the concentration of soluble sugars in the phloem increases.

5. Respiratory inhibitors such as cyanide ions ($CN^-$) reduce or stop the translocation of organic solutes when applied to phloem but not when applied to xylem.

1. Early biologists, including Malpighi and Stephen Hales, demonstrated that the removal of a ring of bark from a tree seriously interrupts the flow of organic solutes down to the roots. They also demonstrated that the ringing procedure removes the phloem but not the xylem, thus indicating that the phloem is the site of solute movements.

**Immediately after ringing:** phloem removed, xylem unaffected.

**Several weeks later:** tissues above ring are swollen with increased solute concentration, tissues below ring show signs of solute depletion.

**One–two years later:** death – roots have inhibited cell division, thus no growth → death of plant since no water or ion absorption.

3. A combination of electron microscopy and autoradiography (microautoradiography) has demonstrated that sucrose and amino acids are transported in the sieve tube elements rather than in any other cells of the phloem.

PHLOEM SIEVE TUBE

COMPANION CELL

PHLOEM PARENCHYMA

# Water potential

**Water potential is a measure of the free kinetic energy of water in a system,** or the tendency of water to leave a system. It is measured in units of pressure (kPa) and is given the symbol $\psi$ ('psi').

For pure water the water potential is arbitrarily given the value 0: this is a reference point, rather like the redox potential system used in chemistry.

i.e. for pure water $\psi = 0$

In a solution the presence of molecules of solute prevents water molecules leaving. Thus

$$\psi_{SOLUTION} < 0$$

(In the solution the solute molecules 'hinder' the movement of the water molecules, thus the kinetic energy of the water

**Water moves down a gradient of water potential,** i.e. from a less negative (e.g. -500 kPa) to a more negative (e.g. -1000 kPa) water potential.

## The advantages of the water potential nomenclature

1. the movement of water is considered from the 'system's' point of view, rather than from that of the environment;

2. comparison between different systems can be made, e.g. between the atmosphere, the air in the spaces of a leaf and the leaf mesophyll cells.

We should remember that:

**Osmosis is the movement of water, through a partially permeable membrane, along a water potential gradient.**

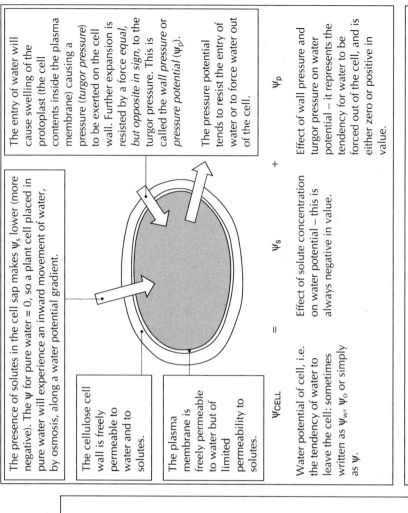

The presence of solutes in the cell sap makes $\psi_s$ lower (more negative). The $\psi$ for pure water = 0, so a plant cell placed in pure water will experience an inward movement of water, by osmosis, along a water potential gradient.

The entry of water will cause swelling of the protoplast (the cell contents inside the plasma membrane) causing a pressure (*turgor pressure*) to be exerted on the cell wall. Further expansion is resisted by a force *equal, but opposite in sign,* to the turgor pressure. This is called the *wall pressure or pressure potential* ($\psi_p$).

The pressure potential tends to resist the entry of water or to force water out of the cell.

The cellulose cell wall is freely permeable to water and to solutes.

The plasma membrane is freely permeable to water but of limited permeability to solutes.

$$\psi_{CELL} \quad = \quad \psi_s \quad + \quad \psi_p$$

Water potential of cell, i.e. the tendency of water to leave the cell: sometimes written as $\psi_w$, $\psi_o$ or simply as $\psi$.

Effect of solute concentration on water potential – this is always negative in value.

Effect of wall pressure and turgor pressure on water potential – it represents the tendency for water to be forced out of the cell, and is either zero or positive in value.

## Water movement between cells:

1. Calculate $\psi$ for each cell from $\psi_s$ and $\psi_p$.

2. Predict direction of water movement since water moves *down the gradient of water potential.*

Cell A

$\psi_s = -1300$ kPa
$\psi_p = -500$ kPa

$\psi = -1300 + 500$
$= -800$ kPa

Cell B

$\psi_s = -1900$ kPa
$\psi_p = 700$ kPa

$\psi = -1900 + 700$
$= -1200$ kPa

Since -800 is a higher number than -1200 *water will move by osmosis down a water potential gradient from A → B.*

WATER POTENTIAL OF SYSTEM kPa

0

−500

−1000

# Water relationships of plant cells

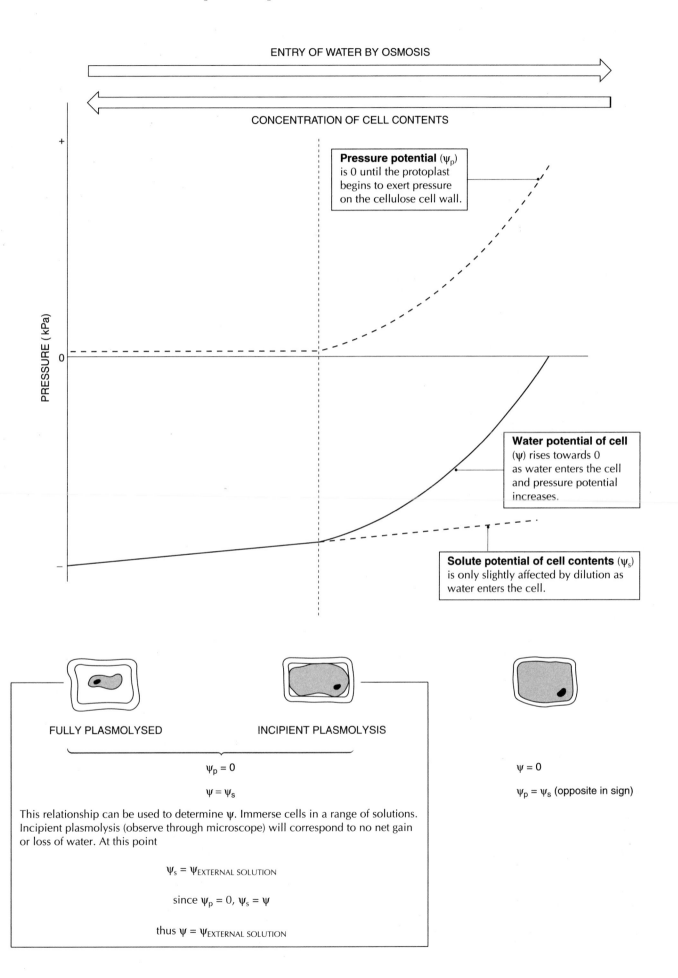

ENTRY OF WATER BY OSMOSIS

CONCENTRATION OF CELL CONTENTS

PRESSURE (kPa)

**Pressure potential** ($\psi_p$) is 0 until the protoplast begins to exert pressure on the cellulose cell wall.

**Water potential of cell** ($\psi$) rises towards 0 as water enters the cell and pressure potential increases.

**Solute potential of cell contents** ($\psi_s$) is only slightly affected by dilution as water enters the cell.

FULLY PLASMOLYSED                    INCIPIENT PLASMOLYSIS

$\psi_p = 0$

$\psi = \psi_s$

This relationship can be used to determine $\psi$. Immerse cells in a range of solutions. Incipient plasmolysis (observe through microscope) will correspond to no net gain or loss of water. At this point

$$\psi_s = \psi_{\text{EXTERNAL SOLUTION}}$$

$$\text{since } \psi_p = 0, \psi_s = \psi$$

$$\text{thus } \psi = \psi_{\text{EXTERNAL SOLUTION}}$$

$\psi = 0$

$\psi_p = \psi_s$ (opposite in sign)

# Stomata represent an important adaptation to life in a terrestrial environment.

**Adjacent epidermal cells:** note that there is no *symplastic* connection (i.e. no *plasmodesmata*) between these cells and the guard cells. The adjacent epidermal cells do not have the chloroplasts or the dense cytoplasm typical of guard cells.

## Guard cells

1. Change *shape* as their *degree of turgor* is altered. The reason for this is twofold:

   a. the inner guard cell wall has microfibrils orientated so that longitudinal expansion is not easy;

   b. the outer wall is less thickened with cellulose so that it elongates much more readily than the inner wall.

2. May alter their *solute potential*, and thus their *water potential*, by the movement of ions, principally potassium ions, K⁺.

An ATP-dependent proton pump moves H⁺ *out of the* guard cells, creating an electrochemical gradient (inside *negative* with respect to *outside*) so that K⁺ can flow passively through K⁺ channels down this electrochemical gradient.

K⁺ movement *in* → reduced water potential → water movement *in*.

## Control of stomatal aperture: must permit

a. entry of enough $CO_2$ to permit photosynthesis;

b. control water loss to prevent desiccation of plant tissues

and has both *internal* (plant growth regulators) and *environmental* (e.g. air humidity) *signals*.

**Stomatal opening** is promoted by:

1. *low intercellular [$CO_2$]*: sensed by guard cells and corresponds to the need for more $CO_2$ to maintain rates of photosynthesis.

2. *high light intensity*: light absorbed by chlorophyll (the PAR photosystem) provides ATP by photophosphorylation – this increases proton pumping and 'opens' stomata when light is available – 'anticipating' the need for more $CO_2$ for photosynthesis. This is a *feedforward response*. There is a second (blue-light photosystem) response for opening stomata in shady conditions, or at dawn.

**Stomatal closure** is triggered by:

1. *low environmental humidity*;

2. *increasing leaf temperature*; both of which are signals that the need to conserve water must override the need to allow $CO_2$ uptake. This response is triggered by the water content of leaf epidermal and mesophyll cells and it is a *feedback response*. (N.B. at very high temperatures stomata may open very wide to allow maximum leaf cooling by evapotranspiration from mesophyll cells.)

3. *Abscisic acid secretion*: severe drought stress is detected in epidermal cells which secrete ABA into the apoplast causing rapid and immediate stomatal closure (possibly by inhibiting the proton pump).

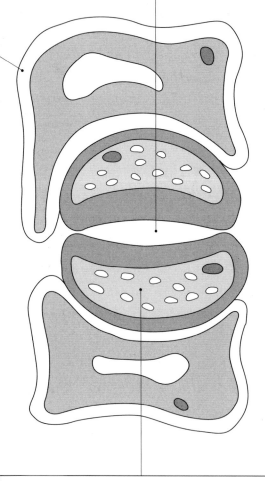

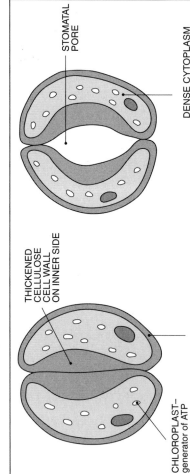

STOMATAL PORE

DENSE CYTOPLASM WITH STARCH GRAINS

**Open:** Guard cells are *turgid* because water has been gained from the *apoplast system* of the epidermis.

**Reason:** [K⁺] in guard cells has risen – low water potential thus allows water to enter the guard cells.

THICKENED CELLULOSE CELL WALL ON INNER SIDE

THIN OUTER WALL

CHLOROPLAST – generator of ATP

**Closed:** guard cells are *flaccid* because water has been lost to the *apoplast system* of the epidermis.

**Reason:** [K⁺] in guard cells has fallen – high water potential thus allows water to leave the guard cells.

# Cohesion–tension theory of transpiration

**4. Water moves through leaf tissues** via *apoplast* (cell wall), *symplast* (cytoplasmic) and *vacuolar* pathways.

**1. Water evaporates** from the surface of epidermal cells.

**5. Water leaves the xylem** via vessels with very little lignification (i.e. with freely permeable cellulose cell walls). Moves into apoplast due to *cohesion* and into symplast/vacuoles by *osmosis* along a *water potential gradient.*

**3. Water evaporates** from the cellulose cell walls of cells of the palisade and spongy mesophyll into the sub-stomatal chamber.

**2. Water diffuses** from sub-stomatal chamber into the atmosphere: the rate of movement will be influenced by any factor which changes the water potential gradient between this chamber and the atmosphere.

**6. Water is drawn up xylem** since transpiration causes a state of *tension* or *negative pressure* in the xylem vessels. The replacement molecules of water form a continuous stream due to *cohesion* (attractive forces between water molecules caused by hydrogen bonding) and *adhesion* (attractive forces between molecules of water and the inside surfaces of the lignified xylem vessels).

**8. Casparian band** (impregnation of cell wall suberin) of the *endodermis* prevents water movement via apoplast pathway – all water movement via *symplast/vacuolar* pathways, from endodermis to pericycle.

**9. Water uptake** occurs by *osmosis* along a *water potential gradient* from the soil solution primarily, but not completely, into *root hair cells.*

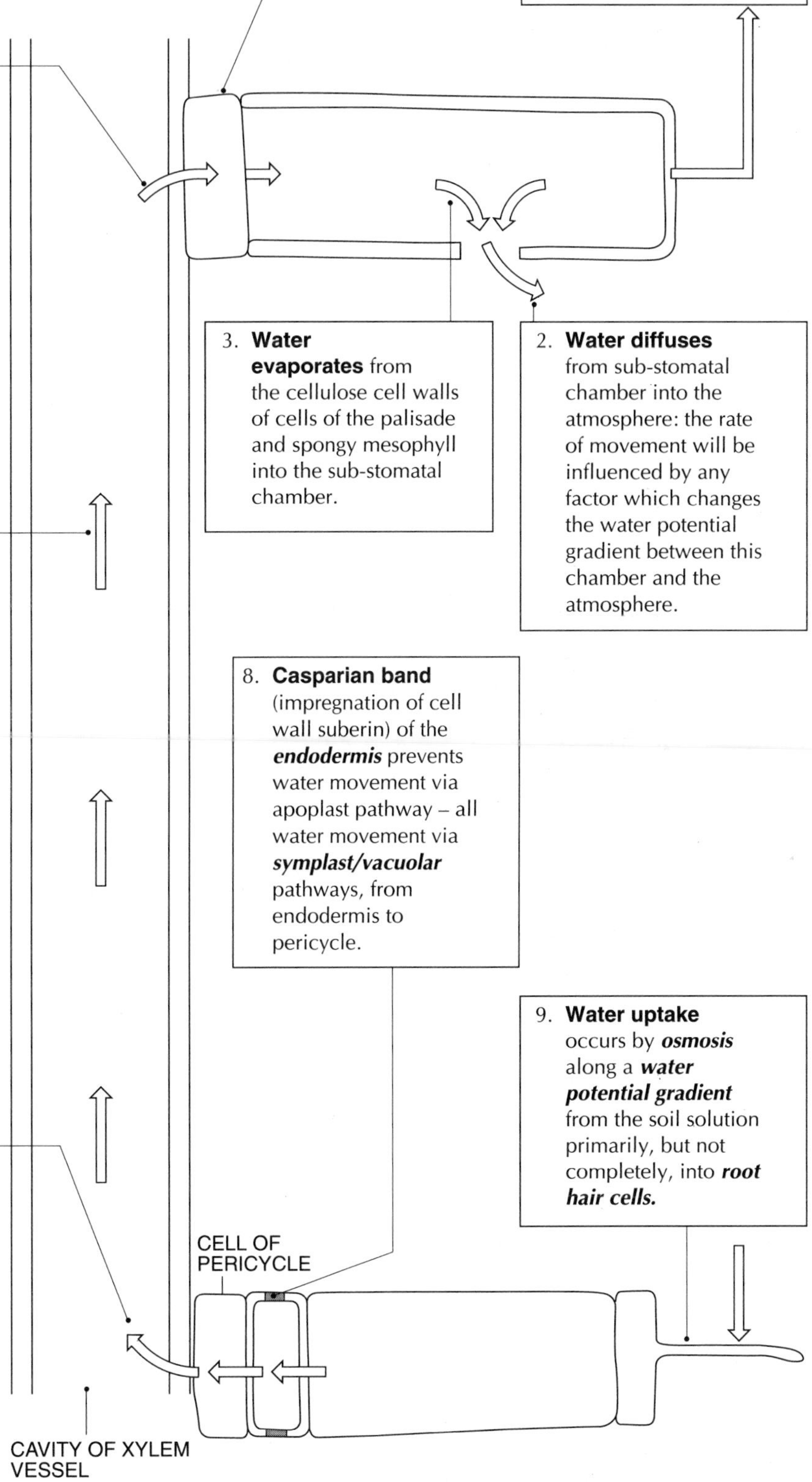

**7. Water enters xylem** through poorly lignified cell walls due to *cohesion* (from apoplast) and *osmosis* along a *water potential gradient* from the symplast/vacuolar pathways.

CELL OF PERICYCLE

CAVITY OF XYLEM VESSEL

**Water movement through the plant** occurs as a result of very large differences in water potential between the atmosphere and the soil solution. The process begins with *evaporation* from the leaf surfaces, is continued due to *cohesion* between water molecules and *tension* in the xylem vessels and is completed by *osmosis* from the soil solution.

# The bubble potometer

measures **water uptake** (= water loss by transpiration + water consumption for cell expansion and photosynthesis).

## PROCEDURE

1. The leafy shoot must be cut *under water*, the apparatus must be filled *under water* and the shoot fixed to the potometer *under water* to prevent air locks in the system.

2. Allow plant to equilibrate (5 min) before introduction of air bubble. Take at least three readings of rate of bubble movement, and use reservoir to return bubble to zero on each occasion. Calculate mean of readings. Record air temperature.

3. Scale can be calibrated by introducing a known mass of mercury into the capillary tubing and using $\rho = m/v$ ($\rho$ for mercury is known, $m$ can be measured, thus $v$ corresponding to a measured distance of bubble movement can be determined).

4. Rate of water uptake per unit area of leaves can be calculated by measurement of leaf area.

## EXTERNAL FACTORS AFFECTING TRANSPIRATION

**Light intensity:** use bench lamp (with water bath to act as heat filter) to increase light intensity. To simulate 'darkness' enclose shoot in black polythene bag.

**Humidity:** enclose shoot in clear plastic bag to *increase* relative humidity of atmosphere – include water absorbant such as calcium chloride to *decrease* relative humidity.

**Wind:** use small electric fan with 'cool' control to mimic air movements whilst avoiding effects of temperature changes.

May also determine relative importance of upper surface/lower surface/stem/petiole in water loss by smearing with vaseline (acts like a waxy cuticle) as appropriate.

N.B. It is sometimes difficult to change only one condition at a time, e.g. enclosure in a black bag to eliminate light will also increase the relative humidity of the atmosphere.

**Water uptake**

Water 'lost' by transpiration (98%)

Water used in photosynthesis (1%)

Water used in building of protoplasm (1%)

**Reservoir of water:** may be connected to capillary tubing if the tap is opened. This is used to prevent the air bubble entering the plant, and to move the bubble back along the capillary tube.

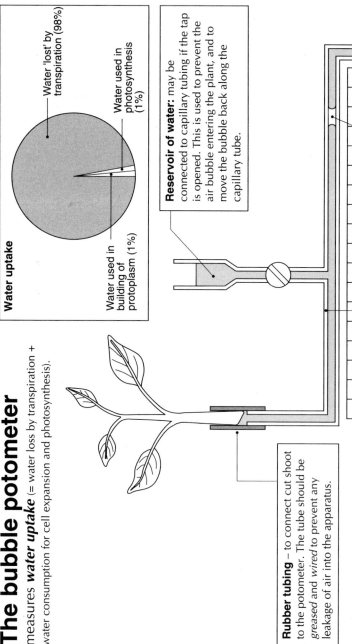

**Capillary tube:** must be kept horizontal to prevent the bubble moving due to its density compared with water.

**Air bubble:** inserted by removal of tube end from beaker of water. Movement corresponds to water uptake by the cut shoot.

**Graduated scale:** permits direct reading of bubble movement/water uptake.

**Rubber tubing** – to connect cut shoot to the potometer. The tube should be *greased* and *wired* to prevent any leakage of air into the apparatus.

**Atmometer control:** The atmometer is an instrument which can measure evaporation from a non-living surface. When subjected to the same conditions as a potometer the changes in the rate of evaporation from a plant and from a purely physical system can be compared – for example, a reduction in light intensity will show a decrease in water loss *only from a potometer* (due to stomatal closure). The atmometer control indicates when the potometer is acting as a free evaporator and when it is affected by physiological factors such as photosynthesis and stomatal closure.

This porous pot replaces the cut shoot

# Plant growth substances

**Auxins** are used as defoliants, e.g. during the Vietnam War to clear areas of vegetation and make bombing of bridges, roads, and troops easier. Also used to remove vegetation from overhead power lines – manual removal would be costly and dangerous.

A mixture of *auxin*, *cytokinin* and *gibberellin* will inhibit apical growth and allow limited development of lateral buds. This mixture applied to hedges promotes dense, bushy growth and limits the need for mechanical trimming to one or two occasions per year.

**Giberellic acid** may mimic red light: control of flowering time (promote long-day species, inhibit short-day species) means flowers can be available 'out of season'.

**Ethene** sprayed onto day-neutral species such as pineapple can synchronize flowering/fruiting so that crop picking can be more efficient.

**Auxins** used as pre-emergent herbicides to prevent germination of weed species and as post-emergent herbicides to remove scrub or competitors for crops.

**Auxin** can inhibit 'sprouting' (lateral bud development) in stored potatoes.

**Cytokinins** delay leaf senescence and are used to maintain the life of fresh, leafy crops such as lettuce.

---

**Lateral bud development** is inhibited by *auxin* but promoted by *cytokinin* (*antagonism*).

**Stomatal closure** under stress may be promoted by *abscisic acid*.

**Flowering** may be triggered by *florigen*.

**Root growth** of adventitious roots is promoted by *auxin*.

N.B. Many commercial applications of these growth phenomena rely on *plant growth regulators*, which are synthetic derivatives of the natural compounds, but are usually more effective in lower concentrations because they are degraded less rapidly by the plant.

## NATURAL PLANT GROWTH HORMONES

**Ethene** is used to accelerate ripening – ideal for grapes which can be picked earlier and thus have a longer drying period for forming raisins. Ripening can be delayed by keeping fruits in an oxygen-free atmosphere: ethene can then induce ripening as required.

**Growth of stem**: cell enlargement is promoted by *auxin* and *gibberellin*. Redistribution of *auxin* causes phototropism.

**Seed dormancy** is maintained by *abscisic acid* but is broken by *gibberellic acid*.

**Leaf fall** is promoted by *abscisic acid*.

**Root growth** is *promoted* by *auxin* at *low* concentration but *inhibited* at *high auxin* concentration.

**Gibberellins** increase fruit size in grapes if applied just after flowers open since some ovules abort – 'crowding' is reduced allowing more nutrients to reach remaining fruits and limiting fungal infections.

**Cytokinin** can promote fruit growth, and synergistically with *auxin* and *gibberellin* can promote parthenocarpy. This is useful if seed fails to 'set' due to poor pollinating conditions, and 'seedless' (parthenocarpic) fruits are popular with consumers.

**Auxin** can prevent premature fruit drop (windfall losses) since it is antagonistic to *abscisic acid*.

**Auxin** can act as a selective lawn weed killer since broad leaved 'weed' species are killed by *auxin* concentrations which do not affect monocotyledons.

# Structure of a typical flower

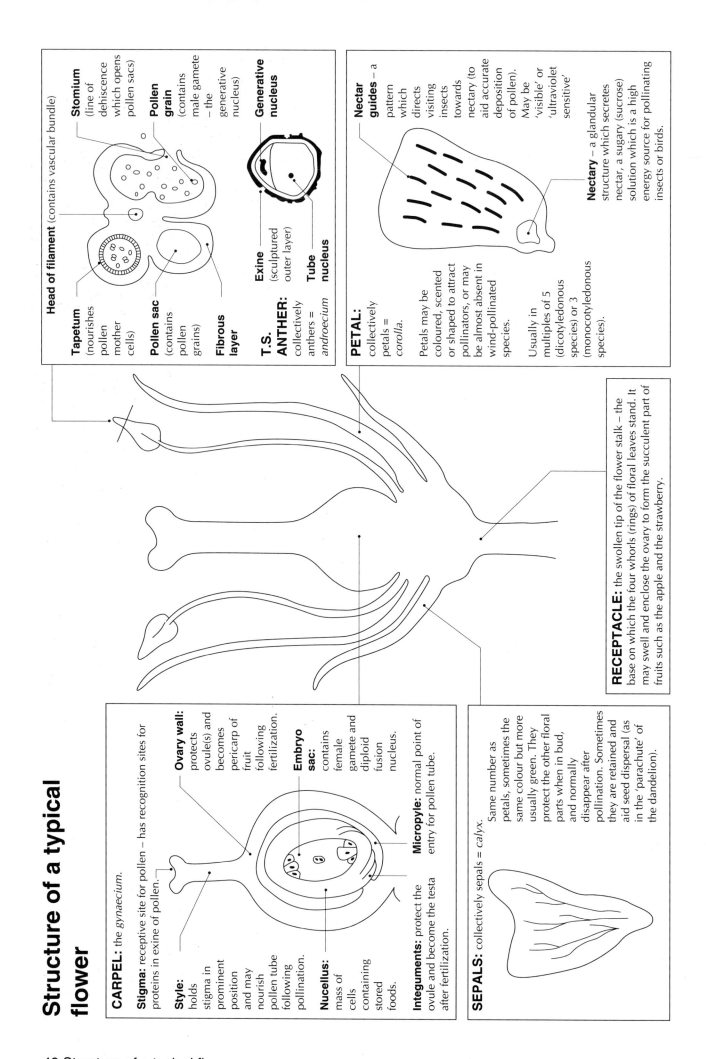

**Head of filament** (contains vascular bundle)

**Stomium** (line of dehiscence which opens pollen sacs)

**Pollen grain** (contains male gamete – the generative nucleus)

**Generative nucleus**

**Tapetum** (nourishes pollen mother cells)

**Pollen sac** (contains pollen grains)

**Fibrous layer**

**Exine** (sculptured outer layer)

**Tube nucleus**

**T.S. ANTHER:** collectively anthers = *androecium*

**Nectar guides** – a pattern which directs visiting insects towards nectary (to aid accurate deposition of pollen). May be 'visible' or 'ultraviolet sensitive'

**Nectary** – a glandular structure which secretes nectar, a sugary (sucrose) solution which is a high energy source for pollinating insects or birds.

**PETAL:** collectively petals = *corolla*.

Petals may be coloured, scented or shaped to attract pollinators, or may be almost absent in wind-pollinated species.

Usually in multiples of 5 (dicotyledonous species) or 3 (monocotyledonous species).

**RECEPTACLE:** the swollen tip of the flower stalk – the base on which the four whorls (rings) of floral leaves stand. It may swell and enclose the ovary to form the succulent part of fruits such as the apple and the strawberry.

**CARPEL:** the *gynaecium*.

**Stigma:** receptive site for pollen – has recognition sites for proteins in exine of pollen.

**Style:** holds stigma in prominent position and may nourish pollen tube following pollination.

**Ovary wall:** protects ovule(s) and becomes pericarp of fruit following fertilization.

**Embryo sac:** contains female gamete and diploid fusion nucleus.

**Micropyle:** normal point of entry for pollen tube.

**Nucellus:** mass of cells containing stored foods.

**Integuments:** protect the ovule and become the testa after fertilization.

**SEPALS:** collectively sepals = *calyx*.

Same number as petals, sometimes the same colour but more usually green. They protect the other floral parts when in bud, and normally disappear after pollination. Sometimes they are retained and aid seed dispersal (as in the 'parachute' of the dandelion).

# Wind-pollinated (anemophilous) flowers

are typically grasses or forest tree species which occur in dense groups covering very large areas.

# Insect-pollinated (entomophilous) flowers

typically belong to species which are solitary or exist in small groups.

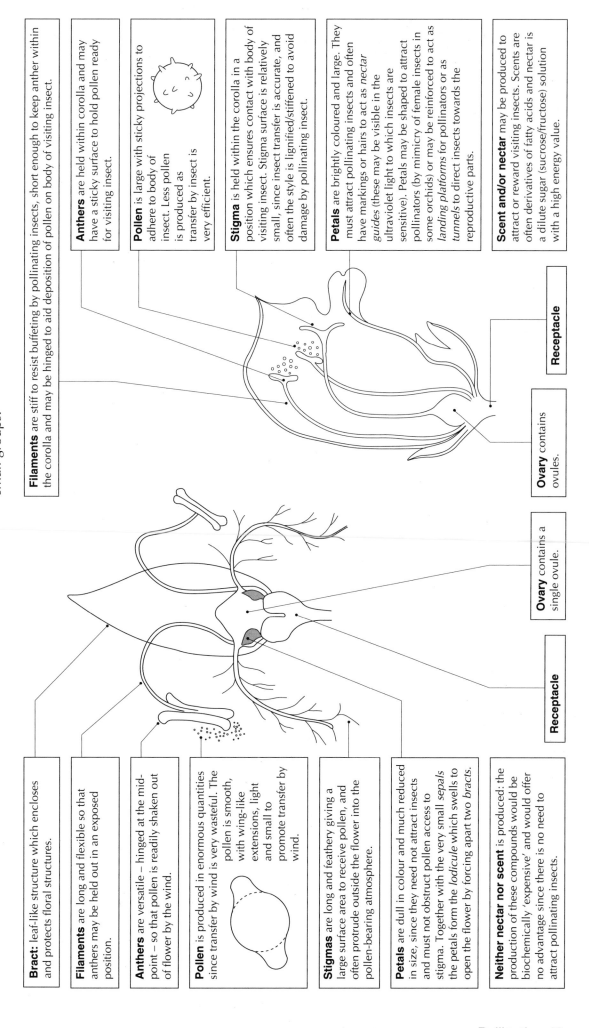

**Filaments** are stiff to resist buffeting by pollinating insects, short enough to keep anther within the corolla and may be hinged to aid deposition of pollen on body of visiting insect.

**Anthers** are held within corolla and may have a sticky surface to hold pollen ready for visiting insect.

**Pollen** is large with sticky projections to adhere to body of insect. Less pollen is produced as transfer by insect is very efficient.

**Stigma** is held within the corolla in a position which ensures contact with body of visiting insect. Stigma surface is relatively small, since insect transfer is accurate, and often the style is lignified/stiffened to avoid damage by pollinating insect.

**Petals** are brightly coloured and large. They must attract pollinating insects and often have markings or hairs to act as *nectar guides* (these may be visible in the ultraviolet light to which insects are sensitive). Petals may be shaped to attract pollinators (by mimicry of female insects in some orchids) or may be reinforced to act as *landing platforms* for pollinators or as *tunnels* to direct insects towards the reproductive parts.

**Scent and/or nectar** may be produced to attract or reward visiting insects. Scents are often derivatives of fatty acids and nectar is a dilute sugar (sucrose/fructose) solution with a high energy value.

**Receptacle**

**Ovary** contains ovules.

**Bract:** leaf-like structure which encloses and protects floral structures.

**Filaments** are long and flexible so that anthers may be held out in an exposed position.

**Anthers** are versatile – hinged at the mid-point – so that pollen is readily shaken out of flower by the wind.

**Pollen** is produced in enormous quantities since transfer by wind is very wasteful. The pollen is smooth, with wing-like extensions, light and small to promote transfer by wind.

**Stigmas** are long and feathery giving a large surface area to receive pollen, and often protrude outside the flower into the pollen-bearing atmosphere.

**Petals** are dull in colour and much reduced in size, since they need not attract insects and must not obstruct pollen access to stigma. Together with the very small *sepals* the petals form the *lodicule* which swells to open the flower by forcing apart two *bracts*.

**Neither nectar nor scent** is produced: the production of these compounds would be biochemically 'expensive' and would offer no advantage since there is no need to attract pollinating insects.

**Receptacle**

**Ovary** contains a single ovule.

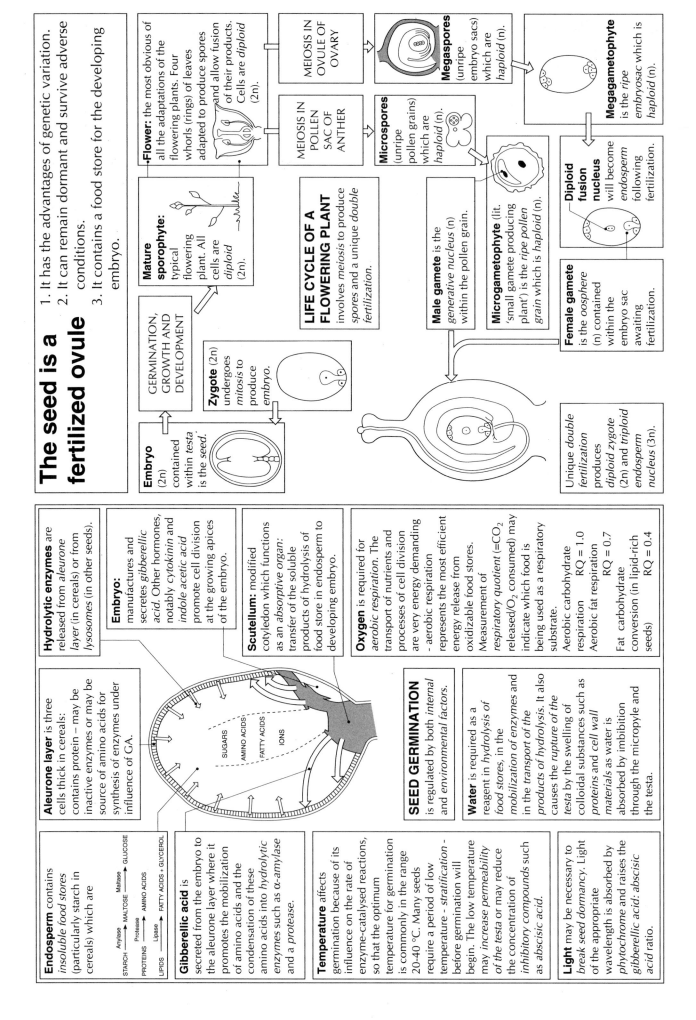

# The seed is a fertilized ovule

1. It has the advantages of genetic variation.
2. It can remain dormant and survive adverse conditions.
3. It contains a food store for the developing embryo.

**Flower:** the most obvious of all the adaptations of the flowering plants. Four whorls (rings) of leaves adapted to produce spores and allow fusion of their products. Cells are *diploid* (2n).

**MEIOSIS IN OVULE OF OVARY**

**Megaspores** (unripe embryo sacs) which are *haploid* (n).

**Megagametophyte** is the ripe embryosac which is *haploid* (n).

**Mature sporophyte:** typical flowering plant. All cells are *diploid* (2n)

**MEIOSIS IN POLLEN SAC OF ANTHER**

**Microspores** (unripe pollen grains) which are *haploid* (n).

**Microgametophyte** (lit. 'small gamete producing plant') is the *ripe pollen grain* which is *haploid* (n).

**LIFE CYCLE OF A FLOWERING PLANT**
involves *meiosis* to produce *spores* and a unique *double fertilization*.

**Male gamete** is the *generative nucleus* (n) within the pollen grain.

**Diploid fusion nucleus** will become *endosperm* following fertilization.

**GERMINATION, GROWTH AND DEVELOPMENT**

**Zygote** (2n) undergoes *mitosis* to produce *embryo*.

**Female gamete** is the *oosphere* (n) contained within the embryo sac awaiting fertilization.

**Embryo** (2n) contained within *testa* is the *seed*.

Unique *double fertilization* produces *diploid zygote* (2n) and *triploid endosperm nucleus* (3n).

---

**Endosperm** contains *insoluble food stores* (particularly starch in cereals) which are

STARCH — Amylase → MALTOSE — Maltase → GLUCOSE
PROTEINS — Protease → AMINO ACIDS
LIPIDS — Lipase → FATTY ACIDS + GLYCEROL

**Gibberellic acid** is secreted from the embryo to the aleurone layer where it promotes the mobilization of amino acids and the condensation of these amino acids into *hydrolytic* enzymes such as *α-amylase* and a *protease*.

**Aleurone layer** is three cells thick in cereals: contains protein – may be inactive enzymes or may be source of amino acids for synthesis of enzymes under influence of GA.

**Hydrolytic enzymes** are released from *aleurone layer* (in cereals) or from *lysosomes* (in other seeds).

**Embryo:** manufactures and secretes *gibberellic acid*. Other hormones, notably *cytokinin* and *indole acetic acid* promote cell division at the growing apices of the embryo.

**Scutellum:** modified cotyledon which functions as an *absorptive organ:* transfer of the soluble products of hydrolysis of food store in endosperm to developing embryo.

SUGARS
AMINO ACIDS
FATTY ACIDS
IONS

**Temperature** affects germination because of its influence on the rate of enzyme-catalysed reactions, so that the optimum temperature for germination is commonly in the range 20–40 °C. Many seeds require a period of low temperature - *stratification* - before germination will begin. The low temperature may *increase permeability of the testa* or may reduce the concentration of inhibitory compounds such as *abscisic acid.*

**SEED GERMINATION** is regulated by both *internal* and *environmental* factors.

**Water** is required as a reagent in *hydrolysis of food stores*, in the *mobilization of enzymes* and in the *transport of the products of hydrolysis*. It also causes the *rupture of the testa* by the swelling of colloidal substances such as *proteins* and *cell wall* materials as water is absorbed by imbibition through the micropyle and the testa.

**Oxygen** is required for *aerobic respiration*. The transport of nutrients and processes of cell division are very energy demanding - aerobic respiration represents the most efficient energy release from oxidizable food stores. Measurement of *respiratory quotient* (=$CO_2$ released/$O_2$ consumed) may indicate which food is being used as a respiratory substrate.

Aerobic carbohydrate respiration   RQ = 1.0
Aerobic fat respiration   RQ = 0.7
Fat carbohydrate conversion (in lipid-rich seeds)   RQ = 0.4

**Light** may be necessary to *break seed dormancy*. Light of the appropriate wavelength is absorbed by *phytochrome* and raises the *gibberellic acid: abscisic acid* ratio.

**Ecology** is the 'study of living organisms in relation to their environment'.

A more recent definition is 'the scientific study of the interactions that determine the distribution and abundance of organisms'.

**Synecology** is the study of groups of organisms associated to form a functional unit of the environment.

Two useful terms are

**Community** *(biotic community):* all of the populations occupying a given, defined physical area, e.g. all the organisms within a rock pool.

**Ecosystem:** the biotic community together with the physical (non-living or abiotic) environment, e.g. a rock pool.

**Autecology** is the study of *single organisms* or *populations of single species* and their relationship to their environment, e.g. Common limpet (*Patella vulgaris*) – an animal of the rocky shore.

What does it **feed on**?

How does it **avoid drying out**?

How does it **minimize damage from wave action**?

What are its **predators**?

How does it **reproduce**?

How do its young **disperse**?

What are its **competitors**?

A **rock pool ecosystem** is maintained by a series of *interactions*.

**Abiotic factors** (including temperature, volume of water, pH, salinity, substrate).

interacting with

**The biotic community**

N.B. The rock pool is not self-sustaining and relies on the twice-daily tidal cycle for maintenance of optimum abiotic (e.g. temperature, salinity) and biotic (e.g. nutrients, new colonizers) factors.

**Autotrophes** – the *producers* – which require an input of light and inorganic nutrients. Include algae and phytoplankton.

interacting with

**Heterotrophes** – the *consumers* – which include herbivores, carnivores, omnivores and decomposers

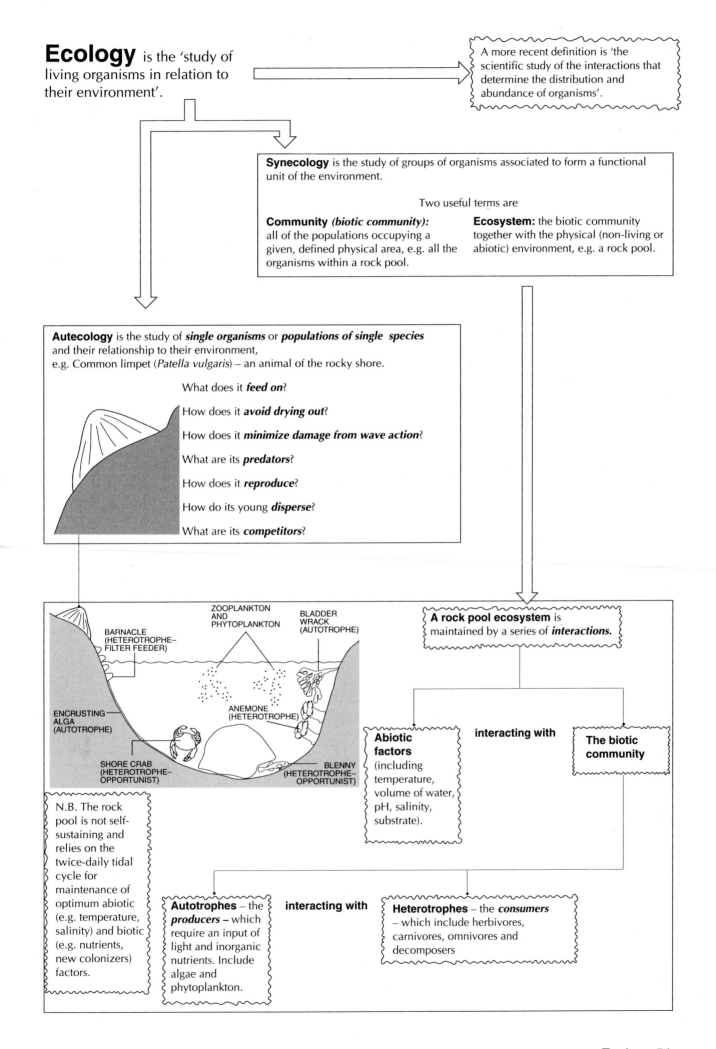

ZOOPLANKTON AND PHYTOPLANKTON

BLADDER WRACK (AUTOTROPHE)

BARNACLE (HETEROTROPHE– FILTER FEEDER)

ENCRUSTING ALGA (AUTOTROPHE)

ANEMONE (HETEROTROPHE)

SHORE CRAB (HETEROTROPHE– OPPORTUNIST)

BLENNY (HETEROTROPHE– OPPORTUNIST)

# Energy flow through an ecosystem: I

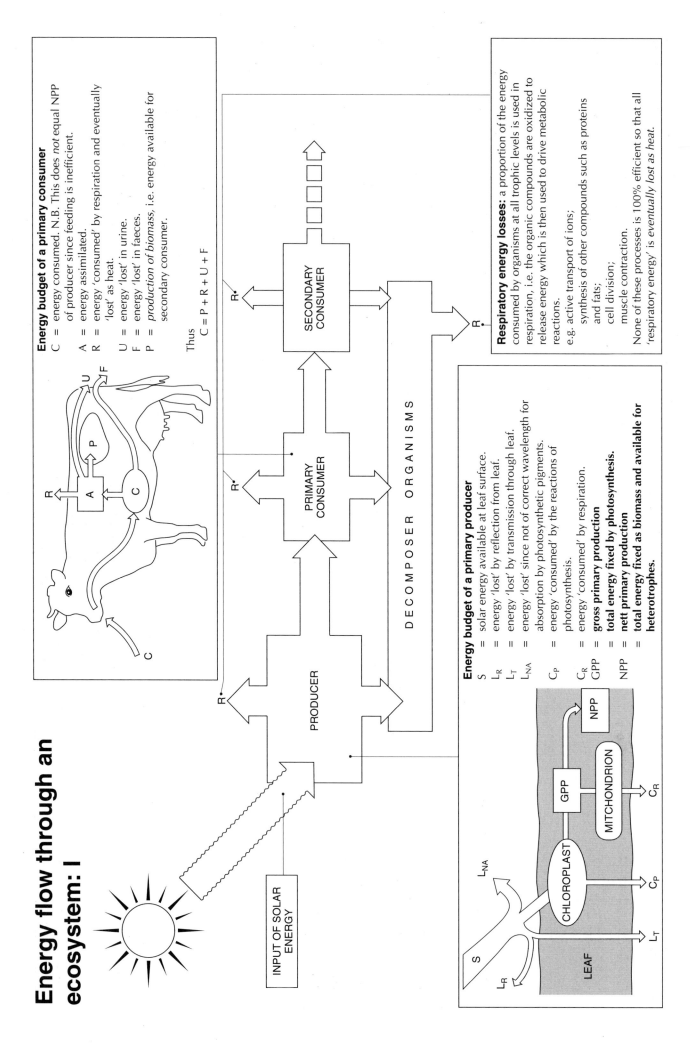

**Energy budget of a primary consumer**

C = energy consumed. N.B. This does *not* equal NPP of producer since feeding is inefficient.

A = energy assimilated.

R = energy 'consumed' by respiration and eventually 'lost' as heat.

U = energy 'lost' in urine.

F = energy 'lost' in faeces.

P = *production of biomass*, i.e. energy available for secondary consumer.

Thus

$$C = P + R + U + F$$

**Respiratory energy losses:** a proportion of the energy consumed by organisms at all trophic levels is used in respiration, i.e. the organic compounds are oxidized to release energy which is then used to drive metabolic reactions.

e.g. active transport of ions;

synthesis of other compounds such as proteins and fats;

cell division;

muscle contraction.

None of these processes is 100% efficient so that all 'respiratory energy' is eventually *lost as heat.*

**Energy budget of a primary producer**

S = solar energy available at leaf surface.

$L_R$ = energy 'lost' by reflection from leaf.

$L_T$ = energy 'lost' by transmission through leaf.

$L_{NA}$ = energy 'lost' since not of correct wavelength for absorption by photosynthetic pigments.

$C_P$ = energy 'consumed' by the reactions of photosynthesis.

$C_R$ = energy 'consumed' by respiration.

GPP = **gross primary production**
    = **total energy fixed by photosynthesis.**

NPP = **nett primary production**
    = **total energy fixed as biomass and available for heterotrophes.**

PRODUCER

PRIMARY CONSUMER

SECONDARY CONSUMER

D E C O M P O S E R   O R G A N I S M S

INPUT OF SOLAR ENERGY

LEAF

CHLOROPLAST

MITCHONDRION

GPP

NPP

# Energy flow through an ecosystem: II

**A closed ecosystem** is rare: migratory animals may deposit faeces, fruits and seeds may enter or leave during dispersal, and leaves may blow in from surrounding trees.

The *gross primary production (GPP)* – the total energy fixed by photosynthesis – represents only about 0.5–1% of the light energy available to the leaf.

At the equator, the *solar flux* (sunlight which reaches the Earth's upper atmosphere) is almost constant at 1.4 kJ m⁻² s⁻¹. Most of this incoming sunlight energy is reflected by the atmosphere, heats the atmosphere and Earth's surface or causes the evaporation of water. Less than 0.1% actually falls on leaves and is thus available for photosynthesis.

The *net primary production (NPP)* is the energy available for consumption by the heterotrophes. NPP can therefore be used to compare the productivity of different ecosystems. For example:

| ECOSYSTEM | NPP (arbitrary units) |
|---|---|
| Coral reef | 1000 |
| Rainforest | 880 |
| Estuaries | 600 |
| Deciduous forest | 500 |
| Grassland | 260 |
| Open ocean | 50 |
| Desert | 2 |

Productivity may be expressed as *units of energy* (e.g. kJ m⁻² yr⁻¹) or *units of mass* (e.g. kg m⁻² yr⁻¹).

Energy transfer from producer to primary consumer is typically in the order of 5–10% of NPP. This is because
1. Much of plant biomass (NPP) is indigestible to herbivores – there are no animal enzymes to digest lignin and cellulose.
2. Much of the plant biomass may not be consumed by any individual herbivore species – roots may be inaccessible or trampled grass may be considered uneatable.

*Energy transfer from primary consumer (herbivore) to secondary consumer (carnivore)* is typically 10–20% of herbivore biomass. This is more efficient than producer → consumer because
1. animal tissue is more digestible than plant tissue;
2. animal tissue has a higher energy value;
3. carnivores may be extremely specialized for prey consumption;

but is still considerably less than 100% because
a. some animal tissue – bone, hooves and hide for example – is not readily digestible;
b. feeding is not 100% efficient – much digestible material (e.g. food fragments and blood) may be lost to the environment.

*The limit to the number of trophic levels* is determined by:
1. the total producer biomass;
2. the efficiency of energy transfer between trophic levels (only 10%).

In practice, the energy losses limit the number of levels to 3 or 4, very rarely 5 or 6. The longest food chains can only be supported by an enormous producer biomass, e.g. a 6 level chain will only have about 10% x 10% x 10% x 10% of NPP available to the top carnivores. The enormous volume of the oceans can provide sufficient biomass to support the longest food chains.

The **decomposers** are fungi and bacteria which obtain energy and raw materials from animal and plant remains. In some situations 80% or more of the productivity at any trophic level may go through a decomposer pathway (e.g. forest floors of tropical forests). In some ecosystems – peat bogs, for example – the cold, wet, acidic conditions inhibit decomposition to such an extent that only about 10% of the material entering the decomposer food chain is broken down. The remainder accumulates as peat.

SECONDARY CONSUMER

PRIMARY CONSUMER

PRODUCER

DECOMPOSER ORGANISMS

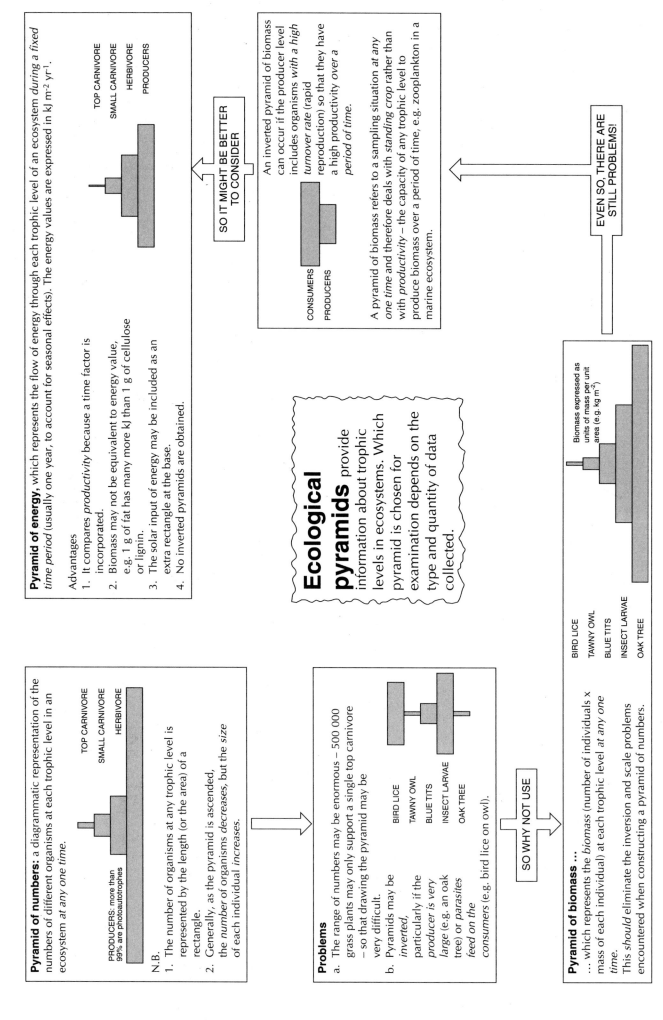

**Ecological pyramids** provide information about trophic levels in ecosystems. Which pyramid is chosen for examination depends on the type and quantity of data collected.

---

**Pyramid of numbers:** a diagrammatic representation of the numbers of different organisms at each trophic level in an ecosystem *at any one time.*

TOP CARNIVORE
SMALL CARNIVORE
HERBIVORE
PRODUCERS: more than 99% are photoautotrophes

N.B.
1. The number of organisms at any trophic level is represented by the length (or the area) of a rectangle.
2. Generally, as the pyramid is ascended, the *number of organisms decreases*, but the *size of each individual increases.*

**Problems**
a. The range of numbers may be enormous – 500 000 grass plants may only support a single top carnivore – so that drawing the pyramid may be very difficult.
b. Pyramids may be *inverted*, particularly if the *producer is very large* (e.g. an oak tree) or *parasites feed on the consumers* (e.g. bird lice on owl).

BIRD LICE
TAWNY OWL
BLUE TITS
INSECT LARVAE
OAK TREE

**SO WHY NOT USE**

**Pyramid of biomass ...**
... which represents the *biomass* (number of individuals x mass of each individual) at each trophic level *at any one time.*
This *should* eliminate the inversion and scale problems encountered when constructing a pyramid of numbers.

Biomass expressed as units of mass per unit area (e.g. kg m⁻²)

BIRD LICE
TAWNY OWL
BLUE TITS
INSECT LARVAE
OAK TREE

**EVEN SO, THERE ARE STILL PROBLEMS!**

An inverted pyramid of biomass can occur if the producer level includes organisms *with a high turnover rate* (rapid reproduction) so that they have a high productivity over a *period of time.*

CONSUMERS
PRODUCERS

A pyramid of biomass refers to a sampling situation at any *one time* and therefore deals with *standing crop* rather than with *productivity* – the capacity of any trophic level to produce biomass over a period of time, e.g. zooplankton in a marine ecosystem.

**SO IT MIGHT BE BETTER TO CONSIDER**

**Pyramid of energy,** which represents the flow of energy through each trophic level of an ecosystem *during a fixed time period* (usually one year, to account for seasonal effects). The energy values are expressed in kJ m⁻² yr⁻¹.

TOP CARNIVORE
SMALL CARNIVORE
HERBIVORE
PRODUCERS

Advantages
1. It compares *productivity* because a time factor is incorporated.
2. Biomass may not be equivalent to energy value, e.g. 1 g of fat has many more kJ than 1 g of cellulose or lignin.
3. The solar input of energy may be included as an extra rectangle at the base.
4. No inverted pyramids are obtained.

**Ecological succession** proceeds via *several stages* to a *climax community* and is characterized by:
1. an increase in *species diversity* and in *complexity of feeding relationships*;
2. a progressive increase in *biomass*;
3. completion when *energy input (community photosynthesis) = energy loss (community respiration)*.

**A COMMUNITY** (all the species present in a given locality at any given time), is the group of interacting populations (all the members of a species in a place at a given time) which represents the biotic component of an ecosystem, and is seldom static. The relative abundance of different species may change, new species may enter the community and others may leave. There are reasons for these changes.

**Catastrophes:** may be natural (e.g. flooding, volcanic eruption) or caused by people (e.g. oil spill, deforestation).

**Seasons:** changes in temperature, rainfall, light intensity and windspeed, for example, may alter the suitability of a habitat for particular species.

**Succession:** long-term directional change in the composition of a community *brought about by the actions of the organisms themselves.*

**Primary succession** occurs when the community develops on bare, uncolonized ground *which has never had any vegetation growing on it* , e.g. mud in river deltas, lava flows, sand dunes, artificial ponds and newly erupted volcanic islands.

LAVA FLOW

CAN BE EITHER

OR

**Secondary succession** occurs on ground *which had previously been colonized* but is now available because the community has been destroyed, typically by fire, flood or as a result of human agricultural or industrial activities. Such ground will not be 'virgin' but will include remnants of soil, organic debris, seeds and even resistant animals and plants which have survived the changes, e.g. fire debris may be rich in minerals, particuarly phosphate.

... BUT ALWAYS PROCEEDS VIA A SERIES OF STAGES

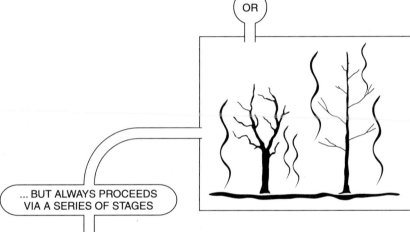

*Migration:* the arrival of seeds and spores. If conditions are suitable immigrant species may become established.

The number of species has risen – further stabilizing soil and adding nutrients. May still be an input of new species so that there will be both *intra-* and *inter-specific competition.* Pioneer species are often poor competitors and will be replaced by higher, more demanding plants such as grasses, shrubs and, eventually, trees.

The end point of succession: the community is now in equilibrium with the environment and is stable. Composition is often determined by one dominant species e.g. *oak woodland.*

BARE GROUND ⇒ PIONEER COMMUNITY (COLONIZERS) ⇒ SECONDARY COMMUNITY ⇒ CLIMAX COMMUNITY

During succession each species modifies the environment, making it *more* suitable for new species and *less* suitable for those already there.

These species are simple plants, e.g. lichens and algae with minimal environmental demands. May show symbiotic relationships to aid their establishment. The community is *open*, i.e. space for further colonizers.

Each of these stages is called a *seral stage* and the complete succession is called a *sere.*

*Hydrosere:* succession in an aquatic environment.
*Xerosere:* succession on dry land.
*Halosere:* succession in a salty environment.
*Lithosere:* succession on a rocky surface.

# The carbon cycle depends upon both biochemical and physical processes.

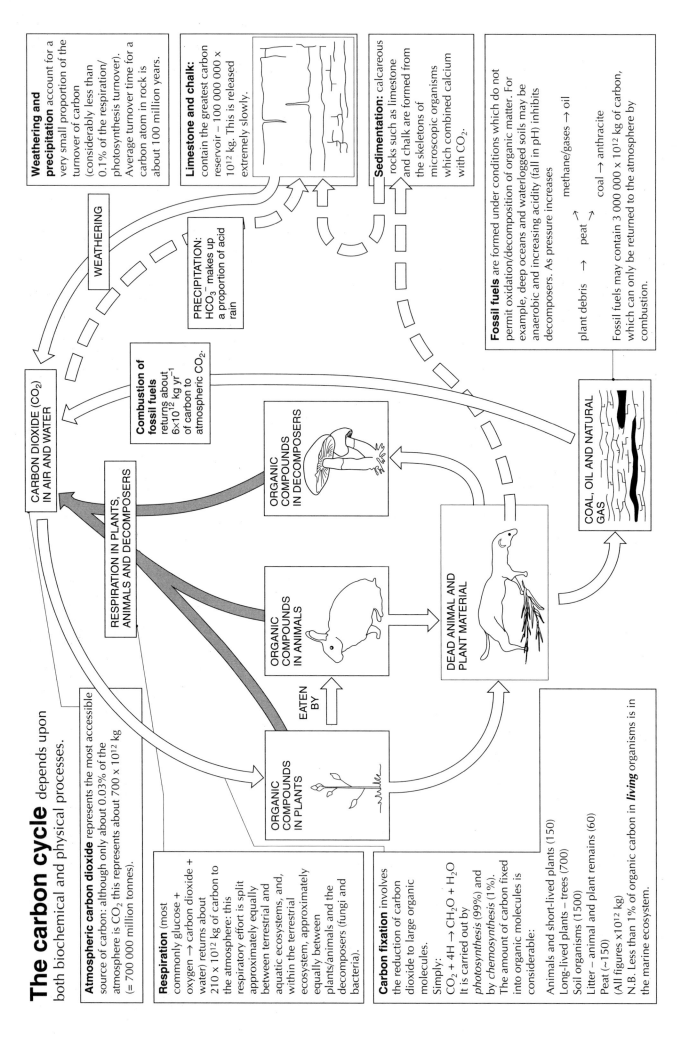

**Weathering and precipitation** account for a very small proportion of the turnover of carbon (considerably less than 0.1% of the respiration/photosynthesis turnover). Average turnover time for a carbon atom in rock is about 100 million years.

**Limestone and chalk:** contain the greatest carbon reservoir – 100 000 000 × $10^{12}$ kg. This is released extremely slowly.

**Sedimentation:** calcareous rocks such as limestone and chalk are formed from the skeletons of microscopic organisms which combined calcium with $CO_2$.

**Fossil fuels** are formed under conditions which do not permit oxidation/decomposition of organic matter. For example, anaerobic and waterlogged soils may be deep oceans and increasing acidity (fall in pH) inhibits decomposers. As pressure increases

plant debris → peat → coal → anthracite

methane/gases → oil

Fossil fuels may contain 3 000 000 × $10^{12}$ kg of carbon, which can only be returned to the atmosphere by combustion.

**PRECIPITATION:** $HCO_3^-$ makes up a proportion of acid rain

**WEATHERING**

**Combustion of fossil fuels** returns about $6 \times 10^{12}$ kg yr$^{-1}$ of carbon to atmospheric $CO_2$.

**Atmospheric carbon dioxide** represents the most accessible source of carbon: although only about 0.03% of the atmosphere is $CO_2$ this represents about 700 × $10^{12}$ kg (= 700 000 million tonnes).

**Respiration** (most commonly glucose + oxygen → carbon dioxide + water) returns about 210 × $10^{12}$ kg of carbon to the atmosphere: this respiratory effort is split approximately equally between terrestrial and aquatic ecosystems, and, within the terrestrial ecosystem, approximately equally between plants/animals and the decomposers (fungi and bacteria).

**Carbon fixation** involves the reduction of carbon dioxide to large organic molecules.
Simply:
$CO_2 + 4H \rightarrow CH_2O + H_2O$
It is carried out by *photosynthesis* (99%) and by *chemosynthesis* (1%).
The amount of carbon fixed into organic molecules is considerable:

Animals and short-lived plants (150)
Long-lived plants – trees (700)
Soil organisms (1500)
Litter – animal and plant remains (60)
Peat (~150)
(All figures ×$10^{12}$ kg)
N.B. Less than 1% of organic carbon in *living* organisms is in the marine ecosystem.

CARBON DIOXIDE ($CO_2$) IN AIR AND WATER

RESPIRATION IN PLANTS, ANIMALS AND DECOMPOSERS

ORGANIC COMPOUNDS IN DECOMPOSERS

ORGANIC COMPOUNDS IN ANIMALS

ORGANIC COMPOUNDS IN PLANTS

EATEN BY

DEAD ANIMAL AND PLANT MATERIAL

COAL, OIL AND NATURAL GAS

# The nitrogen cycle depends on micro-organisms.

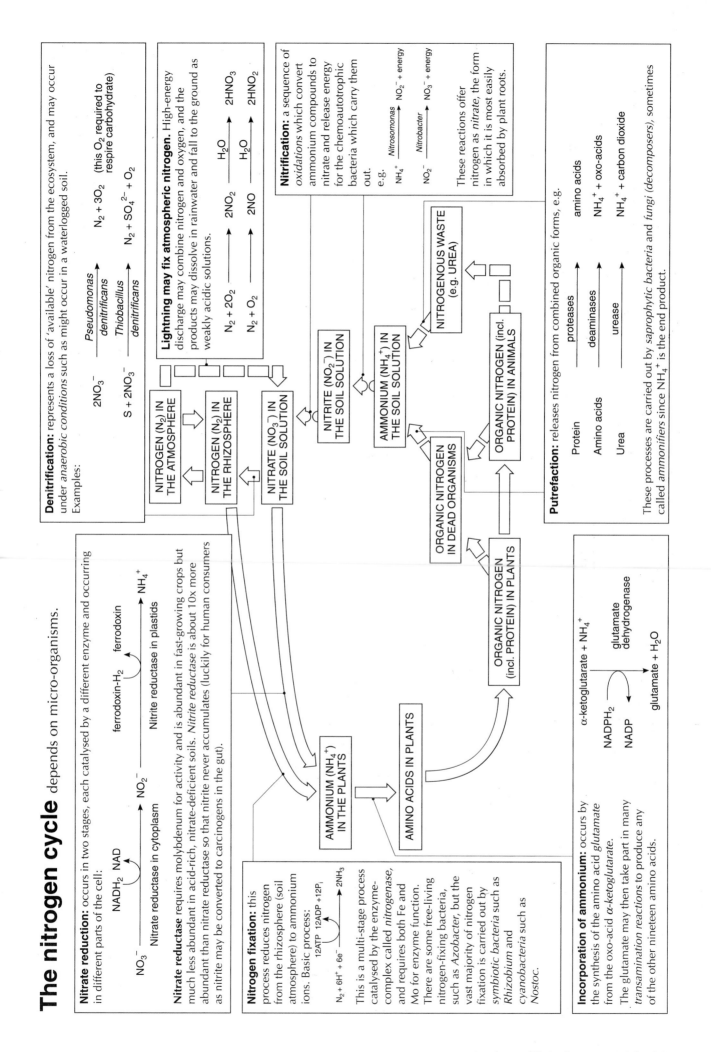

**Nitrate reduction:** occurs in two stages, each catalysed by a different enzyme and occurring in different parts of the cell:

$$NO_3^- \longrightarrow NO_2^-$$
NADH$_2$ NAD

Nitrate reductase in cytoplasm

$$\longrightarrow NH_4^+$$
ferredoxin-H$_2$  ferredoxin

Nitrite reductase in plastids

**Nitrate reductase** requires molybdenum for activity and is abundant in fast-growing crops but much less abundant in acid-rich, nitrate-deficient soils. *Nitrite reductase* is about 10x more abundant than nitrate reductase so that nitrite never accumulates (luckily for human consumers as nitrite may be converted to carcinogens in the gut).

**Nitrogen fixation:** this process reduces nitrogen from the rhizosphere (soil atmosphere) to ammonium ions. Basic process:

$$N_2 + 6H^+ + 6e^- \xrightarrow{\text{12ATP } 12ADP + 12P_i} 2NH_3$$

This is a multi-stage process catalysed by the enzyme-complex called *nitrogenase*, and requires both Fe and Mo for enzyme function. There are some free-living nitrogen-fixing bacteria, such as *Azobacter*, but the vast majority of nitrogen fixation is carried out by *symbiotic bacteria* such as *Rhizobium* and *cyanobacteria* such as *Nostoc*.

**Incorporation of ammonium:** occurs by the synthesis of the amino acid *glutamate* from the oxo-acid *α-ketoglutarate*.
The glutamate may then take part in many *transamination* reactions to produce any of the other nineteen amino acids.

$$\alpha\text{-ketoglutarate} + NH_4^+ \xrightarrow[\text{glutamate dehydrogenase}]{} \text{glutamate} + H_2O$$
NADPH$_2$ → NADP

**Denitrification:** represents a loss of 'available' nitrogen from the ecosystem, and may occur under *anaerobic* conditions such as might occur in a waterlogged soil.
Examples:

$$2NO_3^- \xrightarrow{\textit{Pseudomonas denitrificans}} N_2 + 3O_2 \quad (\text{this } O_2 \text{ required to respire carbohydrate})$$

$$S + 2NO_3^- \xrightarrow{\textit{Thiobacillus denitrificans}} N_2 + SO_4^{2-} + O_2$$

**Lightning may fix atmospheric nitrogen.** High-energy discharge may combine nitrogen and oxygen, and the products may dissolve in rainwater and fall to the ground as weakly acidic solutions.

$$N_2 + 2O_2 \rightarrow 2NO_2 \xrightarrow{H_2O} 2HNO_3$$
$$N_2 + O_2 \rightarrow 2NO \xrightarrow{H_2O} 2HNO_2$$

**Nitrification:** a sequence of *oxidations* which convert ammonium compounds to nitrate and release energy for the chemoautotrophic bacteria which carry them out.
e.g.

$$NH_4^+ \xrightarrow{\textit{Nitrosomonas}} NO_2^- + energy$$
$$NO_2^- \xrightarrow{\textit{Nitrobacter}} NO_3^- + energy$$

These reactions offer nitrogen as *nitrate*, the form in which it is most easily absorbed by plant roots.

**Putrefaction:** releases nitrogen from combined organic forms, e.g.

$$\text{Protein} \xrightarrow{\text{proteases}} \text{amino acids}$$
$$\text{Amino acids} \xrightarrow{\text{deaminases}} NH_4^+ + \text{oxo-acids}$$
$$\text{Urea} \xrightarrow{\text{urease}} NH_4^+ + \text{carbon dioxide}$$

These processes are carried out by saprophytic bacteria and *fungi (decomposers)*, sometimes called *ammonifiers* since NH$_4^+$ is the end product.

NITROGEN (N$_2$) IN THE ATMOSPHERE

NITROGEN (N$_2$) IN THE RHIZOSPHERE

NITRATE (NO$_3^-$) IN THE SOIL SOLUTION

NITRITE (NO$_2^-$) IN THE SOIL SOLUTION

AMMONIUM (NH$_4^+$) IN THE SOIL SOLUTION

NITROGENOUS WASTE (e.g. UREA)

ORGANIC NITROGEN IN DEAD ORGANISMS

ORGANIC NITROGEN (incl. PROTEIN) IN ANIMALS

ORGANIC NITROGEN (incl. PROTEIN) IN PLANTS

AMMONIUM (NH$_4^+$) IN THE PLANTS

AMINO ACIDS IN PLANTS

# The Greenhouse Effect is a

natural feature of the Earth, but when upset may lead to *global warming.*

## ORIGINS OF GREENHOUSE GASES

**Photosynthesis** in forests and grasslands removes carbon dioxide ($CO_2$) from the atmosphere.

**Combustion of fossil fuels** by industrial plants releases large amounts of $CO_2$.

**Car exhaust emissions** contain much $CO_2$ – released to the atmosphere.

**Ruminant fermentation** produces *methane* ($CH_4$) which cattle release into the atmosphere. Intensive cattle ranching increases $CH_4$ release at the expense of $CO_2$ uptake by photosynthesis.

**Aerosol propellants** contain *chlorofluorocarbons (CFCs)* which are $10^5$ x worse than carbon dioxide as greenhouse gases.

**Anaerobic fermentation** in swamps and paddy fields produces $CH_4$. Inorganic fertilizers cause release of nitric oxide (NO).

All living organisms release carbon dioxide by respiration – the additional *greenhouse gases contributed by humans (anthropogenic contributions)* include methane and CFCs in addition to greater quantities of carbon dioxide.

*Phew!*

The Sun, at a temperature of 6000 °C, emits radiation which is mostly in the visible band.

About 10% of the solar energy is reflected back to space by the Earth's atmosphere.

About 83% of the solar energy penetrates the atmosphere, warms the Earth's surface and is re-emitted in the infrared range.

About 7% of short wavelength radiation helps to generate ozone.

Some of the Earth's infrared emissions are re-reflected back to the Earth's surface → *warming,* particularly by $H_2O$ (absorbs and re-emits radiation of 4–7 $\mu m$) and $CO_2$ (absorbs/re-emits at 13–19 $\mu m$), *but most escapes back to space through a 7–13 $\mu m$ 'window'.*

The greenhouse gases close this window and thus allow the Earth's own infrared radiation to warm its surface.

SUN

EARTH

## On the + side

More atmospheric $CO_2$ and higher temperature at Earth's surface

*more rapid photosynthesis*

*more food*

## But on the – side

*Global warming* (observed increase in temperature since 1900 = 0.8 °C)

*Climatic extremes:* altered temperature gradients → cyclones. Heavier rain as water evaporates quicker.

*Rising sea level:* melting of polar ice and thermal expansion of seas.

*Crop losses:* drier weather in most fertile areas → lower yields of staple crops.

*Species migrations:* pests/disease vectors could extend their ranges.

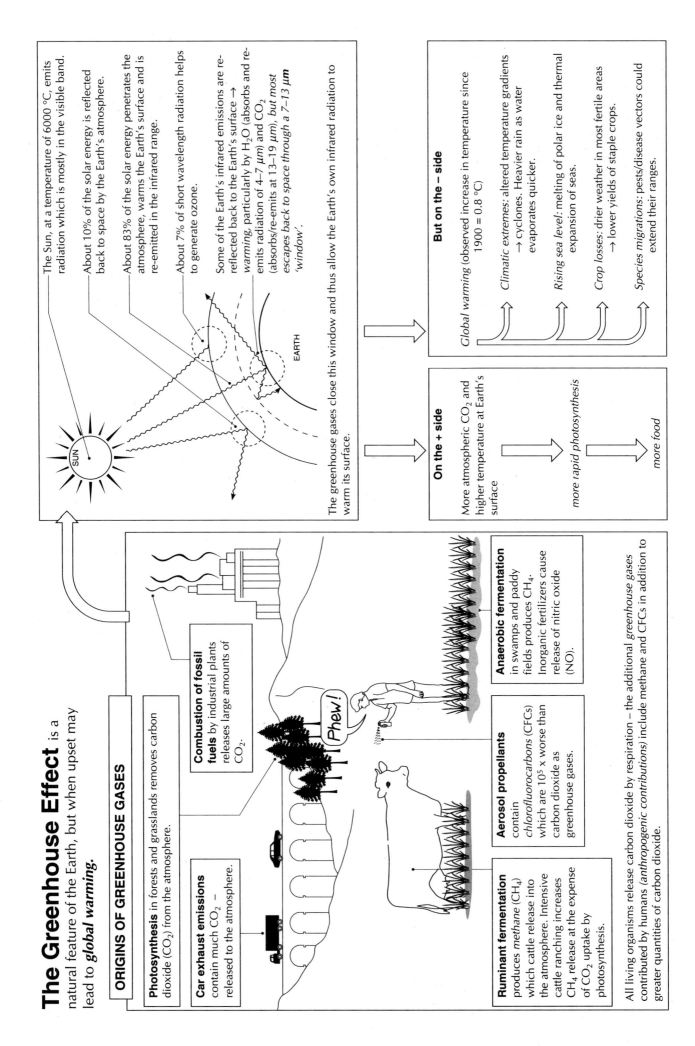

# Acid rain

Sulphur dioxide is an atmospheric pollutant that contributes to acid rain.

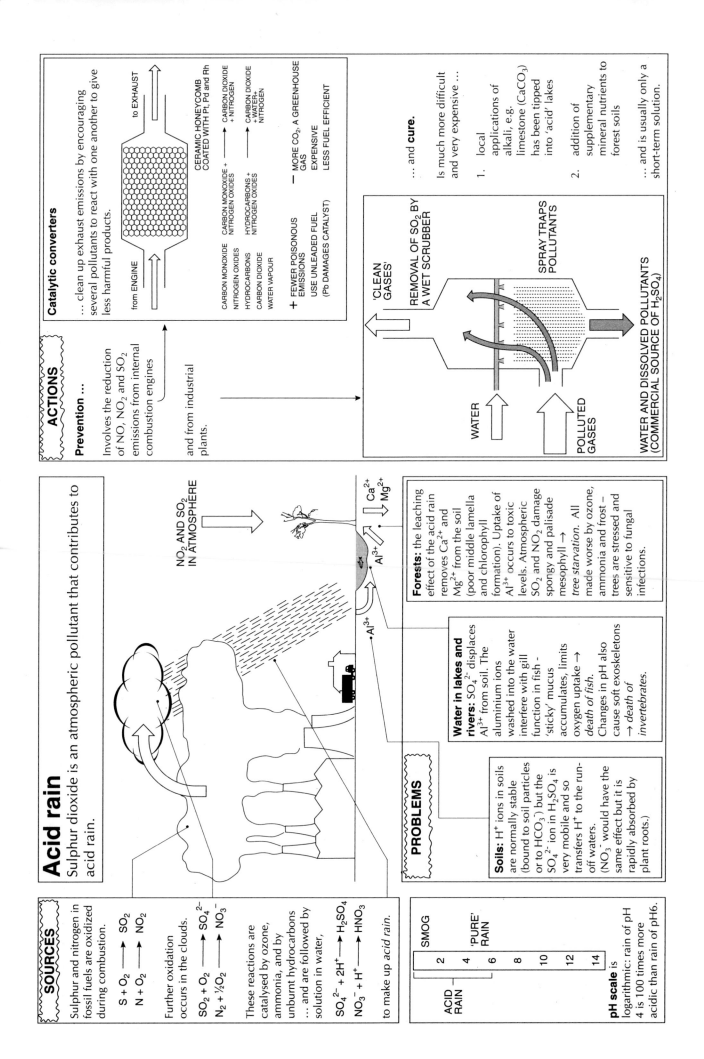

## ACTIONS

**Prevention ...**

Involves the reduction of NO, $NO_2$ and $SO_2$ emissions from internal combustion engines

and from industrial plants.

### Catalytic converters

... clean up exhaust emissions by encouraging several pollutants to react with one another to give less harmful products.

to EXHAUST

CERAMIC HONEYCOMB COATED WITH Pt, Pd and Rh

from ENGINE

CARBON MONOXIDE + NITROGEN OXIDES $\longrightarrow$ CARBON DIOXIDE + NITROGEN

HYDROCARBONS + NITROGEN OXIDES $\longrightarrow$ CARBON DIOXIDE + WATER + NITROGEN

- CARBON MONOXIDE
- NITROGEN OXIDES
- HYDROCARBONS
- CARBON DIOXIDE
- WATER VAPOUR

+ FEWER POISONOUS EMISSIONS

USE UNLEADED FUEL (Pb DAMAGES CATALYST)

− MORE $CO_2$, A GREENHOUSE GAS
 EXPENSIVE
 LESS FUEL EFFICIENT

'CLEAN GASES'

REMOVAL OF $SO_2$ BY A WET SCRUBBER

SPRAY TRAPS POLLUTANTS

WATER

POLLUTED GASES

WATER AND DISSOLVED POLLUTANTS (COMMERCIAL SOURCE OF $H_2SO_4$)

**... and cure.**

Is much more difficult and very expensive ...

1. local applications of alkali; e.g. limestone ($CaCO_3$) has been tipped into 'acid' lakes

2. addition of supplementary mineral nutrients to forest soils

... and is usually only a short-term solution.

## SOURCES

Sulphur and nitrogen in fossil fuels are oxidized during combustion.

$$S + O_2 \longrightarrow SO_2$$
$$N + O_2 \longrightarrow NO_2$$

Further oxidation occurs in the clouds.

$$SO_2 + O_2 \longrightarrow SO_4^{2-}$$
$$N_2 + \tfrac{1}{2}O_2 \longrightarrow NO_3^{-}$$

These reactions are catalysed by ozone, ammonia, and by unburnt hydrocarbons ... and are followed by solution in water,

$$SO_4^{2-} + 2H^+ \longrightarrow H_2SO_4$$
$$NO_3^{-} + H^+ \longrightarrow HNO_3$$

to make up *acid rain*.

$NO_2$ AND $SO_2$ IN ATMOSPHERE

$Ca^{2+}$
$Mg^{2+}$
$Al^{3+}$
$Al^{3+}$

## PROBLEMS

**Soils:** $H^+$ ions in soils are normally stable (bound to soil particles or to $HCO_3^-$) but the $SO_4^{2-}$ ion in $H_2SO_4$ is very mobile and so transfers $H^+$ to the run-off waters.
($NO_3^-$ would have the same effect but it is rapidly absorbed by plant roots.)

**Water in lakes and rivers:** $SO_4^{2-}$ displaces $Al^{3+}$ from soil. The aluminium ions washed into the water interfere with gill function in fish - 'sticky' mucus accumulates, limits oxygen uptake → *death of fish*.
Changes in pH also cause soft exoskeletons → *death of invertebrates*.

**Forests:** the leaching effect of the acid rain removes $Ca^{2+}$ and $Mg^{2+}$ from the soil (poor middle lamella and chlorophyll formation). Uptake of $Al^{3+}$ occurs to toxic levels. Atmospheric $SO_2$ and $NO_2$ damage spongy and palisade mesophyll → *tree starvation*. All made worse by ozone, ammonia and frost – trees are stressed and sensitive to fungal infections.

SMOG

'PURE' RAIN

| | |
|---|---|
| 2 | |
| 4 | |
| 6 | |
| 8 | |
| 10 | |
| 12 | |
| 14 | |

ACID RAIN

**pH scale** is logarithmic: rain of pH 4 is 100 times more acidic than rain of pH 6.

# Ozone in the atmosphere is essential for life

(but too much in the wrong place can be harmful!).

## Stratospheric (high level) ozone offers protection

Ozone absorbs solar *ultraviolet radiation* which would otherwise reach the Earth's surface.

UV-B (290–320 nm) already reaches the Earth

→ sunburn
some forms of skin cancer
cataract

One estimate suggests that a 2.5% reduction in the ozone layer would cause 0.8 million cancer deaths and 40 000 000 additional cases of skin cancer

→ reduced productivity of some plant species, e.g. soya bean.

UV-C (240–290 nm) does not at present reach the Earth but in laboratory tests has been shown to increase damage to DNA (more mutations) and to proteins.

## Human activities reduce ozone in the stratosphere

CFCs (chlorofluorocarbons) used in:
refrigerator coolants;
aerosols;
expanded plastics.

→ **Atmospheric chlorine**

$$Cl + O_3 \rightarrow ClO + O_2$$
$$ClO + O \rightarrow Cl + O_2$$

*i.e. ozone levels are depleted.*
*Chlorine is released to degrade further ozone molecules.*

SOLAR RADIATION

ULTRAVIOLET

VISIBLE AND INFRA RED

35 km

LOWER STRATOSPHERE

15 km

TROPOSPHERE

EARTH'S SURFACE

## Human activities generate ozone in the troposphere

Fossil fuel combustion → $NO_2$

$$NO_2 \xrightarrow[\;\;*\;\;]{\text{sunlight}} NO + O$$

$$O + O_2 \rightarrow O_3 : \text{OZONE}$$

* This occurs more rapidly in the presence of unburned hydrocarbons.

**'Holes' in the ozone layer:** measurements made by British scientists at Halley Bay, Antarctica, showed a thinning of the ozone layer caused by an accumulation of atmospheric chlorine during the winter months. The effect is partially reversed in the summer and may be peculiar to the Antarctic, but is seen as a warning that we must reduce production of long-lived CFCs.

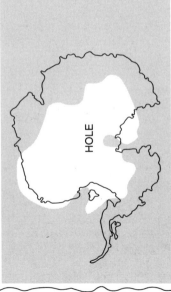

HOLE

*Antarctica*: ozone layer thinned over an area as large as the United States.

## Tropospheric (low level) ozone causes problems

1. It acts as a *greenhouse gas*, absorbing and re-radiating heat which raises the temperature at the Earth's surface.
2. As a result of 1, *thermal inversion occurs* – a layer of warm air traps cool air (containing dust and smoke) close to the Earth causing *smog*.
3. It causes *irritation* of eyes, throat and lungs and may cause death in sufferers from respiratory ailments as breathing is impaired.
4. It severely damages the photosynthetic mesophyll layers of plants by forming powerful oxidizing free radicals: this may lead to a *10% reduction in crop production*.

# Deforestation: the
rapid destruction of woodland.

BULLDOZE, SLASH AND BURN

Has been occurring on a major scale throughout the world.

- Between 1880 and 1980 about 40% of all tropical rainforest was destroyed.

- Britain has fallen from 85% forest cover to about 8% (probably the lowest in Europe).

- Major reasons
    - removal of hardwood for high-quality furnishings;
    - removal of softwoods for chipboards, paper and other wood products;
    - clearance for cattle ranching and for cash crop agriculture;
    - clearance for urban development (roads and towns being built).

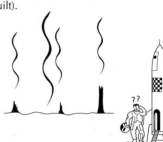

**Current losses:** about 11 hectares *per minute* (that's about 40 soccer or hockey pitches!).

## Reduction in soil fertility
1. Deciduous trees may contain 90% of the nutrients in a forest ecosystem: these nutrients are removed, and are thus not available to the soil, if the trees are cut down and taken away.
2. Soil erosion may be rapid since in the absence of trees
   a. wind and direct rain may remove the soil;
   b. soil structure is no longer stabilized by tree root systems.

N.B. The soil below coniferous forests is often of poor quality for agriculture because the shed pine needles contain toxic compounds which act as germination and growth inhibitors.

## Flooding and landslips
Heavy rainfall on deforested land is not 'held up': normally 25% of rainfall is absorbed by foliage or evaporates and 50% is absorbed by root systems. As a result water may accumulate rapidly in river valleys, often causing landslips from steep hillsides.

## Changes in recycling of materials: Fewer trees mean
1. atmospheric $CO_2$ concentration may rise as less $CO_2$ is removed for photosynthesis;
2. atmospheric $O_2$ – vital for aerobic respiration – is diminished as less is produced by photosynthesis;
3. the atmosphere may become drier and the soil wetter as evaporation (from soil) is slower than transpiration (from trees).

## Climatic changes
1. Reduced transpiration rates and drier atmosphere affect the water cycle and reduce rainfall.
2. Rapid heat absorption by bare soil raises the temperature of the lower atmosphere in some areas, causing thermal gradients which result in more frequent and intense winds.

**Species extinction:** Many species are dependent on forest conditions.

e.g.    mountain gorilla depends on cloud forest of Central Africa; golden lion tamarin depends on coastal rainforest of Brazil; osprey depends on mature pine forests in Northern Europe.

**It is estimated that one plant and one animal species become extinct every 30 minutes due to deforestation.**

Many plant species may have medicinal properties,
e.g.    as tranquilizers, reproductive hormones, anticoagulants, painkillers and antibiotics.
The Madagascan periwinkle, for example, yields one of the most potent known anti-leukaemia drugs.

# River pollution affects animal and plant populations.

**Clean water**

Indicator species (trout, larvae of mayfly and stonefly) tend to be *active* with a **high oxygen demand.**

**Heavily polluted**
Fish are absent – indicator species (e.g. bloodworm, *Tubifex*) often have respiratory pigments to **increase $O_2$ uptake** and are relatively inactive to **reduce oxygen demand.**

**Slightly polluted**
Slower moving fish (pike, carp) return: other indicator species include blackfly larvae and some snail species which have **moderate oxygen demand.**

**Clean water**
Return of *Gammarus* (freshwater shrimp), trout and stonefly larvae is taken as an indication that the BOD of the water is now very low.

*Perla* (Stonefly) nymph

DIRECTION OF RIVER FLOW

INPUT OF SEWAGE

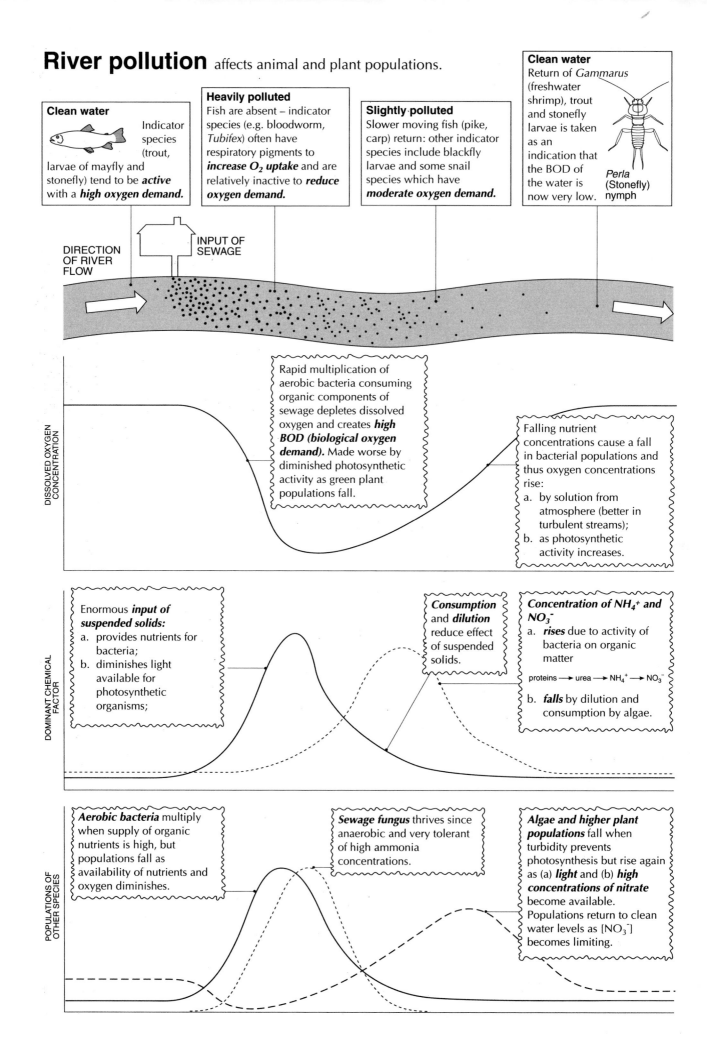

**DISSOLVED OXYGEN CONCENTRATION**

Rapid multiplication of aerobic bacteria consuming organic components of sewage depletes dissolved oxygen and creates **high BOD (biological oxygen demand).** Made worse by diminished photosynthetic activity as green plant populations fall.

Falling nutrient concentrations cause a fall in bacterial populations and thus oxygen concentrations rise:
a. by solution from atmosphere (better in turbulent streams);
b. as photosynthetic activity increases.

**DOMINANT CHEMICAL FACTOR**

Enormous **input of suspended solids:**
a. provides nutrients for bacteria;
b. diminishes light available for photosynthetic organisms;

**Consumption** and **dilution** reduce effect of suspended solids.

**Concentration of $NH_4^+$ and $NO_3^-$**
a. **rises** due to activity of bacteria on organic matter

proteins $\longrightarrow$ urea $\longrightarrow NH_4^+ \longrightarrow NO_3^-$

b. **falls** by dilution and consumption by algae.

**POPULATIONS OF OTHER SPECIES**

**Aerobic bacteria** multiply when supply of organic nutrients is high, but populations fall as availability of nutrients and oxygen diminishes.

**Sewage fungus** thrives since anaerobic and very tolerant of high ammonia concentrations.

**Algae and higher plant populations** fall when turbidity prevents photosynthesis but rise again as (a) **light** and (b) **high concentrations of nitrate** become available. Populations return to clean water levels as $[NO_3^-]$ becomes limiting.

# Nitrates are significant pollutants of water.

**Effects on human health**

1. In the stomach

$$NO_3^- \longrightarrow NITROSAMINES$$

Nitrosamines are highly carcinogenic, and some studies have linked high $[NO_3^-]$ in water supplies with increased incidence of stomach and oesophageal cancer.

2. **Blue baby syndrome** (in children younger than 3 months)

$$NO_3^- \xrightarrow[\text{or water supply}]{\text{bacteria in gut}} NITRITE (NO_2^-)$$

Haemoglobin in baby's red blood cells

*methaemoglobin* (has $Fe^{II}$ oxidized to $Fe^{III}$) which reduces oxygen-carrying capacity of baby's blood

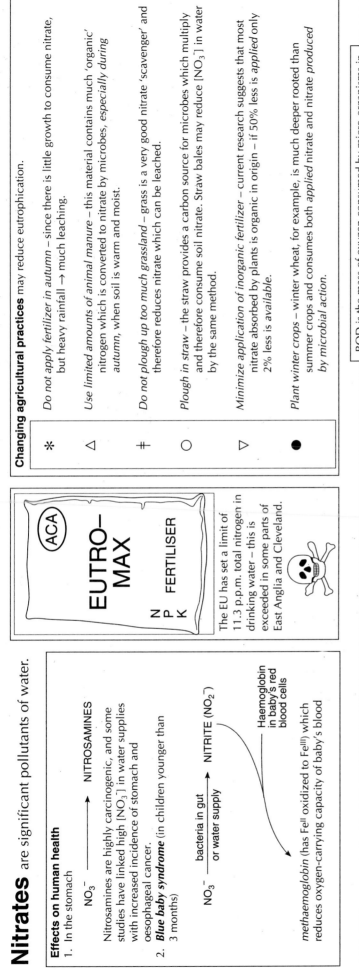

(ACA)

## EUTRO–MAX

N
P FERTILISER
K

The EU has set a limit of 11.3 p.p.m. total nitrogen in drinking water – this is exceeded in some parts of East Anglia and Cleveland.

---

**Changing agricultural practices** may reduce eutrophication.

\* *Do not apply fertilizer in autumn* – since there is little growth to consume nitrate, but heavy rainfall → much leaching.

△ *Use limited amounts of animal manure* – this material contains much 'organic' nitrogen which is converted to nitrate by microbes, *especially during autumn*, when soil is warm and moist.

✣ *Do not plough up too much grassland* – grass is a very good nitrate 'scavenger' and therefore reduces nitrate which can be leached.

○ *Plough in straw* – the straw provides a carbon source for microbes which multiply and therefore consume soil nitrate. Straw bales may reduce $[NO_3^-]$ in water by the same method.

▽ *Minimize application of inorganic fertilizer* – current research suggests that most nitrate absorbed by plants is organic in origin – if 50% less is *applied* only 2% less is *available*.

● *Plant winter crops* – winter wheat, for example, is much deeper rooted than summer crops and consumes both *applied* nitrate and nitrate *produced* by microbial action.

---

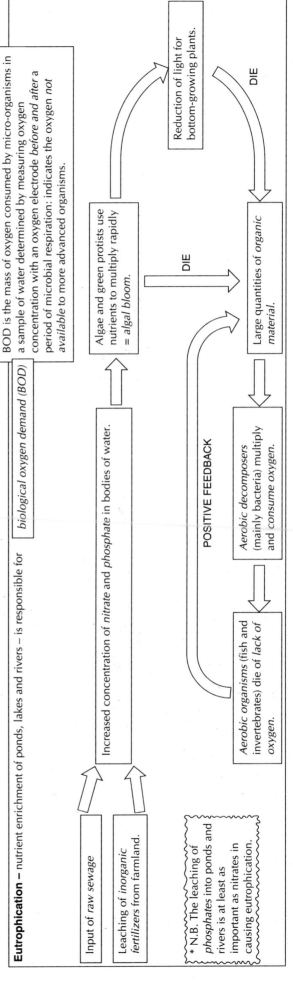

**Eutrophication** – nutrient enrichment of ponds, lakes and rivers – is responsible for

BOD is the mass of oxygen consumed by micro-organisms in a sample of water determined by measuring oxygen concentration with an oxygen electrode *before and after* a period of microbial respiration: indicates the oxygen *not available* to more advanced organisms.

*biological oxygen demand (BOD)*

Input of *raw sewage*

Leaching of *inorganic fertilizers* from farmland.

\* N.B. The leaching of *phosphates* into ponds and rivers is at least as important as nitrates in causing eutrophication.

Increased concentration of *nitrate* and *phosphate* in bodies of water.

Algae and green protists use nutrients to multiply rapidly = *algal bloom.*

Reduction of light for bottom-growing plants.

DIE

DIE

Large quantities of *organic material.*

Aerobic *decomposers* (mainly bacteria) multiply and *consume oxygen.*

POSITIVE FEEDBACK

Aerobic *organisms* (fish and invertebrates) die of *lack of oxygen.*

# Chemical pest control

may involve the use of:

*herbicides* – for control of weeds;

*insecticides* – for control of insects;

*fungicides* – for control of fungi;

*molluscicides* – for control of slugs and snails.

## HERBICIDES may be

1. **Pre-emergent**, i.e. applied *before* emergence of crop.
   a. Contact herbicides, e.g. *Paraquat*, which kill all above-ground parts of all plants.
   b. Residual herbicides, e.g. *Linuron*, which bind to soil particles and kill weed seedlings as they emerge.

   Pre-emergent herbicides can be *non-selective* and are ideal for clearing ground prior to cultivation.

2. **Post-emergent** is applied to both crop and weed, and therefore must be *selective*. Many, such as 2,4-D, are growth regulators.

**Systemic herbicides,** such as *glyphosate*, are absorbed by weeds and translocated to the meristems where they typically act by inhibition of cell division.

## PROBLEMS WITH INSECTICIDES:

these arise since the principal idea behind chemical control is to *kill as many of the pests as possible* – the effects on harmless or beneficial organisms were not studied or were ignored.

1. **Direct killing:** accidental misuse of toxic chemicals may cause death in humans or in domestic animals.

2. **Non-specificity:** non-target species, particularly natural predators of the pest species, may be killed by some wide-spectrum insecticides, e.g. large doses of **dieldrin** killed many birds as well as the Japanese beetle pest which was the intended target organism.

3. **Pest resistance:** genetic variation means that each pest population contains a *few* resistant individuals. The pesticide eliminates the non-resistant forms and thus a resistant population is selected for and may quickly develop (since many pests reproduce rapidly).

4. **Pest replacement:** most crops are susceptible to attack by more than one species – a *pest complex* and the use of a pesticide to eliminate one species may simply allow another species to assume major pest proportions (since a pesticide may be more deadly to one species than another).

5. **Pest resurgence:** non-specific pesticides may kill natural predators as well as pests – a small residual pest population may now multiply without check, creating a worse problem than initially was present.

6. **Bioaccumulation of toxins:** pesticides or their products may be toxic
   a. they may seriously affect micro-organisms and thus alter decomposition in soils;
   b. they may pass along food chains, becoming more concentrated in organisms further up the chain.

e.g. DDT used as an insecticide accumulates in the fatty tissues of carnivorous animals, inhibiting cytochrome oxidase and limiting reproductive success (especially thin eggshells in birds of prey).

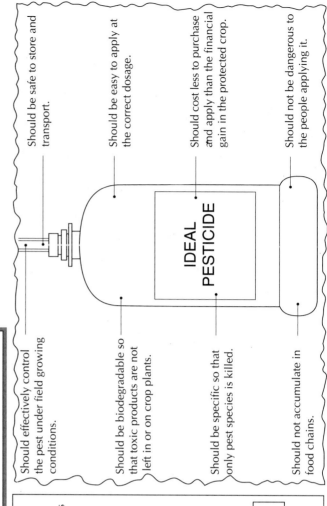

| PHYTOPLANKTON 1 | → | MAYFLY LARVAE 4 | → | TROUT 50 | → | OSPREY 800 |
|---|---|---|---|---|---|---|

Relative DDT concentration along an aquatic food chain.

**IDEAL PESTICIDE**

- Should effectively control the pest under field growing conditions.
- Should be biodegradable so that toxic products are not left in or on crop plants.
- Should be specific so that only pest species is killed.
- Should not accumulate in food chains.
- Should be safe to store and transport.
- Should be easy to apply at the correct dosage.
- Should cost less to purchase and apply than the financial gain in the protected crop.
- Should not be dangerous to the people applying it.

# Biological pest control

reduces the population of one species to levels at which it is no longer a pest by the use of one of the pest species' natural predators.

## TYPICAL BIOLOGICAL CONTROL PROGRAMME

1. Identify the pest and *trace its origins*, i.e. where did it come from?
2. Investigate original site of pest and *identify natural enemies* of the pest.
3. Test the potential *control agent* under careful quarantine to ensure
   a. that it is *specific* (does not prey on other species)
   b. will not change its prey species and *become a pest itself*
   c. has a life cycle which will allow it to *develop a population large enough to act as an economic control*.
4. *Mass culture* of the control agent.
5. Development of the most *effective distribution/release method* for the control agent.

## PRINCIPAL TECHNIQUES IN BIOLOGICAL CONTROL

1. Use a *herbivore* to control a *weed* species,
   e.g. *Cactoblastis* larvae on prickly pear.
2. Use a *carnivore* to control a *herbivorous pest*,
   e.g. hoverfly larvae on aphids.
3. Use a *parasite* to control its *host*,
   e.g. *Encharsia*, a parasitic wasp, on the greenhouse whitefly, *Trialeurodes vaporariorum*.
4. Disrupt the breeding cycle of a pest *if it mates once only in its life*,
   e.g. release of sterilized males of the screw worm fly, a flesh eating parasite of cattle.

Irradiated ♂♂'s ♀♀'s

5. Control of *pest behaviour*,
   e.g. sex attractant pheromones are used to attract apple codling moths into lethal traps.

## IDEAL RELATIONSHIP BETWEEN PEST AND ITS CONTROL AGENT

The *pest species* becomes the *prey* of the control agent: it is the *target* in the system of biological control.

Pest population falls due to *predation* by control agent.

Population size above which the pest is *economically harmful*: often determined by the expected yield and potential value of the crop.

Population of control agent falls because of a food shortage caused by reduction in prey (pest) numbers.

SIZE OF POPULATION / arbitrary units

TIME / arbitrary units

*Control agent* selected according to the criteria outlined above is the *predator* on the prey pest species. Population rises as the agent breeds, if conditions are appropriate.

*Introduction of control agent*: the size of the introduced population must be great enough to ensure a rise in numbers which is rapid enough to ensure control of the pest population within an economic time, e.g. before a crop plant has been extensively damaged.

A *dynamic equilibrium* is set up in which a moderate residual population of the control agent is able to permanently restrict the population of the pest. N.B. the pest species *must not be entirely eliminated* or the control agent will die out and a further introduction will be necessary to prevent re-establishment of economically damaging pest populations.

# An ideal human diet contains fat, protein, carbohydrate, vitamins, minerals, water and fibre *in the correct proportions.*

**An adequate diet** provides sufficient *energy* for the performance of metabolic work, although the 'energy food' is in unspecified form.

**A balanced diet** provides all dietary requirements *in the correct proportions.* Ideally this would be $^1/_7$ *fat*, $^1/_7$ *protein* and $^5/_7$ *carbohydrate.*

In conditions of *undernutrition* the first concern is usually provision of an *adequate diet*, but to avoid symptoms of *malnutrition* a *balanced diet* must be provided.

**Proteins** are *building blocks* for growth and repair of many body tissues (e.g. myosin in muscle, collagen in connective tissues), as *enzymes*, as *transport systems* (e.g. haemoglobin), as *hormones* (e.g. insulin) and as *antibodies.*

Common source: meat, fish, eggs and legumes/pulses. Must contain eight *essential amino acids* since humans are not able to synthesize them. Animal sources generally contain more of the essential amino acids.

Digested in stomach, duodenum and ileum and absorbed as *amino acids.*

**Water** is required as a solvent, a transport medium, a substrate in hydrolytic reactions and for lubrication. A human requires $2-3 \ dm^3$ of water daily, most commonly from drinks and liquid foods.

**Minerals** have a range of *specific* roles (direct structural components, e.g. $Ca^{2+}$ in bones; constituents of macromolecules, e.g. $PO_4^{3-}$ in DNA; part of pumping systems, e.g. $Na^+$ in glucose uptake; enzyme cofactors, e.g. $Fe^{3+}$ in catalase; electron transfer, e.g. $Cu^{2+}$ in cytochromes) and *collectively* help to maintain solute concentrations essential for control of water movement. They are usually ingested with other foods – dairy products and meats are particularly important sources.

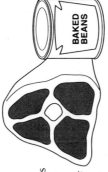

## Carbohydrates

Principally as a *respiratory substrate*, i.e. to be oxidized to release *energy* for active transport, synthesis of macromolecules, cell division and muscle contraction.

Common sources: rice, potatoes, wheat and other cereal grains, i.e. as *starch* and as refined sugar, *sucrose* in food sweetenings and preservatives.

Digested in duodenum and ileum and absorbed as *glucose.*

## Lipids

Highly reduced and therefore can be oxidized to release *energy*. Also important in *cell membranes* and as a component of *steroid hormones.*

Common sources: meat and animal foods are rich in *saturated fats* and *cholesterol*, plant sources such as sunflower and soya are rich in *unsaturated fats.*

Digested in duodenum and ileum and absorbed as *fatty acids and glycerol.*

## Vitamins

**Vitamins** have no common structure or function but are essential in small amounts to use other dietary components efficiently. *Fat-soluble vitamins* (e.g. A, D and E) are ingested with fatty foods and *water-soluble vitamins* (B group, C) are common in fruits and vegetables.

## Fibre

**Fibre** (originally known as *roughage*) is mainly cellulose from plant cell walls and is common in fresh vegetables and cereals. It *may* provide some energy but mainly serves to aid faeces formation, prevent constipation and ensure the continued health of the muscles of large intestine.

# Human digestive system: I

**Palate:** separates breathing and feeding pathways, allowing both processes to go on simultaneously so different types of teeth evolved.

**Teeth:** cut, tear and grind food so that solid foods are reduced to smaller particles for swallowing, and the food has a larger surface area for enzyme action.

**Salivary glands:** produce *saliva*, which is 99% water plus mucin, chloride ions (activate amylase), hydrogen carbonate and phosphate (maintain pH about 6.5), lysozyme and salivary amylase.

**Paratoid**

**Sublingual**

**Submandibular**

**Tongue:** manoeuvres food for chewing and rolls food into a bolus for swallowing. Mixes food with saliva.

**Diaphragm:** a muscular 'sheet' separating the thorax and abdomen.

**Liver:** an accessory organ which produces bile and stores it in the gall bladder.

**Bile duct:** carries bile from gall bladder to duodenum.

**Pancreas:** an accessory organ producing a wide range of digestive secretions, as well as hormones.

**Duodenum:** the first 30 cm of the small intestine. Receives pancreatic secretions and bile and produces an alkaline mucus for protection, lubrication and chyme neutralization.

**Ileum:** up to 6 m in length – main site for absorption of soluble products of digestion.

**Appendix:** no function in humans. It is a vestige of the caecum in other mammals (herbivores).

**Anal sphincter:** regulates release of faeces (defecation).

**Uvula:** extension of soft palate which separates nasal chamber from pharynx.

**Epiglottis:** muscular flap which reflexly closes the trachea during swallowing to prevent food entry to respiratory tree.

**Oesophagus:** muscular tube which is dorsal to the trachea and connects the buccal cavity to the stomach. Muscular to generate peristaltic waves, which drive bolus of food downwards, and glandular to lubricate bolus with mucus. Semi-solid food passes to stomach in 4–8 seconds, very soft foods and liquids take only 1 second.

**Cardiac sphincter:** allows entry of food to stomach. Helps to retain food in stomach.

**Stomach:** a muscular bag which is distensible to permit storage of large quantities of food. Mucosal lining is glandular, with numerous gastric pits which secrete digestive juices. Three muscle layers including an oblique layer churn the stomach contents to ensure thorough mixing and eventual transfer of chyme to the duodenum.

**Pyloric sphincter:** opens to permit passage of chyme into duodenum and closes to prevent backflow of food from duodenum to stomach.

**Colon (large intestine):** absorbs water from faeces. Some B vitamins and vitamin K are synthesized by colonic bacteria. Mucus glands lubricate faeces.

**Rectum:** stores faeces before expulsion.

There are only *radial* muscle fibres in sphincters (including the bladder sphincter).
When the fibres are *relaxed* the sphincter is *closed*.
When the fibres are *contracted* the sphincter is *open*.
Since the sphincter is closed for most of the time, the muscle fibres are relaxed and there is no fatigue.

# Human digestive system: II

Digestion of protein, fat and carbohydrate

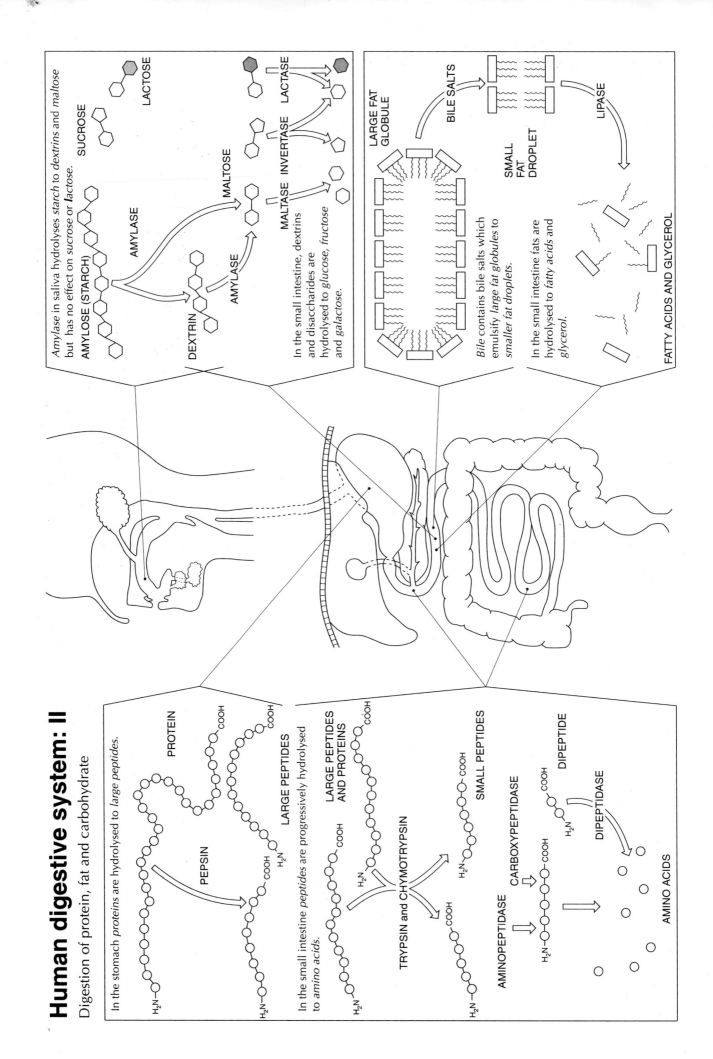

*Amylase in saliva hydrolyses starch to dextrins and maltose but has no effect on sucrose or lactose.*

LACTOSE
SUCROSE
MALTOSE
LACTASE
INVERTASE
MALTASE
AMYLASE
AMYLASE
AMYLASE
AMYLOSE (STARCH)
DEXTRIN

*In the small intestine, dextrins and disaccharides are hydrolysed to glucose, fructose and galactose.*

LARGE FAT GLOBULE
BILE SALTS
SMALL FAT DROPLET
LIPASE
FATTY ACIDS AND GLYCEROL

*Bile contains bile salts which emulsify large fat globules to smaller fat droplets.*

*In the small intestine fats are hydrolysed to fatty acids and glycerol.*

*In the stomach proteins are hydrolysed to large peptides.*

PROTEIN
PEPSIN
LARGE PEPTIDES

*In the small intestine peptides are progressively hydrolysed to amino acids.*

LARGE PEPTIDES AND PROTEINS
TRYPSIN and CHYMOTRYPSIN
SMALL PEPTIDES
CARBOXYPEPTIDASE
AMINOPEPTIDASE
DIPEPTIDE
DIPEPTIDASE
AMINO ACIDS

# Absorption of the products of digestion is aided by a large surface area, specific uptake systems and well-developed transport network.

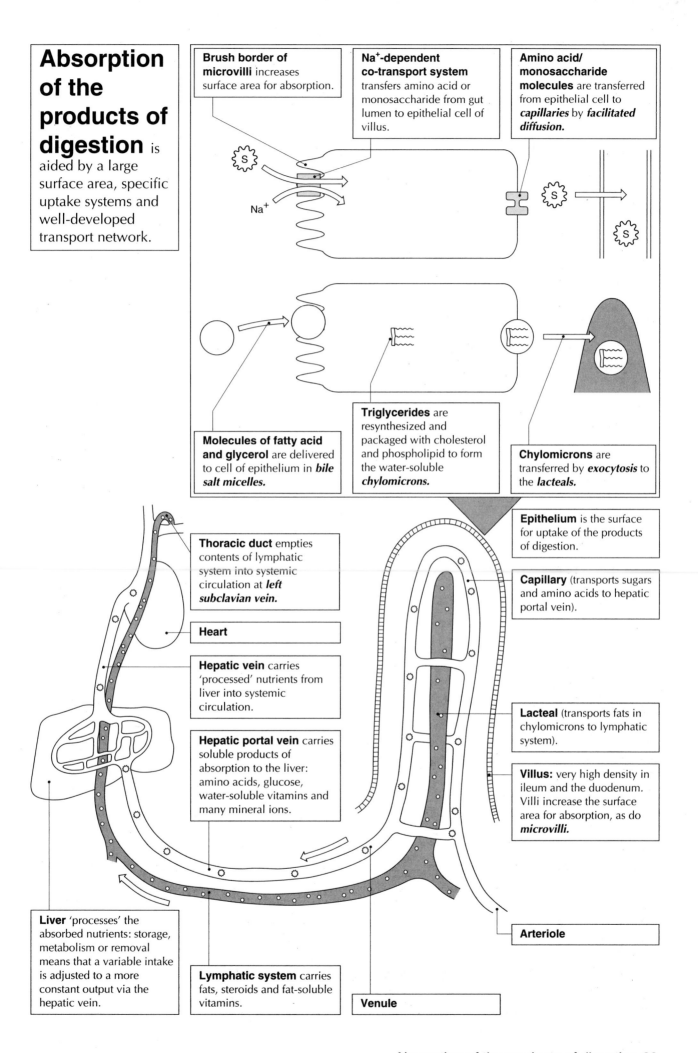

**Brush border of microvilli** increases surface area for absorption.

**Na⁺-dependent co-transport system** transfers amino acid or monosaccharide from gut lumen to epithelial cell of villus.

**Amino acid/ monosaccharide molecules** are transferred from epithelial cell to *capillaries* by *facilitated diffusion*.

$Na^+$

**Molecules of fatty acid and glycerol** are delivered to cell of epithelium in *bile salt micelles*.

**Triglycerides** are resynthesized and packaged with cholesterol and phospholipid to form the water-soluble *chylomicrons*.

**Chylomicrons** are transferred by *exocytosis* to the *lacteals*.

**Thoracic duct** empties contents of lymphatic system into systemic circulation at *left subclavian vein*.

**Heart**

**Hepatic vein** carries 'processed' nutrients from liver into systemic circulation.

**Hepatic portal vein** carries soluble products of absorption to the liver: amino acids, glucose, water-soluble vitamins and many mineral ions.

**Liver** 'processes' the absorbed nutrients: storage, metabolism or removal means that a variable intake is adjusted to a more constant output via the hepatic vein.

**Lymphatic system** carries fats, steroids and fat-soluble vitamins.

**Venule**

**Arteriole**

**Epithelium** is the surface for uptake of the products of digestion.

**Capillary** (transports sugars and amino acids to hepatic portal vein).

**Lacteal** (transports fats in chylomicrons to lymphatic system).

**Villus:** very high density in ileum and the duodenum. Villi increase the surface area for absorption, as do *microvilli*.

# Principles of respiration: a number of processes are involved in the provision/consumption of *oxygen* and the excretion/production of *carbon dioxide.*

| | |
|---|---|
| **Pulmonary ventilation** | moves gases between atmosphere and respiratory surface. |
| **External respiration** | occurs when gases diffuse across the respiratory surface. |
| **Internal respiration** | occurs when gases diffuse between circulating blood and respiring cells. |
| **Tissue/cell respiration** | occurs when oxygen is consumed and carbon dioxide is produced during the oxidation of foods to release energy. |

**Ventilation** is the movement of the respiratory medium to and from the respiratory surface: this helps to maintain adequate concentration gradients of $O_2$ and $CO_2$ so that diffusion may take place across the respiratory surface.

**Respiratory medium** supplies *oxygen* and accepts excreted *carbon dioxide.*

**Respiratory surface** across which *oxygen absorption* and *carbon dioxide release* occurs is *thin* (minimum diffusion distance only 0.5 μm in humans), *moist* (so that diffusion may occur in solution) and of *great surface area* ( about 70 m² in humans) so that adequate gas movement can occur within a limited time, and has a contact with the transport medium to move gases and maintain the diffusion gradient.

**Erythrocytes** (red blood cells) contain haemoglobin, which plays a part in both $O_2$ and $CO_2$ transport.

**Oxygen is transported** in the circulating blood: approx. 98% as $Hb(O_2)_4$ *(oxyhaemoglobin)* in the erythrocytes; approx. 2% in solution in the plasma.

**Circulating blood** returns $CO_2$ to respiratory surface: approx. 85% as $HCO_3^-$ *carried* in the plasma but *formed* in erythrocytes; approx. 10% as Hb-$CO_2$ *(carbamino-haemoglobin)* carried in erythrocytes; approx. 5% dissolved in the plasma.

**Oxygen is released** from oxyhaemoglobin under conditions of low oxygen tension and diffuses to respiring cells via the tissue fluid.

**Respiration in cells:** most efficient energy release demands oxygen and produces carbon dioxide.

**Carbon dioxide** is a product of cell respiration and diffuses from the respiring cell, via the tissue fluid, to the circulating blood.

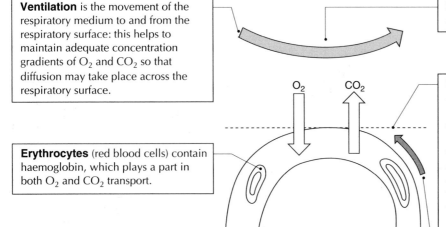

| FEATURE | INSECT | FISH | MAMMAL |
|---|---|---|---|
| RESPIRATORY MEDIUM | AIR | WATER | AIR |
| SURFACE | TRACHEOLES contact cells directly | LAMELLAE of gills | ALVEOLI of lungs |
| TRANSPORT SYSTEM | NONE | Blood in SINGLE CIRCULATION | Blood in DOUBLE CIRCULATION |
| VENTILATION | Little – some ABDOMINAL MOVEMENT | Muscular movements drive ONE-WAY flow of water | Negative pressure system initiates TIDAL FLOW of air |

# Lung structure and function may be affected by a variety of disease conditions.

**Epiglottis** covers trachea when swallowing to prevent entry of food to lungs.

**Lung cancer** arises from a tumour which develops in the bronchus and then invades adjacent tissues. It causes loss of function and pain, and tumour cells may spread via the bloodstream to other parts of the body.

**Turbinate bones** direct flow of air so that inspired air is warmed and moistened.

**Palate** separates nasal and buccal cavities to permit breathing and feeding at the same time.

**Nasal hairs** trap dust particles and some air-borne pathogens.

**Sternum** for ventral attachment of ribs.

**Pulmonary artery,** which delivers deoxygenated blood to the lungs.

**Bronchus** with cartilaginous rings to prevent collapse during inspiration.

**Pulmonary vein,** which returns oxygenated blood to the heart.

**Terminal bronchiole** with no cartilage support.

**Alveolus,** which is the actual site of gas exchange between air and blood.

**Domed muscular diaphragm,** whose contraction may increase the volume of the thorax.

**Emphysema** is linked to tobacco smoking, which stimulates the release of proteolytic enzymes from mast cells in the lungs. These enzymes break down alveolar walls producing single large chambers. Thus the effective surface area of the lungs is decreased, causing reduced oxygenation of the blood.

**Laryngitis** is an inflammation of the larynx caused by a viral infection, often followed by a secondary bacterial infection.

**Larynx** containing vocal cords which snap shut during hiccoughs.

**Trachea** with C-shaped rings of cartilage to support trachea in open position when thoracic pressure falls.

**Lining of ciliated epithelium** to trap and remove pathogens and particles of dust and smoke.

**External intercostal muscles** which contract to lift rib cage upwards and outwards.

**Pleural membranes** are moist to reduce friction as lungs move in chest.

**Heart** is close to lungs to drive pulmonary circulation.

**Cut end of rib:** ribs protect lungs and heart.

**Pleural cavity** at negative pressure so that passive lungs follow movement of rib cage.

**Chronic bronchitis** is a progressive inflammatory disease caused by exposure to irritants, including tobacco smoke, sulphur dioxide and urban fog. The mucous membrane is damaged causing swelling and fluid secretion, and reduced ciliary activity allows excess mucus to collect. There may be difficulty in breathing, and bacteria may infect the stagnant mucus, leading to pus formation. Continued shortage of oxygen leads to pulmonary hypertension and death.

**Pleurisy** is infection of the pleural membranes, causing painful breathing and impairment of the negative pressure breathing system.

# Fine structure of the lung: exchange of gases in the alveolus requires

1. A tube for the movement of gases to and from the atmosphere (e.g. **bronchiole).**
2. A surface across which gases may be transported between air and blood (i.e. **alveolar membrane).**
3. A vessel which can take away oxygenated blood or deliver carboxylated blood (i.e. a **branch of the pulmonary circulation).**

**Inspired air**

**Expired air**

**Terminal bronchiole** has no rings of cartilage and collapses when external pressure is high – dangerous when diving as trapped air in alveolus may give up nitrogen to blood, where it forms damaging bubbles.

**Alveolar duct (atrium)**

**Alveolus (air sac)**

**Elastic fibres** in alveolus permit optimum extension during inspiration – properties are adversely affected by tobacco smoke → **emphysema.**

**Branch of pulmonary artery** delivers deoxygenated blood to the alveolar capillaries.

**Surfactant** is a phospholipid produced by **septal cells** in the alveolar wall. It reduces surface tension of the alveolar walls and prevents them sticking together following expiration - its absence in the newborn may lead to **respiratory distress syndrome,** and even to death, since the effort needed

**Bronchiole** has supporting rings of cartilage to prevent collapse during low pressure phase of breathing cycle.

**P$_{450}$** is a cytochrome which speeds oxygen transfer across the alveolar membrane by facilitating diffusion, and is also involved in the detoxification of some harmful compounds by oxidation. Toxins in tobacco smoke may drive P$_{450}$ to **consume** $O_2$ rather than **transport** it, leading to **anoxia** (oxygen deficiency).

**Alveolar-capillary (respiratory) membrane** consists of
1. **Alveolar wall:** squamous epithelium and alveolar macrophages.
2. **Epithelial** and **capillary basement membranes.**
3. **Endothelial cells of the capillary wall.**
Despite the number of layers this membrane averages only 0.5 μm in thickness.

**Tributary of pulmonary vein** returns oxygenated blood to the four pulmonary veins and thence to the left atrium of the heart.

**Alveolar capillaries** adjacent to the alveolus are the site of oxygen and carbon dioxide transfer between the air in the alveolus (air sac) and the circulating blood.

**Stretch receptors** provide sensory input, which initiates the **Hering-Breuer reflex** control of the breathing cycle.

## Changes in composition of inspired and expired air

|  | INSPIRED | ALVEOLAR | EXPIRED |  |
|---|---|---|---|---|
| $O_2$ | 20.95 | 13.80 | 16.40 | Oxygen diffuses from alveoli into blood: expired air has an increased proportion of oxygen due to additional oxygen added from the anatomical dead space. |
| $CO_2$ | 0.04 | 5.50 | 4.00 | Carbon dioxide concentration in alveoli is high because $CO_2$ diffuses from blood: the apparent fall in $CO_2$ concentration in expired air is due to dilution in the anatomical dead space. |
| $N_2$ | 79.01 | 80.70 | 79.60 | The apparent increase in the concentration of nitrogen, a metabolically inert gas, is due to a **relative** decrease in the proportion of oxygen rather than an **absolute** increase in nitrogen. |
| $H_2O(g)$ | VARI–ABLE | SATURATED | | The moisture lining the alveoli evaporates into the alveolar air and is then expired unless the animal has anatomical adaptations to prevent this (e.g. the extensive nasal hairs in desert rats). |
| Temp. | ATMOS–PHERIC | BODY | | Heat lost from the blood in the pulmonary circulation raises the temperature of the alveolar air. |

# Pulmonary ventilation is a result of changes in pressure within the thorax.

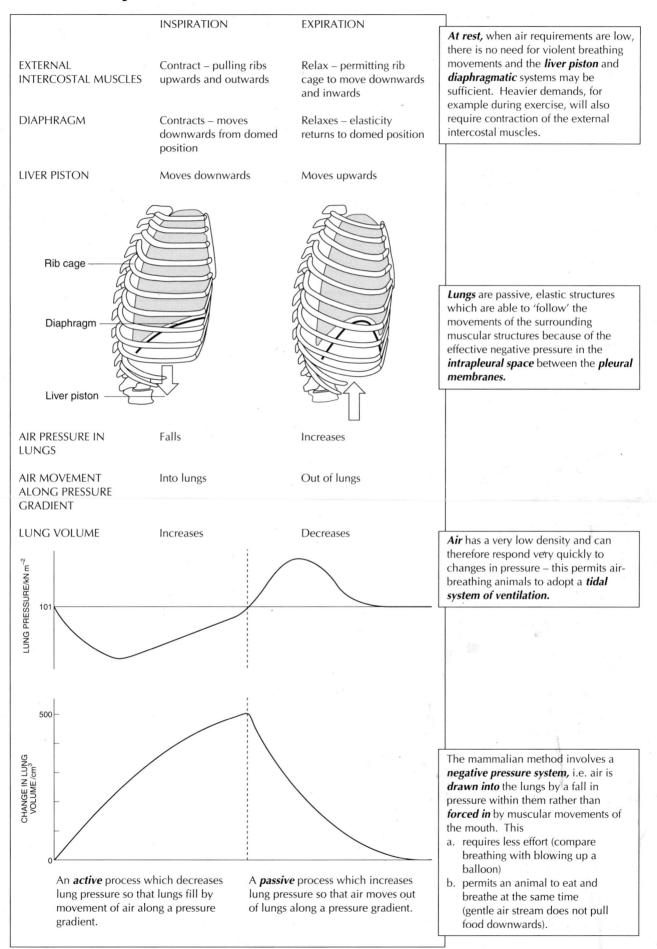

|  | INSPIRATION | EXPIRATION |
|---|---|---|
| EXTERNAL INTERCOSTAL MUSCLES | Contract – pulling ribs upwards and outwards | Relax – permitting rib cage to move downwards and inwards |
| DIAPHRAGM | Contracts – moves downwards from domed position | Relaxes – elasticity returns to domed position |
| LIVER PISTON | Moves downwards | Moves upwards |

| AIR PRESSURE IN LUNGS | Falls | Increases |
|---|---|---|
| AIR MOVEMENT ALONG PRESSURE GRADIENT | Into lungs | Out of lungs |
| LUNG VOLUME | Increases | Decreases |

Rib cage

Diaphragm

Liver piston

LUNG PRESSURE/kN m$^{-2}$

101

CHANGE IN LUNG VOLUME /cm$^3$

500

0

An **active** process which decreases lung pressure so that lungs fill by movement of air along a pressure gradient.

A **passive** process which increases lung pressure so that air moves out of lungs along a pressure gradient.

**At rest,** when air requirements are low, there is no need for violent breathing movements and the **liver piston** and **diaphragmatic** systems may be sufficient. Heavier demands, for example during exercise, will also require contraction of the external intercostal muscles.

**Lungs** are passive, elastic structures which are able to 'follow' the movements of the surrounding muscular structures because of the effective negative pressure in the **intrapleural space** between the **pleural membranes.**

**Air** has a very low density and can therefore respond very quickly to changes in pressure – this permits air-breathing animals to adopt a **tidal system of ventilation.**

The mammalian method involves a **negative pressure system,** i.e. air is **drawn into** the lungs by a fall in pressure within them rather than **forced in** by muscular movements of the mouth. This

a. requires less effort (compare breathing with blowing up a balloon)

b. permits an animal to eat and breathe at the same time (gentle air stream does not pull food downwards).

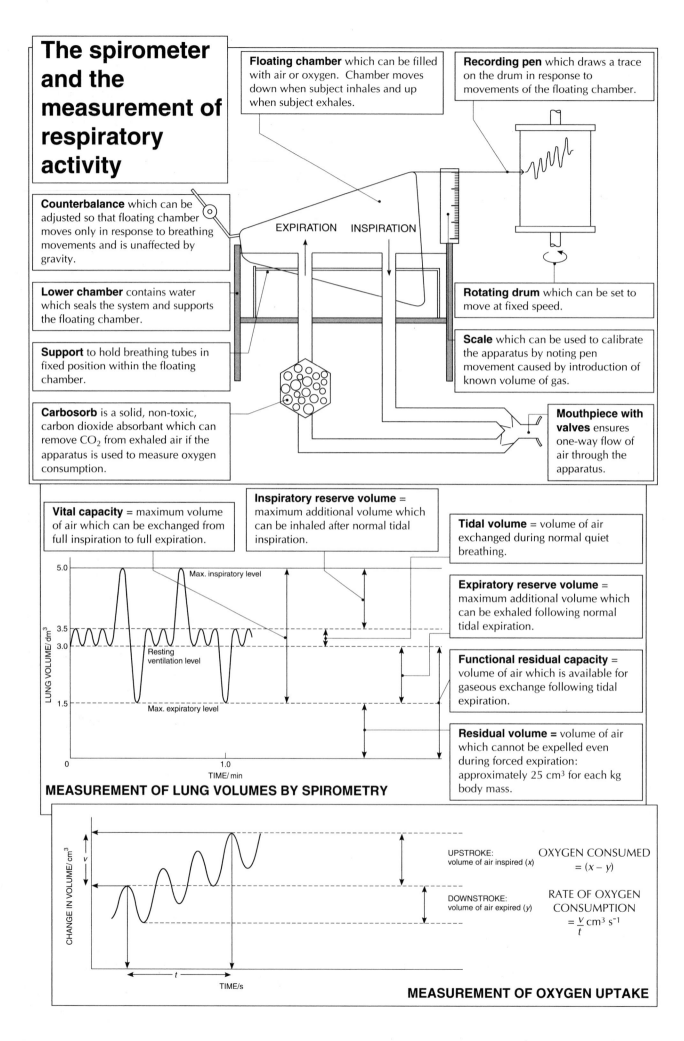

# The spirometer and the measurement of respiratory activity

**Floating chamber** which can be filled with air or oxygen. Chamber moves down when subject inhales and up when subject exhales.

**Recording pen** which draws a trace on the drum in response to movements of the floating chamber.

**Counterbalance** which can be adjusted so that floating chamber moves only in response to breathing movements and is unaffected by gravity.

EXPIRATION    INSPIRATION

**Lower chamber** contains water which seals the system and supports the floating chamber.

**Rotating drum** which can be set to move at fixed speed.

**Support** to hold breathing tubes in fixed position within the floating chamber.

**Scale** which can be used to calibrate the apparatus by noting pen movement caused by introduction of known volume of gas.

**Carbosorb** is a solid, non-toxic, carbon dioxide absorbant which can remove $CO_2$ from exhaled air if the apparatus is used to measure oxygen consumption.

**Mouthpiece with valves** ensures one-way flow of air through the apparatus.

**Vital capacity** = maximum volume of air which can be exchanged from full inspiration to full expiration.

**Inspiratory reserve volume** = maximum additional volume which can be inhaled after normal tidal inspiration.

**Tidal volume** = volume of air exchanged during normal quiet breathing.

**Expiratory reserve volume** = maximum additional volume which can be exhaled following normal tidal expiration.

**Functional residual capacity** = volume of air which is available for gaseous exchange following tidal expiration.

**Residual volume** = volume of air which cannot be expelled even during forced expiration: approximately 25 cm³ for each kg body mass.

Max. inspiratory level

Resting ventilation level

Max. expiratory level

LUNG VOLUME/dm³

TIME/ min

**MEASUREMENT OF LUNG VOLUMES BY SPIROMETRY**

CHANGE IN VOLUME/cm³

TIME/s

UPSTROKE: volume of air inspired (x)

DOWNSTROKE: volume of air expired (y)

OXYGEN CONSUMED $= (x - y)$

RATE OF OXYGEN CONSUMPTION $= \frac{v}{t}$ cm³ s⁻¹

**MEASUREMENT OF OXYGEN UPTAKE**

# Blood cells differ in structure and function.

If blood is spun for a few minutes in a high speed centrifuge it separates into two layers.

**Serum** is the name given to plasma from which the soluble protein fibrinogen (a protein involved in blood clotting) has been removed.

PLASMA (55%)

CELLS (45%)

**Blood cells** originate from *stem cells* in the bone marrow by the process of *haemopoiesis*.

UNCOMMITTED STEM CELL

LYMPHOBLAST

HAEMOCYTOBLAST

MEGA KARYOCYTE

MONOBLAST

PROERYTHROBLAST

MYELOBLAST

PLATELETS

LYMPHOCYTE

ERYTHROCYTE

LEUCOCYTE

MACROPHAGE

**Erythrocytes (red blood cells)** are the most numerous of blood cells – about 5 000 000 per mm³ of adult blood. They function in the transport of $O_2$ and $CO_2$, and they contribute to the buffering capacity of the blood. The red colour is due to the presence of the pigment haemoglobin. There are several advantages in packing the haemoglobin into cells rather than leaving it free in the cytoplasm – it keeps the blood viscosity low, it allows the best arrangement of enzymes and solutes for functioning of haemoglobin and it prevents a dramatic reduction in blood water potential. The typical lifespan of a red cell is 90–120 days, before they are destroyed in the spleen.

**Platelets (thrombocytes)** are fragments of cells which are involved in blood clotting (they disintegrate to release thromboplasts).

**Neutrophils** are the most abundant of the leucocytes (white blood cells). They are very short-lived (12–72 h), contain non-staining granules, and are responsible for the phagocytosis of micro-organisms. They migrate from the blood to the tissues, and are so active in phagocytosis that they are replaced at the rate of about 100 000 000 000 per day.

**Monocytes** are the largest of the leucocytes. They are agranulocytes (have non-granular cytoplasm) and have a large, bean-shaped nucleus. They spend a short time (2–3 days) in the circulatory system before moving into the tissues where they mature into phagocytic macrophages.

**Lymphocytes** make up about 30% of the circulating leucocytes. Although they are produced in the bone marrow they continue to develop and mature in the lymph nodes, the thymus gland and the spleen. They are responsible for the specific immune response – the B-lymphocytes produce antibodies and the T-lymphocytes have a number of roles, including co-ordination of the immune response and direct cell destruction. They are best identified by the prominent, deeply staining nucleus and the thin 'halo' of clear cytoplasm.

**Basophils** have an S-shaped nucleus and granules which stain blue. They secrete large amounts of histamine (which increases inflammation) and heparin (which helps to keep a balance between blood clotting and not clotting).

SCALE
5 µm

**Eosinophils** have a double-lobed nucleus and granules which stain red with the acid dye eosin. They help control the allergic response – for example, they secrete enzymes which inactivate histamine. Their numbers increase during allergic reactions and in response to some parasitic infections (e.g. tapeworm and hookworm).

# Tissue fluid (interstitial or intercellular fluid)

is the immediate environment of the cells, and represents the 'internal environment' described by Claude Bernard in his definition of homeostasis.

**Plasma proteins** do not move from plasma to tissue fluid (cannot cross capillary endothelium) - largely responsible for solute potential of plasma.

**Movement from tissue fluid to plasma**
> **Water**
> **Carbon dioxide**
> **Nitrogenous waste**
> **Hormones and other secretions**

ARTERIAL END
OF CAPILLARY

VENOUS END
OF CAPILLARY

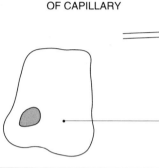

**Living cells** place demands on the tissue fluid.

**Movement from plasma to tissue fluid**
> *Water*
> *Oxygen*
> *Soluble products of digestion*
> *Hormones*

## FORCES WHICH REGULATE THE FORMATION AND RECLAMATION OF TISSUE FLUID

**Pressure potential (hydrostatic potential)** is the pressure exerted on a fluid by its surroundings, e.g. by *pumping action of heart* and *elastic recoil of arteries.*

*Net force driving fluid movement at any point*
*= pressure potential gradient – solute potential gradient*

**Solute potential (osmotic potential)** is the force of attraction towards water molecules caused by dissolved solutes, particularly *ions* and *plasma proteins*.

PRESSURE POTENTIAL GRADIENT

**Venous end of capillaries:** the PP gradient has fallen (1) as distance from pumping heart increases and (2) as volume of fluid in vessels falls. High concentration of plasma proteins means that blood solute potential is high.

SP GRADIENT > PP GRADIENT

*Net movement of water from tissues to plasma.*

DIRECTION OF BLOOD FLOW

SOLUTE POTENTIAL GRADIENT

**Arterial end of capillaries:** the PP gradient between plasma and tissue fluid is high due to pumping of heart and recoil of artery walls.

PP GRADIENT > SP GRADIENT

*Net movement of water from plasma to tissue fluid.*

In *most capillaries* there is a net flow of fluid from the blood to the tissue fluid. This depends on the pressure potential and solute potential gradients between blood plasma and tissue fluid – because the pressure potential falls as blood travels through the capillaries whereas blood solute potential remains fairly constant water tends to leave the capillaries at the high pressure end and enter at the low pressure end. Any net loss drains to the lymphatic system.

# Functions of blood

## TRANSPORT

**Soluble products of digestion/absorption** (such as glucose, amino acids, vitamins and minerals) from the gut to the liver and then to the general circulation. Fatty acids are transported from the gut to the lymph system and then to the general circulation.

**Waste products of metabolism** (such as urea, creatinine and lactate) from sites of production to sites of removal, such as the liver and kidney.

**Hormones** (such as insulin, a peptide, testosterone, a steroid, and adrenaline, a catecholamine) from their sites of production in the glands to the target organs where they exert their effects.

**Respiratory gases** (oxygen and carbon dioxide) from their sites of uptake or production to their sites of utilization or removal. Oxygen transport is more closely associated with red blood cells, and carbon dioxide transport with the plasma.

**Plasma proteins** secreted from the liver and present in the circulating blood include fibrinogen (a blood clotting agent), globulins (involved with specific transport functions, e.g. of thyroxine, iron and copper) and albumin (which binds plasma $Ca^{2+}$ ions).

## REGULATORY

**Blood solutes** affect the water potential of the blood, and thus the water potential gradient between the blood and the tissue fluid. The size of this water potential gradient, determined principally by plasma concentrations of $Na^+$ ions and plasma proteins, thus *regulates water movement* between blood and tissues.

The **water content** of the blood plays a part in *regulation of body temperature* since it may transfer heat between thermogenic (heat-generating) centres, such as the liver, skeletal muscle and brown fat, and heat sinks such as the skin, the brain and the kidney.

**pH maintenance** is an important function of *blood buffer systems* such as the hydrogencarbonate and phosphate equilibria, and is a secondary role of haemoglobin and some plasma proteins.

## PROTECTIVE

**Platelets, plasma proteins** (e.g. fibrinogen) and many other plasma factors (e.g. $Ca^{2+}$) protect against *blood loss* and the *entry of pathogens* by the clotting mechanism.

**Leucocytes** protect against *toxins and potential pathogens* by both non-specific (e.g. phagocytosis) and specific (e.g. antibody production and secretion) immune responses.

# Haemoglobin and myoglobin

**OXYGEN DISSOCIATION CURVES OF HAEMOGLOBIN** show the relationship between haemoglobin and oxygen (i.e. the percentage of haemoglobin in the form of oxyhaemoglobin) and the partial pressure of oxygen in the environment (the $pO_2$ or oxygen tension).

The S-shape of the curve is most significant. Simply put, it means that oxygen associates with haemoglobin, and remains associated with it, at oxygen tensions typical of the alveolar capillaries, the pulmonary vein, the aorta and the arteries, but that it very rapidly dissociates from haemoglobin at oxygen tensions typical of those found in respiring tissues. Furthermore, this dissociation is almost complete at the low oxygen tensions found in the most active tissues. In other words, oxygen release from oxyhaemoglobin is tailored to the tissues' demand for this gas.

The reason for this S-shapedness is that haemoglobin and oxygen illustrate co-operative binding, that is, the binding of the first oxygen molecule to haemoglobin alters the shape of the haemoglobin molecule slightly so that the binding of a second molecule of oxygen is made easier, and so on until haemoglobin has its full complement of four molecules of oxygen. Conversely, when one molecule of oxygen dissociates from the oxyhaemoglobin, the haemoglobin shape is adjusted to make release of successive molecules of oxygen increasingly easy.

---

**$pO_2$ typical of lungs, pulmonary veins and systemic arteries:** haemoglobin is saturated with oxygen – the 'flatness' of the curve means that the Hb remains saturated (i.e. very little $O_2$ is released) despite a small reduction in $O_2$. **Ideal for the transport of oxygen.**

**Steepness of curve** corresponds to easy dissociation of oxyhaemoglobin (much release of $O_2$) as $pO_2$ falls to values typical of blood in capillaries of respiring tissues.

**$pO_2$ typical of respiring tissues:** almost complete dissociation of $Hb(O_2)_4$ (most $O_2$ has been released).

PERCENTAGE SATURATION OF HAEMOGLOBIN

OXYGEN TENSION ($pO_2$)/ mm Hg

---

## MYOGLOBIN, MUSCLE AND MARATHONS

The muscles of mammals contain a red pigment called **myoglobin** which is structurally similar to one of the four subunits of haemoglobin. This pigment may also bind to oxygen, but since there is only one haem group there can be no co-operative binding and the myoglobin–oxygen dissociation curve is hyperbolic rather than sigmoidal.

The significance of this is that at any particular oxygen tension myoglobin has a higher affinity for oxygen than does haemoglobin. Thus when oxyhaemoglobin in blood passes through tissues such as muscle, oxygen is transferred to the myoglobin. Further analysis of the myoglobin–oxygen dissociation curve will show that myoglobin does not release oxygen until oxygen tension is very low indeed, and myoglobin therefore represents an excellent **store** of oxygen.

Muscles which have a high oxygen demand during exercise, or which may be exposed to low oxygen tension in the circulating blood, commonly have particularly large myoglobin stores and are called 'red' muscles. A high proportion of red muscle is of considerable advantage to marathon runners, who must continue to respire efficiently even when their blood is severely oxygen-depleted.

**Oxygen** can be transferred from oxyhaemoglobin owing to the latter's high oxygen affinity. Thus oxygen stores in muscle can be replenished from circulating blood.

At low $pO_2$ all oxygen from the $Hb(O_2)_4$ has been released but myoglobin retains a store of oxygen which is only released when $pO_2$ is almost zero.

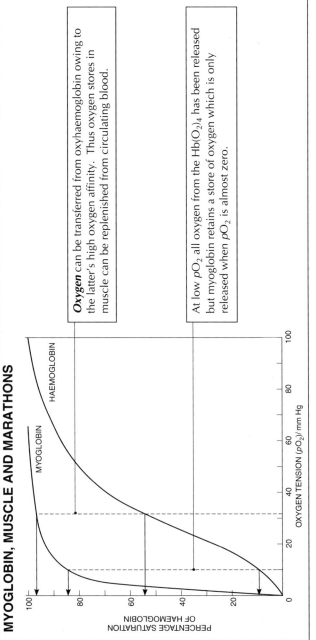

MYOGLOBIN

HAEMOGLOBIN

PERCENTAGE SATURATION OF HAEMOGLOBIN

OXYGEN TENSION ($pO_2$)/ mm Hg

# The transport of carbon dioxide from tissue to lung

The red cell and haemoglobin both play a significant part in this process as well as in the transport of oxygen.

**At the respiring tissue:** carbon dioxide produced in the mitochondria diffuses out of the cells, through the plasma, and into the erythrocytes, where it combines with water to produce carbonic acid, $H_2CO_3$, under the influence of the enzyme carbonic anhydrase.

① 

The reaction proceeds rapidly since the equilibrium is disturbed by the rapid removal of the hydrogen ions ($H^+$) by association with haemoglobin to form haemoglobinic acid (H.Hb). By accepting hydrogen ions in this way haemoglobin is acting as a buffer, permitting the transport of large quantities of carbon dioxide without any significant change in blood pH.

②

As a result of these changes the hydrogencarbonate concentration in the erythrocyte rises and these ions begin to diffuse along a concentration gradient into the plasma. However, this movement of negative ions is not balanced by an equivalent outward flow of positive ions since the membrane of the erythrocyte is relatively impermeable to sodium and potassium ions, which are therefore retained within the cell. This could potentially be disastrous, since positively charged erythrocytes would repel one another, a situation which would not enhance their function as oxygen carriers in the confines of a closed circulatory system! The situation is avoided, and electrical neutrality maintained, by an inward diffusion of chloride ions from the plasma sufficient to balance the $HCO_3^-$ moving out. This movement of chloride ions to maintain erythrocyte neutrality is called the *chloride shift*.

③

**At the lungs:** the reverse takes place. In the presence of oxygen haemoglobinic acid dissolves so that oxyhaemoglobin ($Hb.O_2$) may be formed. This releases hydrogen ions which combine with hydrogencarbonate in the plasma to produce carbonic acid.

④

Carbonic acid dissociates to water and carbon dioxide, which can diffuse along the concentration gradient into the alveoli and out of the body.

⑤

The hydrogencarbonate concentration in the red cells falls, more diffuses in from the plasma, and the process continues so that more carbon dioxide is released. Once more electrical neutrality of the erythrocytes is maintained by the chloride shift, but this time the chloride ions are moving in the opposite direction, from the cell to the plasma.

⑥

MITOCHONDRION IN TISSUE

$CO_2$

$O_2$

PLASMA

$CO_2$ IN SOLUTION

ALVEOLUS

$CO_2$

$O_2$

$CO_2$ IN SOLUTION

**ERYTHROCYTE AT TISSUE**

$CO_2 + Hb.NH_2 \rightleftharpoons Hb.NH\ COOH$ CARBAMINO HAEMOGLOBIN

$CO_2 + H_2O \rightleftharpoons H_2CO_3 \rightleftharpoons H^+ + HCO_3^-$ ①

5% 10% 85%

$O_2 + Hb \rightleftharpoons Hb.O_2$

H.Hb HAEMOGLOBINIC ACID ②

**ERYTHROCYTE AT ALVEOLUS**

$Hb.NHCOOH \rightleftharpoons Hb.NH_2 + CO_2$

$HCO_3^- + H^+ \rightleftharpoons H_2CO_3 \rightleftharpoons H_2O + CO_2$ ⑤

$H^+ + Hb.O_2 \rightleftharpoons H.Hb + O_2$ ④

$HCO_3^-$ ⑥

$Cl^-$ CHLORIDE SHIFT ③

# Mammalian double circulation comprises *pulmonary* (heart – lung – heart) and *systemic* (heart – rest of body – heart) *circuits*.

The complete separation of the two circuits permits rapid, high-pressure distribution of oxygenated blood essential in active, endothermic animals. There are many subdivisions of the systemic circuit, including **coronary, cerebral, hepatic portal** and, during fetal life only, **fetal circuits**. The circuits are typically named for the organ or system which they service – thus each kidney has a **renal** artery and vein. Each organ has an artery bringing oxygenated blood and nutrients, and a vein removing deoxygenated blood and waste.

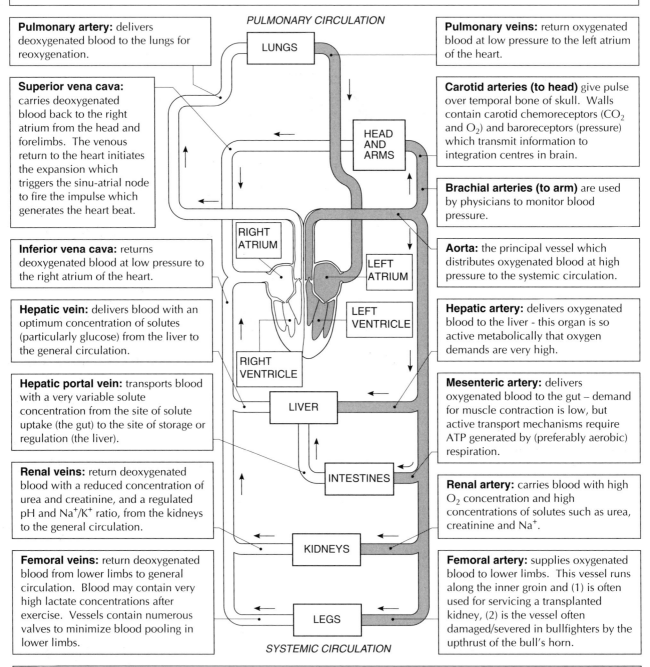

**PULMONARY CIRCULATION**

**Pulmonary artery:** delivers deoxygenated blood to the lungs for reoxygenation.

**Pulmonary veins:** return oxygenated blood at low pressure to the left atrium of the heart.

**Superior vena cava:** carries deoxygenated blood back to the right atrium from the head and forelimbs. The venous return to the heart initiates the expansion which triggers the sinu-atrial node to fire the impulse which generates the heart beat.

**Carotid arteries (to head)** give pulse over temporal bone of skull. Walls contain carotid chemoreceptors ($CO_2$ and $O_2$) and baroreceptors (pressure) which transmit information to integration centres in brain.

**Brachial arteries (to arm)** are used by physicians to monitor blood pressure.

**Inferior vena cava:** returns deoxygenated blood at low pressure to the right atrium of the heart.

**Aorta:** the principal vessel which distributes oxygenated blood at high pressure to the systemic circulation.

**Hepatic vein:** delivers blood with an optimum concentration of solutes (particularly glucose) from the liver to the general circulation.

**Hepatic artery:** delivers oxygenated blood to the liver - this organ is so active metabolically that oxygen demands are very high.

**Hepatic portal vein:** transports blood with a very variable solute concentration from the site of solute uptake (the gut) to the site of storage or regulation (the liver).

**Mesenteric artery:** delivers oxygenated blood to the gut – demand for muscle contraction is low, but active transport mechanisms require ATP generated by (preferably aerobic) respiration.

**Renal veins:** return deoxygenated blood with a reduced concentration of urea and creatinine, and a regulated pH and $Na^+/K^+$ ratio, from the kidneys to the general circulation.

**Renal artery:** carries blood with high $O_2$ concentration and high concentrations of solutes such as urea, creatinine and $Na^+$.

**Femoral veins:** return deoxygenated blood from lower limbs to general circulation. Blood may contain very high lactate concentrations after exercise. Vessels contain numerous valves to minimize blood pooling in lower limbs.

**Femoral artery:** supplies oxygenated blood to lower limbs. This vessel runs along the inner groin and (1) is often used for servicing a transplanted kidney, (2) is the vessel often damaged/severed in bullfighters by the upthrust of the bull's horn.

Diagram labels: LUNGS, HEAD AND ARMS, RIGHT ATRIUM, LEFT ATRIUM, LEFT VENTRICLE, RIGHT VENTRICLE, LIVER, INTESTINES, KIDNEYS, LEGS

**SYSTEMIC CIRCULATION**

The **flow of blood** is maintained in three ways.

1. *The pumping action of the heart:* the ventricles generate pressures great enough to drive blood through the arteries into the capillaries.

2. *Contraction of skeletal muscle:* the contraction of muscles during normal movements compress and relax the thin-walled veins causing pressure changes within them. Pocket valves in the veins ensure that this pressure directs the blood to the heart, without backflow.

3. *Inspiratory movements:* reducing thoracic pressure caused by chest and diaphragm movements during inspiration helps to draw blood back towards the heart.

# Mammalian heart: structure and function

The pressure generated by the left ventricle is greater than that generated by the right ventricle as the systemic circuit is more extensive than the pulmonary circuit.

The pressure generated by the atria is less than that generated by the ventricles since the distance from atria to ventricles is less than that from ventricles to circulatory system.

**Volume:** the same volume of blood passes through each side of the heart, so circulating volumes are also equal in pulmonary and systemic circuits.

**Aortic (semilunar) valve:** prevents backflow from aorta to left ventricle.

**Bicuspid (mitral, left atrioventricular) valve:** ensures blood flow from left ventricle into aortic arch.

**Left ventricle:** generates pressure to force blood into the systemic circulation.

**Chordae tendineae:** short, inextensible fibres – mainly composed of collagen – which connect to free edges of atrioventricular valves to prevent 'blow-back' of valves when ventricular pressure rises during contraction of myocardium.

**Papillary muscles:** contract as wave of excitation spreads through ventricular myocardium and tighten the chordae tendineae just before the ventricles contract.

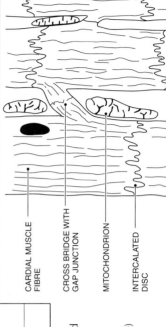

CARDIAL MUSCLE FIBRE

CROSS BRIDGE WITH GAP JUNCTION

MITOCHONDRION

INTERCALATED DISC

**Aorta:** carries oxygenated blood from the left ventricle to the systemic circulation. It is a typical elastic (conducting) artery with a wall that is relatively thin in comparison to the lumen, and with more elastic fibres than smooth muscle. This allows the wall of the aorta to accommodate the surges of blood associated with the alternative contraction and relaxation of the heart - as the ventricles contract the artery expands and as the ventricle relaxes the elastic recoil of the artery forces the blood onwards.

**Left atrium**

**Pulmonary arteries**

**Right atrium**

**Right ventricle:** generates pressure to pump deoxygenated blood to pulmonary circulation.

**Myocardium** is composed of cardiac muscle: intercalated discs separate muscle fibres, strengthen the muscle tissue and aid impulse conduction; cross-bridges promote rapid conduction throughout entire myocardium; numerous mitochondria permit rapid aerobic respiration. Cardiac muscle is myogenic (can generate its own excitatory impulse) and has a long refractory period (interval between two consecutive effective excitatory impulses), which eliminates danger of cardiac fatigue.

**Pulmonary (semilunar) valve:** is composed of three cusps or watchpocket flaps which are forced together then the pressure in the pulmonary artery exceeds that in the right ventricle, thus preventing backflow of blood into the relaxing chambers of the heart.

$P$ ventricle > $P$ artery

$P$ ventricle < $P$ artery

**Tricuspid (right atrioventricular) valve:** has three fibrous flaps with pointed ends which point into the ventricle. The flaps are pushed together when the ventricular pressure exceeds the atrial pressure so that blood is propelled past the inner edge of the valve through the pulmonary artery instead of through the valve and back into the atrium.

**Superior (anterior) vena cava:** carries deoxygenated blood back to the right atrium of the heart. As with other veins the wall is thin, with little elastic tissue or smooth muscle. In contrast to veins returning blood from below the heart there are no venous valves, since blood may return under the influence of gravity.

**Control of heartbeat**
1. The heartbeat is initiated in the *sinu-atrial node* (particularly excitable myogenic tissue in the wall of the right atrium).
2. *Intrinsic* heart rate is about 78 beats per minute.
3. *External (extrinsic)* factors may modify basic heart rate:
   a. *vagus* nerve decreases heart rate;
   b. *accelerator (sympathetic)* nerve increases heart rate;
   c. *adrenaline* and *thyroxine* increase heart rate.
Resting heart rate of 70 beats per minute indicates that heart has *vagal tone*.

# The lymphatic system

**Tonsils** are aggregations of large lymphatic nodules embedded in a mucous membrane. There is a single *pharyngeal* tonsil or *adenoid*, and two pairs (the *palatine* and the *lingual* tonsils), all arranged in a ring at the junction of the pharynx and the oral cavity. They protect against the invasion of foreign substances from the mouth, and produce lymphocytes and antibodies.

**Right lymphatic duct** receives lymph drainage from the right side of the head, the right upper trunk and the right arm, and empties the lymph into the systemic blood circulation at the junction of the right subclavian and right jugular veins.

The **thymus gland** is a paired organ most obvious in the pre-pubertal individual. It has a significant role in the immune response since it produces the T-lymphocytes which have a number of roles in the hierarchy of the immune system.

**Peyer's patches** are aggregated lymph nodes in the wall of the ileum, where they are ideally situated to offer protection against the invasion of potential pathogens or absorption of toxins from the gut contents.

The **lymphatic vessels** form a low-pressure return system for reclaimed tissue fluid. Since their contents are at low pressure the lymphatics are well-supplied with semi-lunar valves to ensure flow in one direction (towards the heart).

**Thoracic duct** receives lymph drained from all other areas of the body, and returns it to the blood circulation at the junction of the left jugular and left subclavian veins.

**The spleen** is the largest mass of lymphatic tissue in the body, and has the role of filtration of *blood* (not lymph, like the other lymph nodes). In the spleen the blood, plus any potential pathogens, is exposed to lymphocytes which may then be triggered to produce appropriate antibodies. The spleen also phagocytoses bacterial and worn-out red blood cells, acts as a blood reservoir and, during fetal development, produces red blood cells.

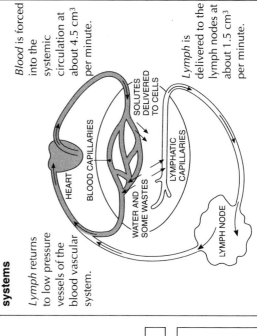

**Lymph nodes** are located along the lymphatic vessels, usually in groups, some *superficial* (easily located during infection) and some *deep*. As lymph passes through these nodes it is filtered of foreign substances which are trapped within a network of fibres and then phagocytosed by *macrophages* or destroyed by products of *T-cells*. Lymph nodes also produce *lymphocytes*, which may release antibodies, or may themselves leave the node and circulation to other parts of the body.

EFFERENT VESSEL

AFFERENT VESSEL

FIBROUS NETWORK WITH LYMPHOCYTES AND PHAGOCYTES

## Relationship between lymphatic and blood vascular systems

*Blood* is forced into the systemic circulation at about 4.5 cm$^3$ per minute.

*Lymph* returns to low pressure vessels of the blood vascular system.

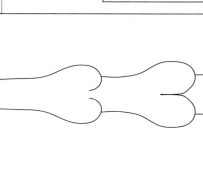

SOLUTES DELIVERED TO CELLS

HEART

BLOOD CAPILLARIES

WATER AND SOME WASTES

LYMPHATIC CAPILLARIES

LYMPH NODE

*Lymph* is delivered to the lymph nodes at about 1.5 cm$^3$ per minute.

At the lymph node, *phagocytes* remove toxins and pathogens, and **lymphocytes** secrete antibodies.

# Control systems in biology

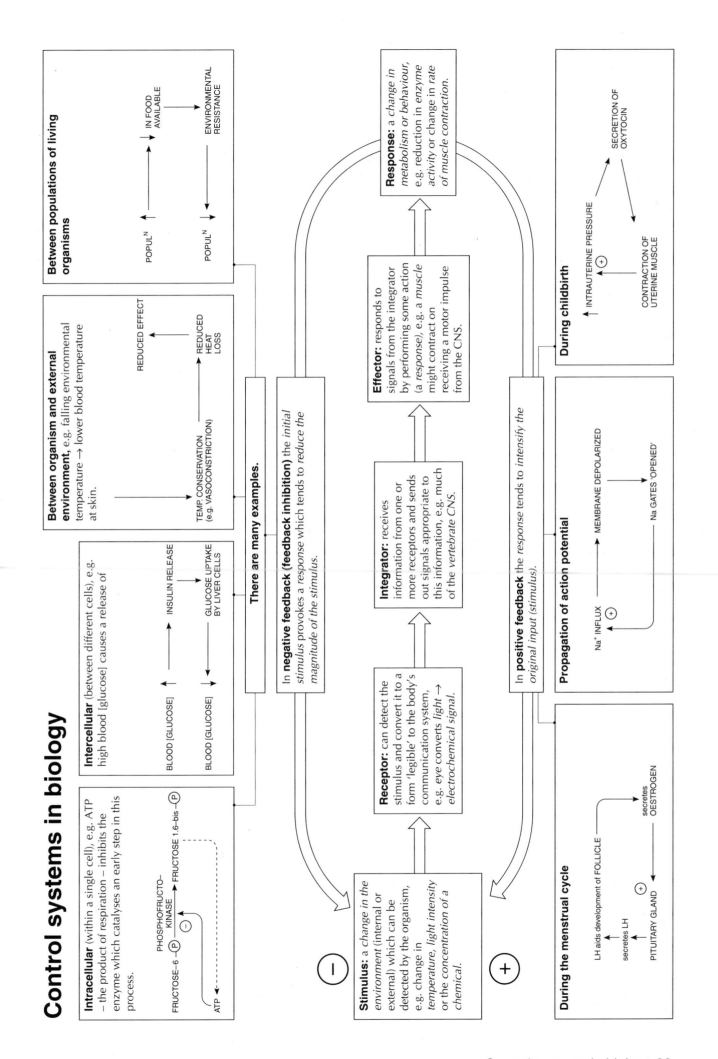

**Intracellular** (within a single cell), e.g. ATP – the product of respiration – inhibits the enzyme which catalyses an early step in this process.

PHOSPHOFRUCTO-KINASE

FRUCTOSE-6–Ⓟ ──(–)── FRUCTOSE 1,6-bis–Ⓟ

ATP

**Intercellular** (between different cells), e.g. high blood [glucose] causes a release of

BLOOD [GLUCOSE] ─→ INSULIN RELEASE

BLOOD [GLUCOSE] ←── GLUCOSE UPTAKE BY LIVER CELLS

**There are many examples.**

**Between organism and external environment,** e.g. falling environmental temperature → lower blood temperature at skin.

REDUCED EFFECT

REDUCED HEAT LOSS

TEMP. CONSERVATION (e.g. VASOCONSTRICTION)

**Between populations of living organisms**

POPUL^N ⟷ IN FOOD AVAILABLE

POPUL^N ⟷ ENVIRONMENTAL RESISTANCE

In **negative feedback (feedback inhibition)** the *initial stimulus provokes a response which tends to reduce the magnitude of the stimulus.*

**Response:** *a change in metabolism or behaviour,* e.g. reduction in enzyme activity or change in rate of muscle contraction.

**Effector:** responds to signals from the integrator by performing some action (*a response*), e.g. *a muscle might contract on receiving a motor impulse from the CNS.*

**Integrator:** receives information from one or more receptors and sends out signals appropriate to this information, e.g. much of the *vertebrate CNS.*

**Receptor:** can detect the stimulus and convert it to a form 'legible' to the body's communication system, e.g. *eye converts light → electrochemical signal.*

**Stimulus:** *a change in the environment* (internal or external) *which can be detected by the organism,* e.g. *change in temperature, light intensity or the concentration of a chemical.*

In **positive feedback** the *response tends to intensify the original input (stimulus).*

**During childbirth**

INTRAUTERINE PRESSURE → SECRETION OF OXYTOCIN

(+) CONTRACTION OF UTERINE MUSCLE

**Propagation of action potential**

Na⁺ INFLUX → MEMBRANE DEPOLARIZED → Na GATES 'OPENED'

(+)

**During the menstrual cycle**

LH aids development of FOLLICLE → secretes OESTROGEN

secretes LH

PITUITARY GLAND

(+)

Ⓘ

(+)

# Hormones of the pancreas regulate blood glucose concentration by negative feedback.

Claude Bernard: '…the maintenance of a constant internal environment is a necessity for a free life'.

There are severe consequences of any lengthy diversion of blood glucose concentration from its optimum.

**Blood glucose concentration: optimum** ~90–100 mg 100 cm⁻³

**Classic homeostatic principle:**

Stimulus

is

detected

and

regulation system

controls

effectors

which produce

response

to cancel out

stimulus

---

Increased uptake of glucose and amino acids from blood (particularly into skeletal muscle)
Increased glycogenesis in liver and muscle

PHOSPHORYLASE
Glucose ⟶ Glycogen

Increased lipogenesis, especially in adipose cells
Decreased gluconeogenesis
   i.e. less AMINO ACIDS → GLUCOSE
Decreased glycogenolysis
   i.e. less GLYCOGEN → GLUCOSE

Decreased absorption of dietary glucose

Inhibition of action of glucagon

Increased release of glucose from the liver into the blood

Increased gluconeogenesis
   i.e. more AMINO ACIDS → GLUCOSE
Increased glycogenolysis
   i.e. less GLUCOSE → GLYCOGEN
Decreased glycogenesis

---

INSULIN — β CELLS

SOMATOSTATIN — δ CELLS

GLUCAGON — α CELLS

ISLETS OF LANGERHANS IN PANCREAS

**Lowered blood glucose concentration**

**Reduces initial stimulus**

Blood [glucose] caused by dietary intake

Blood [glucose] caused by assimilation or loss

**Reduces initial stimulus**

**Raised blood glucose concentration**

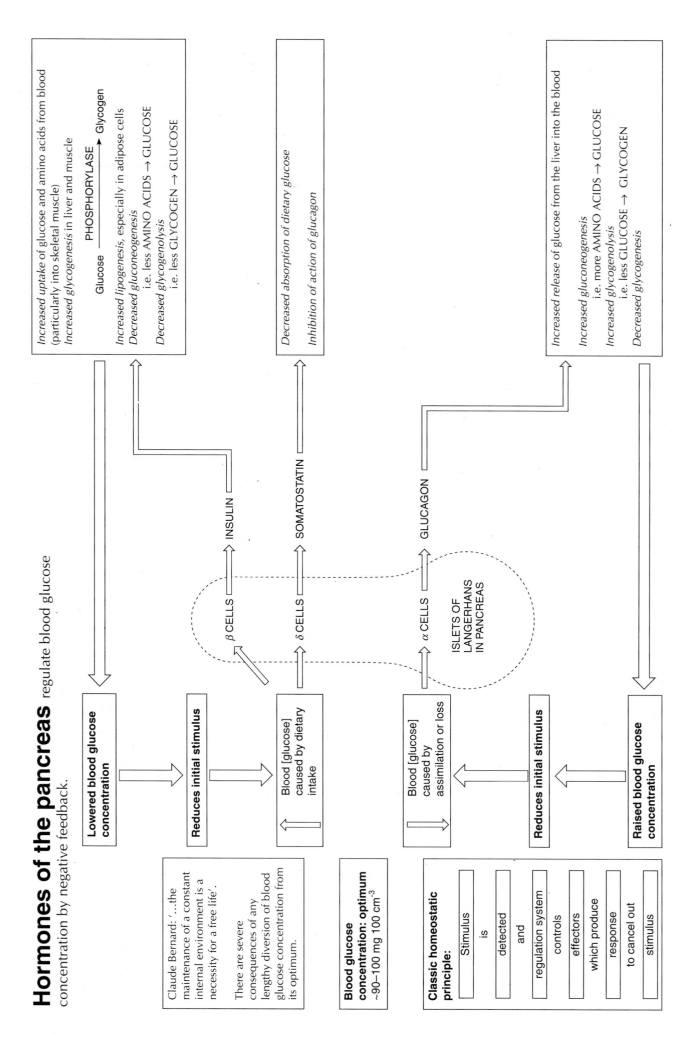

# The urinary system

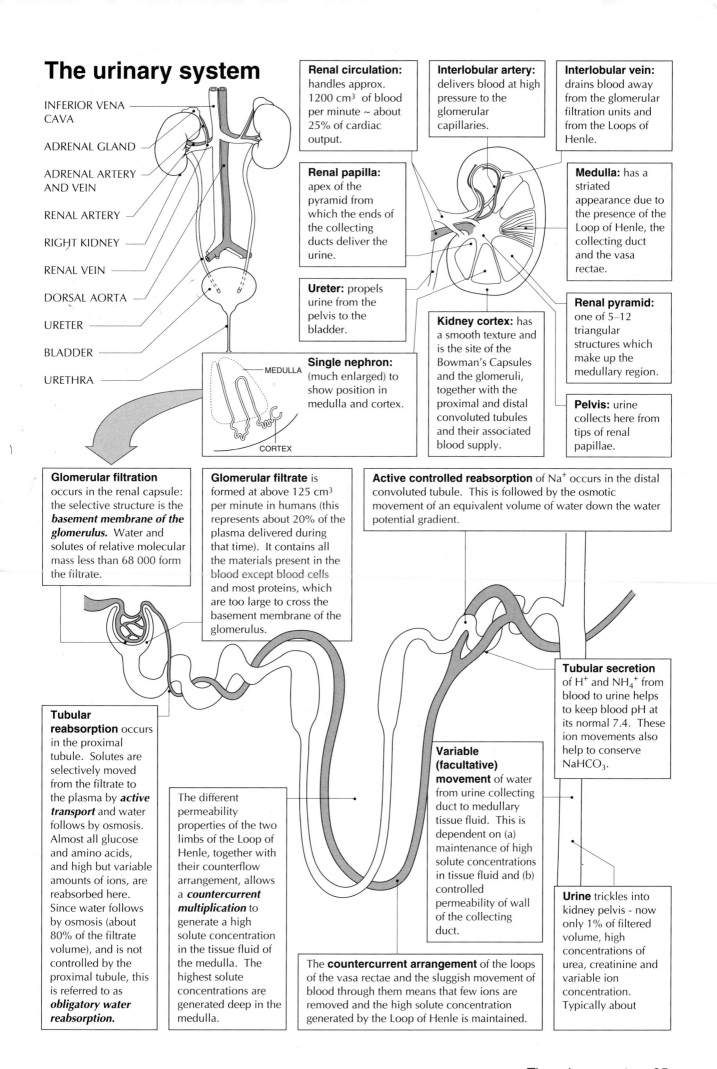

INFERIOR VENA CAVA

ADRENAL GLAND

ADRENAL ARTERY AND VEIN

RENAL ARTERY

RIGHT KIDNEY

RENAL VEIN

DORSAL AORTA

URETER

BLADDER

URETHRA

**Renal circulation:** handles approx. 1200 cm³ of blood per minute ~ about 25% of cardiac output.

**Interlobular artery:** delivers blood at high pressure to the glomerular capillaries.

**Interlobular vein:** drains blood away from the glomerular filtration units and from the Loops of Henle.

**Renal papilla:** apex of the pyramid from which the ends of the collecting ducts deliver the urine.

**Medulla:** has a striated appearance due to the presence of the Loop of Henle, the collecting duct and the vasa rectae.

**Ureter:** propels urine from the pelvis to the bladder.

**Kidney cortex:** has a smooth texture and is the site of the Bowman's Capsules and the glomeruli, together with the proximal and distal convoluted tubules and their associated blood supply.

**Renal pyramid:** one of 5–12 triangular structures which make up the medullary region.

**Pelvis:** urine collects here from tips of renal papillae.

MEDULLA

**Single nephron:** (much enlarged) to show position in medulla and cortex.

CORTEX

**Glomerular filtration** occurs in the renal capsule: the selective structure is the **basement membrane of the glomerulus.** Water and solutes of relative molecular mass less than 68 000 form the filtrate.

**Glomerular filtrate** is formed at above 125 cm³ per minute in humans (this represents about 20% of the plasma delivered during that time). It contains all the materials present in the blood except blood cells and most proteins, which are too large to cross the basement membrane of the glomerulus.

**Active controlled reabsorption** of Na⁺ occurs in the distal convoluted tubule. This is followed by the osmotic movement of an equivalent volume of water down the water potential gradient.

**Tubular reabsorption** occurs in the proximal tubule. Solutes are selectively moved from the filtrate to the plasma by **active transport** and water follows by osmosis. Almost all glucose and amino acids, and high but variable amounts of ions, are reabsorbed here. Since water follows by osmosis (about 80% of the filtrate volume), and is not controlled by the proximal tubule, this is referred to as **obligatory water reabsorption.**

The different permeability properties of the two limbs of the Loop of Henle, together with their counterflow arrangement, allows a **countercurrent multiplication** to generate a high solute concentration in the tissue fluid of the medulla. The highest solute concentrations are generated deep in the medulla.

**Variable (facultative) movement** of water from urine collecting duct to medullary tissue fluid. This is dependent on (a) maintenance of high solute concentrations in tissue fluid and (b) controlled permeability of wall of the collecting duct.

**Tubular secretion** of H⁺ and NH₄⁺ from blood to urine helps to keep blood pH at its normal 7.4. These ion movements also help to conserve NaHCO₃.

The **countercurrent arrangement** of the loops of the vasa rectae and the sluggish movement of blood through them means that few ions are removed and the high solute concentration generated by the Loop of Henle is maintained.

**Urine** trickles into kidney pelvis - now only 1% of filtered volume, high concentrations of urea, creatinine and variable ion concentration. Typically about

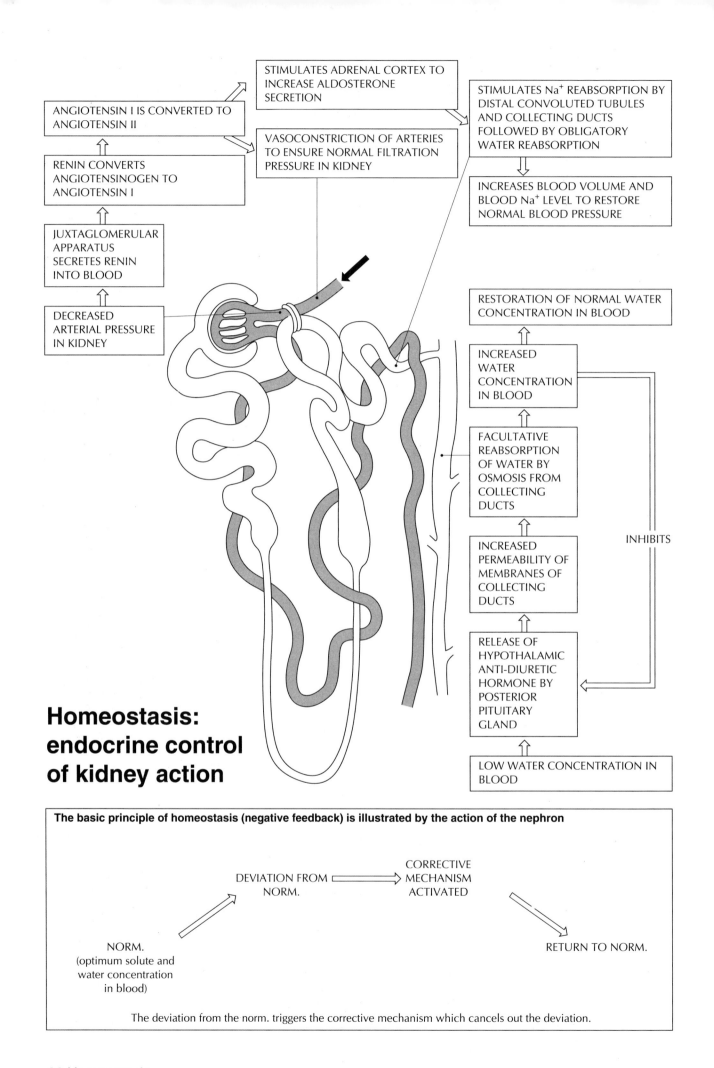

STIMULATES ADRENAL CORTEX TO INCREASE ALDOSTERONE SECRETION

ANGIOTENSIN I IS CONVERTED TO ANGIOTENSIN II

RENIN CONVERTS ANGIOTENSINOGEN TO ANGIOTENSIN I

VASOCONSTRICTION OF ARTERIES TO ENSURE NORMAL FILTRATION PRESSURE IN KIDNEY

STIMULATES Na$^+$ REABSORPTION BY DISTAL CONVOLUTED TUBULES AND COLLECTING DUCTS FOLLOWED BY OBLIGATORY WATER REABSORPTION

JUXTAGLOMERULAR APPARATUS SECRETES RENIN INTO BLOOD

INCREASES BLOOD VOLUME AND BLOOD Na$^+$ LEVEL TO RESTORE NORMAL BLOOD PRESSURE

DECREASED ARTERIAL PRESSURE IN KIDNEY

RESTORATION OF NORMAL WATER CONCENTRATION IN BLOOD

INCREASED WATER CONCENTRATION IN BLOOD

FACULTATIVE REABSORPTION OF WATER BY OSMOSIS FROM COLLECTING DUCTS

INCREASED PERMEABILITY OF MEMBRANES OF COLLECTING DUCTS

INHIBITS

RELEASE OF HYPOTHALAMIC ANTI-DIURETIC HORMONE BY POSTERIOR PITUITARY GLAND

LOW WATER CONCENTRATION IN BLOOD

# Homeostasis: endocrine control of kidney action

**The basic principle of homeostasis (negative feedback) is illustrated by the action of the nephron**

DEVIATION FROM NORM.

CORRECTIVE MECHANISM ACTIVATED

NORM.
(optimum solute and water concentration in blood)

RETURN TO NORM.

The deviation from the norm. triggers the corrective mechanism which cancels out the deviation.

**Protein metabolism**

**Deamination** of excess amino acids

Amino acid + oxygen → oxo acid + ammonia

and subsequent formation of **urea**

$$2\,NH_3 + CO_2 \longrightarrow \begin{Bmatrix} CO(NH_2)_2 \\ \end{Bmatrix} + H_2O$$

**Transamination** involves the transfer of an -NH$_2$ group from an amino acid to a different carbon skeleton

Amino acid I + oxo acid → Amino acid II + oxo acid I

The eight 'essential' amino acids cannot be synthesized in this way.

**Synthesis of plasma proteins,** including albumin, globulins, heparin, fibrinogen, prothrombin, factor VIII.

**Heat production**

High metabolic rate and considerable energy consumption make the liver the main heat-producing organ in the body. Metabolic rate and hence heat production is under the control of thyroxine.

**Küppfer cell**

A fixed cell of the reticulo-endothelial system which removes old ('effete') red blood cells. Iron is stored as ferritin, globin → amino acid pool and pyrrole rings are excreted as bile pigments.

**Lipid metabolism**

1. Excess carbohydrate is converted to fat.
2. Desaturation of stored fats prior to oxidation.
3. Synthesis/degradation of phospholipids and cholesterol.
4. Synthesis of lipid-transporting globulins.

**Storage of minerals and vitamins** principally *iron* (as ferritin), some potassium, copper and trace elements.

mainly the *fat-soluble* vitamins A, D, E. *Small* amounts of B$_{12}$, C. Synthesis of vitamin A from carotene.

**Branch of hepatic vein (intralobular vein)**

Delivers blood with a *constant concentration* of products to the circulation.

**Detoxification**

Often by *oxidation* (e.g. alcohol → ethanal), often by the protein P450, sometimes by *reduction* or *methylation*. Many drugs damage the liver, in original or intermediate forms, e.g. chloroform, paracetamol, tetracyclines, alcohol, anabolic steroids. Detoxified products are usually excreted but sometimes stored (e.g. DDT).

**Macrophage**

Wandering cells of the reticulo-endothelial system which identify and remove pathogens by phagocytosis.

**Branch of the hepatic portal vein (interlobular vein)**

Delivers blood from the absorptive regions of the gut carrying a *variable concentration* of the soluble products of digestion.

**Branch of hepatic artery (interlobular artery)**

Delivers oxygenated blood at high pressure – hepatocytes have a high oxygen demand and are very vulnerable to hypoxia. Also delivers lactate from anaerobic respiration in skeletal muscle.

**Bile ductile**

Takes away *bile* to be stored in the gall bladder. Bile is 90% water + *bile salts* (aid emulsification of fats) + *bile pigments* (an excretory product) + *cholesterol + salts.* Release is triggered by CCK-PZ from wall of duodenum.

**Carbohydrate metabolism**

*Glycogenesis:*
– promoted by *insulin*

glucose ⇌ gluc. 6 Ⓟ ⇌ gluc. 1 Ⓟ ⇌ glycogen

*Glycogenolysis:*
– promoted by *glucagon*

glycogen ⇌ gluc. 1 Ⓟ ⇌ gluc. 6 Ⓟ ⇌ glucose

*Lactate metabolism:*
– initiated by *lactate dehydrogenase*

lactate → pyruvate → glucose → glycogen

*Gluconeogenesis:*
– promoted by *cortisone* and *adrenaline*
Non-carbohydrate sources → glucose (e.g. glycerol, amino acids)

**Hormone removal**

Rapid inactivation of testosterone and aldosterone. More gradual breakdown of insulin, glucagon, thyroxine, cortisone, oestrogen and progesterone.

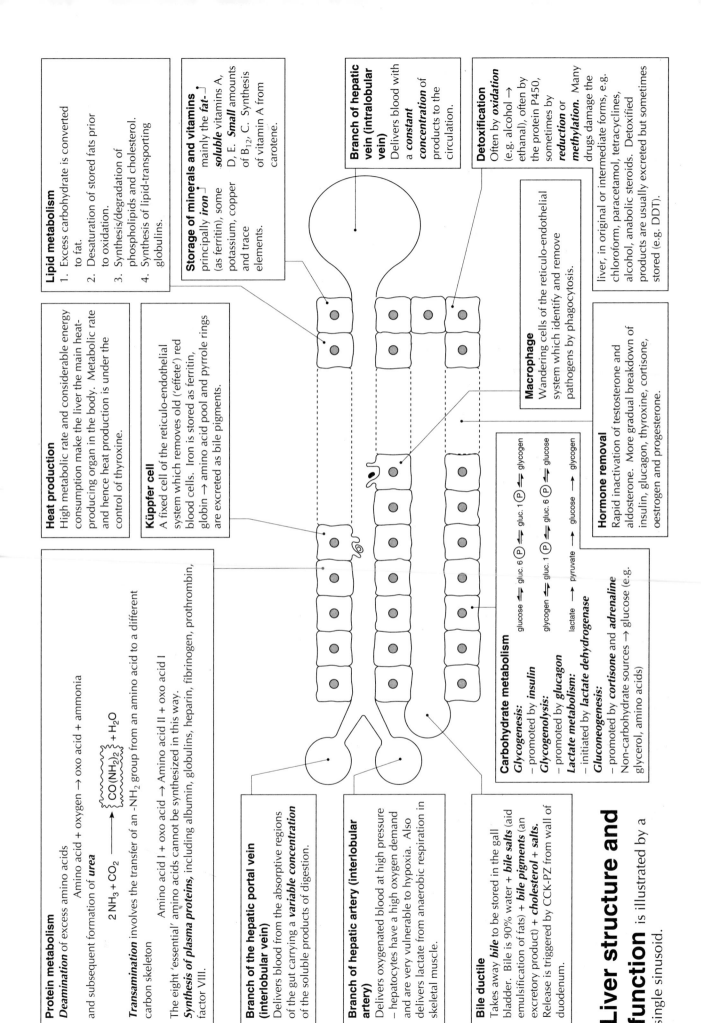

# Liver structure and function is illustrated by a single sinusoid.

# Control of body temperature in mammals

### EXTERNAL TEMPERATURE HIGH

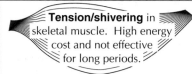

Pilo-erector muscles relaxed: hair shafts 'flatten' and allow free circulation of air over hairs. Moving air is a good convector of heat.

### EXTERNAL TEMPERATURE LOW

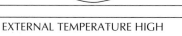

Pilo-erector muscles contracted: hair shafts perpendicular to skin surface. Trapped air is a poor conductor of heat so warm skin is insulated (similar effect by adding layers of clothing).

### EXTERNAL TEMPERATURE HIGH

Fluid overflows here

Fluid flows up duct

Sweat changed into vapour, taking latent heat of evaporation from the body to do this (about 2.5 kJ for each gram evaporated). Sweat glands extract larger volume of fluid from blood.

### EXTERNAL TEMPERATURE LOW

Skin surface comparatively dry – no evaporation and no cooling effect.

Sweat glands extract very little fluid from blood.

### Non-shivering heat response

triggers a general increase in metabolic rate. This is particularly noticeable in **brown adipose tissue** of newborns and animals that become acclimatized to cold. The **liver** of adults is also affected.

## Changes in behaviour

Dressing/undressing; moving in and out of shade; rest/activity cycles may all affect heat loss or production.

**Hypothalamus** contains the thermoregulatory centre which compares sensory input with a set point and initiates the appropriate motor responses. The set point may be raised by the action of pyrogens during pyrexia (fever).

**Core temperature** affects temperature of circulating blood which is monitored in the thermoregulatory centre.

**Skin temperature** is detected by skin thermoreceptors which deliver sensory input to hypothalamus via cutaneous nerves.

Automatic responses

Voluntary responses

CEREBRAL CORTEX

Releasing hormones

ANTERIOR PITUITARY GLAND

Sympathetic neurones

VASOMOTOR CENTRE in medulla oblongata

Sympathetic neurones

Thyrotrophic hormone

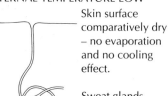

ADRENAL MEDULLA

THYROID GLAND

THYROXINE

ADRENALINE

### EXTERNAL TEMPERATURE HIGH

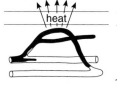

heat

epidermis

dermis

**Vasodilation:** sphincters/dilation of superficial arterioles allow blood close to surface. Heat lost by radiation – body cooled.

### EXTERNAL TEMPERATURE LOW

heat

epidermis

dermis

**Vasoconstriction:** superficial arterioles are constricted so that blood is shunted away from surface – heat is conserved.

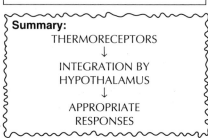

**Summary:**

THERMORECEPTORS
↓
INTEGRATION BY HYPOTHALAMUS
↓
APPROPRIATE RESPONSES

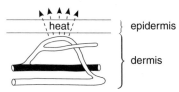

# Ectotherms

**Ectotherms** attempt to maintain body temperature by **behavioural** rather than **physiological** methods. These methods are less precise and so thermoregulation is more difficult.

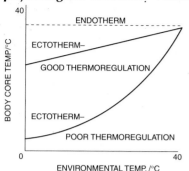

Graph: BODY CORE TEMP./°C (0 to 40) vs ENVIRONMENTAL TEMP./°C (0 to 40)
- ENDOTHERM
- ECTOTHERM– GOOD THERMOREGULATION
- ECTOTHERM– POOR THERMOREGULATION

**Reorientation** of the body with respect to solar **radiation** can vary the surface area exposed to heating. A terrestrial ectotherm may gain heat rapidly by aligning itself at right angles to the Sun's rays but as its body temperature rises it may reduce the exposed surface by reorientating itself parallel to the Sun's rays.

**Thermal gaping** is used by some larger ectotherms such as alligators and crocodiles. The open mouth allows heat loss by **evaporation** from the moist mucous surfaces. Some tortoises have been observed to use a similar principle by spreading saliva over the neck and front legs which then acts as an evaporative surface.

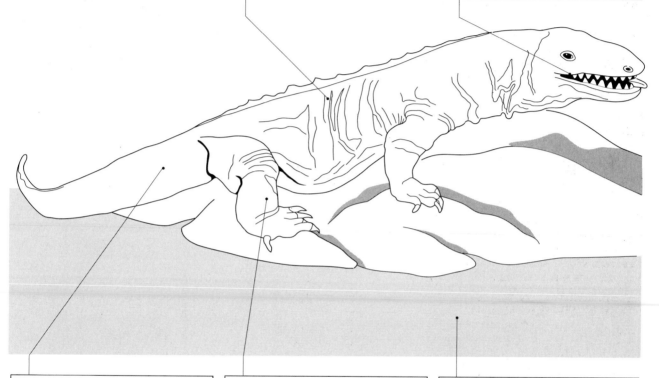

**Colour changes** of the skin may alter the ability of the body to absorb **radiated** heat energy. A dark-bodied individual will absorb heat more rapidly than a light-bodied one – thus some ectotherms begin the day with a dark body to facilitate 'warming-up' but then lighten the body as the environmental temperature rises.

**Body raising** is used by ectotherms to minimize heat gains by **conduction** from hot surfaces such as rocks and sand. The whole body may be lifted and the animal may reduce the area of contact to the absolute minimum by balancing on alternate diagonal pairs of feet.

**Burrowing** is a widely used behavioural device which enables ectotherms to avoid the greater temperature fluctuations on the surface of their habitat. The temperature in even a shallow burrow may only fluctuate by 5°C over a 24 h period whereas the surface temperature may range over 40°C during the same time. Amphibious and semi-aquatic reptiles such as alligators and crocodiles may return to water rather than burrow, since the high heat capacity of water means that its temperature is relatively constant.

**The marine iguana and bradycardia** The marine iguana of the Galapagos Islands feeds by browsing on seaweed gathered from the sea around the rocky shores on which it lives. When basking on the rocks it normally maintains a body temperature of 37°C but during the time spent feeding in the sea it is exposed to environmental temperatures of 22–25°C. In order to avoid losing heat rapidly by **conduction and convection** the iguana reduces the flow of blood between its core tissues (at 37°C) and its skin (22°C) by slowing its heart rate (bradycardia).

**Heat transfer** between the body of an organism and its environment depends on the **magnitude** and **direction** of the **thermal gradient** (i.e. the temperature difference between the organism and its surroundings). Heat may be **lost** or **gained** by
**conduction** (heat transfer by physical contact)
**convection** (heat transfer to the air) and
**radiation** (heat transfer in the form of long-wave, infra-red electromagnetic waves) but can only be **lost** by
**evaporation** (heat consumption during the conversion of water to water vapour).

# Immune response I: cells

The immune response involves a wide range of cells and their products in defence against diseases.

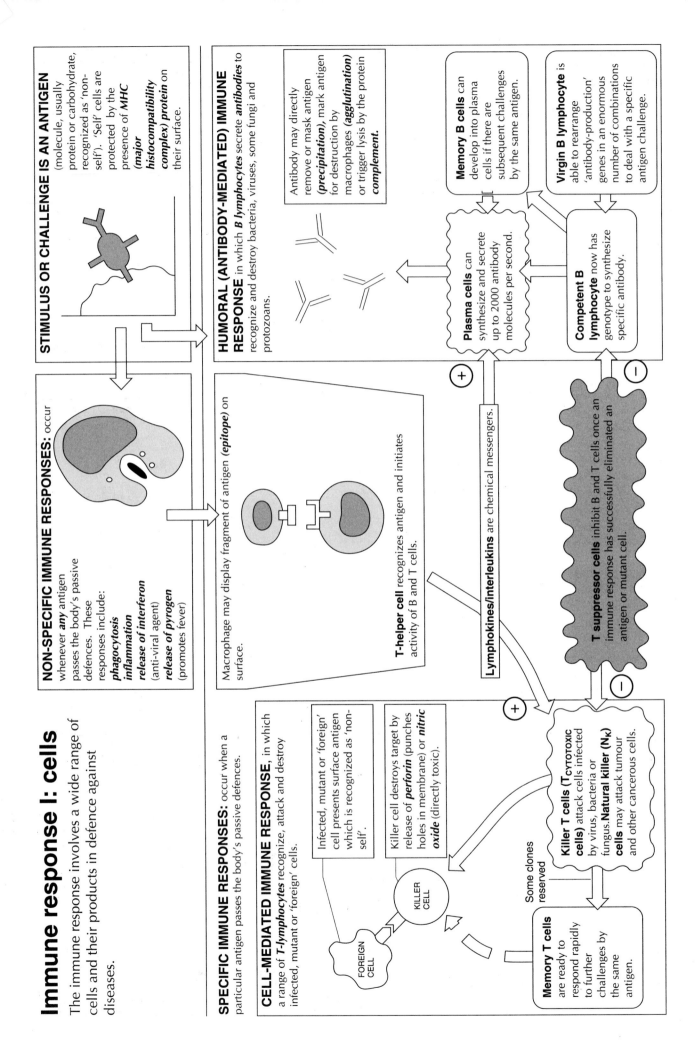

## STIMULUS OR CHALLENGE IS AN ANTIGEN

(molecule, usually protein or carbohydrate, recognized as 'non-self'). 'Self' cells are protected by the presence of *MHC* (*major histocompatibility complex*) *protein* on their surface.

## NON-SPECIFIC IMMUNE RESPONSES: occur

whenever *any* antigen passes the body's passive defences. These responses include:
**phagocytosis**
**inflammation**
**release of interferon** (anti-viral agent)
**release of pyrogen** (promotes fever)

## HUMORAL (ANTIBODY-MEDIATED) IMMUNE

RESPONSE in which *B lymphocytes* secrete *antibodies* to recognize and destroy bacteria, viruses, some fungi and protozoans.

Antibody may directly remove or mask antigen (*precipitation*), mark antigen for destruction by macrophages (*agglutination*) or trigger lysis by the protein *complement.*

**Memory B cells** can develop into plasma cells if there are subsequent challenges by the same antigen.

**Virgin B lymphocyte** is able to rearrange 'antibody-production' genes in an enormous number of combinations to deal with a specific antigen challenge.

**Plasma cells** can synthesize and secrete up to 2000 antibody molecules per second.

**Competent B lymphocyte** now has genotype to synthesize specific antibody.

**Lymphokines/interleukins** are chemical messengers.

**T suppressor cells** inhibit B and T cells once an immune response has successfully eliminated an antigen or mutant cell.

## SPECIFIC IMMUNE RESPONSES: occur when a

particular antigen passes the body's passive defences.

Macrophage may display fragment of antigen (*epitope*) on surface.

**T-helper cell** recognizes antigen and initiates activity of B and T cells.

## CELL-MEDIATED IMMUNE RESPONSE, in which

a range of *T-lymphocytes* recognize, attack and destroy infected, mutant or 'foreign' cells.

Infected, mutant or 'foreign' cell presents surface antigen which is recognized as 'non-self'.

Killer cell destroys target by release of *perforin* (punches holes in membrane) or *nitric oxide* (directly toxic).

KILLER CELL

FOREIGN CELL

Some clones reserved

**Killer T cells** (**T**CYTOTOXIC **cells**) attack cells infected by virus, bacteria or fungus. **Natural killer (N**K**) cells** may attack tumour and other cancerous cells.

**Memory T cells** are ready to respond rapidly to further challenges by the same antigen.

# Immune response II: antibodies and immunity

An antibody is a protein molecule synthesized by an animal in response to a specific antigen.

The basic structure of an antibody has the shape of the letter Y. Each molecule is composed of four polypeptide chains, two heavy and two light, all linked by disulphide bridges.

**Constant (C) region of light chain**

**Constant (C) region of heavy chain**

The constant regions determine the *general class* of the antibody:

IgG and IgM participate in the *precipitation, agglutination* and *complement* reactions.
IgA in tears, mucous secretions and saliva specifically binds to *surface antigens on bacteria.*
IgD helps to *activate lymphocytes.*
IgE is bound to mast cells and provokes *allergies.*

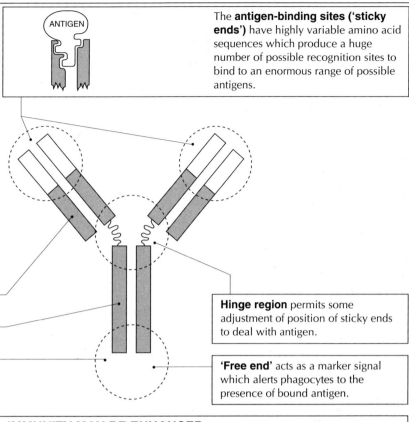

The **antigen-binding sites ('sticky ends')** have highly variable amino acid sequences which produce a huge number of possible recognition sites to bind to an enormous range of possible antigens.

**Hinge region** permits some adjustment of position of sticky ends to deal with antigen.

**'Free end'** acts as a marker signal which alerts phagocytes to the presence of bound antigen.

## MEMORY CELLS SPEED UP IMMUNE RESPONSE

**Secondary response:** curve is steeper, peak is higher (commonly $10^3$ x the primary response), lag period is negligible *due to the presence of B-memory cells.* Dominant antibody is IgG which is more stable and has a greater affinity for the antigen.

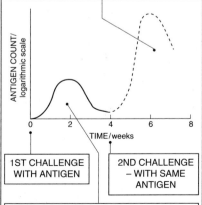

ANTIGEN COUNT/ logarithmic scale

TIME/weeks

1ST CHALLENGE WITH ANTIGEN

2ND CHALLENGE – WITH SAME ANTIGEN

**Primary response:** typical lag period is 3 days with peak at 11–14 days. Dominant antibody molecule is IgM.

## IMMUNITY MAY BE ENHANCED

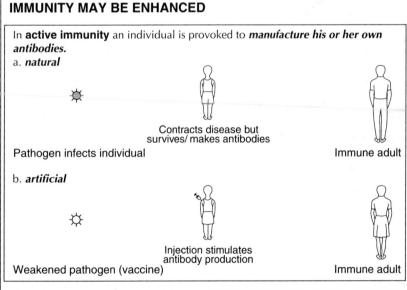

In **active immunity** an individual is provoked to *manufacture his or her own antibodies.*
a. *natural*

Pathogen infects individual

Contracts disease but survives/ makes antibodies

Immune adult

b. *artificial*

Weakened pathogen (vaccine)

Injection stimulates antibody production

Immune adult

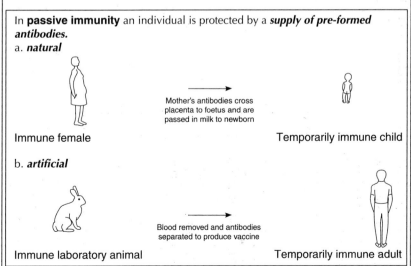

In **passive immunity** an individual is protected by a *supply of pre-formed antibodies.*
a. *natural*

Immune female

Mother's antibodies cross placenta to foetus and are passed in milk to newborn

Temporarily immune child

b. *artificial*

Immune laboratory animal

Blood removed and antibodies separated to produce vaccine

Temporarily immune adult

# The eye as a sense organ

The eye is a *generator region* (the retina) and a range of *ancillary structures* (e.g. lens, iris and choroid) to ensure optimum operation of the sensory cells.

**Choroid:** a thin pigmented layer which absorbs light to prevent internal reflection and multiple image formation. It has a well developed blood vascular supply which services the cells of the retina.

**Retina:** contains light-sensitive cells, the rods and cones, and a series of neurones which enhance image formation and transmit action potentials to the optic nerve.

**Fovea centralis/yellow spot:** region in which only cones (no rods) are found and thus the area of greatest visual acuity.

**Blind spot:** this region contains no light-sensitive cells and thus an image falling on this area cannot be perceived. The blind spot corresponds to the exit of the axons of the ganglion cells of the optic nerve.

**Optic nerve:** transmits impulses generated in the retina to the visual cortex of the cerebral cortex.

**Retinal blood vessels:** delivery of nutrients/removal of waste products to/from cells of retina.

**Vitreous humour:** this is produced during embryonic life and never replaced. It helps to maintain the shape of the eyeball, supports the lens and keeps the retina firmly applied to the choroid. There is considerable refraction of light at the posterior edge of the lens where it meets the vitreous humour.

**Lens:** is normally completely transparent. It allows light to enter the posterior chamber of the eye and is responsible for the refraction necessary to complete the fine focusing of an image on to the retina. The lens is composed of numerous layers of protein fibres in an elastic capsule.

**Sclera:** a tough coat of collagen fibres which protects the eyeball against mechanical damage, helps to maintain the shape of the eyeball, and provides attachment for the tendons of the rectus muscles.

**Rectus muscle:** one of three pairs of striated muscles which adjust the position of the eyeball within the orbit (eye socket).

**Ciliary body:** contains both circular and radial muscles which are able to alter the shape of the lens. The ciliary body also supports the lens behind the pupil, and secretes the aqueous humour into the anterior chamber of the eye.

**Aqueous humour:** maintains the curvature of the choroid.

**Conjunctiva:** protects the cornea at the front of the eyeball against friction and minor mechanical damage. Cells are replaced very rapidly.

**Cornea:** transparent to admit light to anterior chamber. Most light refraction occurs at the cornea/aqueous humour boundary.

**Pupil:** the circular opening which admits light to the lens.

**Canal of Schlemm:** a sinus which contains venous drainage products of the sclera and choroid.

**Iris:** a pigmented muscular structure which controls the entry of light via the pupil. Has both radial and circular muscles – there is a well developed cranial reflex which alters the diameter of the pupil to ensure optimum illumination of the retina. Degree of pigmentation (by melanin) is genetically determined.

**Suspensory ligaments:** attach the lens capsule to the muscular ciliary process, thus permitting adjustment of the lens shape during accommodation.

Optic axis

Hyaloid canal

# Structure and function of the retina

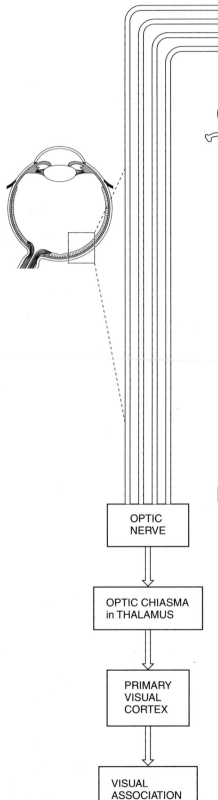

**Ganglion cell:** transmits action potential (depending on generator potential of photo-sensitive cells) along neurones of optic nerve.

**Amacrine cell:** interconnects sets of bipolar and ganglion cells – allows *visual field pathways* to influence one another and thus increase *contrast and discrimination.*

**Bipolar cell:** these form an intermediate which connects photosensitive cells to ganglion cells – important in summation (see below).

**Horizontal cell:** interconnects rods and cones with bipolar cells – helps function of amacrine cells (see above).

**Rod cell:** sensitive to low levels of illumination but unable to discriminate between 'colours'.

**Cone cell:** contains pigment which is only sensitive to high levels of illumination but exists in different forms, so these cells can detect 'colours'.

**Pigmented epithelium of retina**

OPTIC NERVE

OPTIC CHIASMA in THALAMUS

PRIMARY VISUAL CORTEX

VISUAL ASSOCIATION CORTEX

## RODS, SUMMATION AND SENSITIVITY

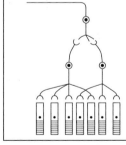

The responses of many rods may be 'summed' by the anatomical arrangement of the bipolar cells, which may synapse with several rods but only a single ganglion cell. This *synaptic convergence* permits great *visual sensitivity,* and rods are thus of great value for *night vision.* Since rods are more abundant away from the fovea, objects are often seen more clearly at night by not looking directly at them.

## CONES AND VISUAL ACUITY

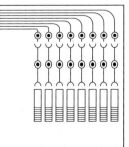

Each cone is connected, via a bipolar cell, to a single ganglion cell. Since cones are packed closely together, especially at the fovea, these cells are able to discriminate between light stimuli which arrive in close proximity – the retina is able to resolve two light sources falling on cones separated only by a single other cone.
The *absence of synaptic convergence* offers *acuity* but *poor sensitivity.*

# Endocrine control depends upon chemical messengers secreted from cells and binding to specific hormone receptors

**A hormone** is a chemical produced in one part of an organism which is transported throughout the organism and produces a specific response in target cells.

## Hormones fall into *three broad chemical categories*

1. **Proteins** (e.g. insulin) and **peptides** (e.g. oxytocin).

OXYTOCIN

$S$ ──── $S$

CYS — TYR — ILE — GLN — ASN — CYS — PRO — LEU — GLY — NH$_2$

2. **Amines** (e.g. adrenaline) are derivatives of amino acids.

3. **Steroids** (e.g. testosterone) derived from cholesterol.

## Hormone-secreting cells may be

a. **Endocrine** – secrete hormones into the bloodstream
   e.g. **adrenal medulla/adrenaline**

b. **Paracrine** – secrete hormones that affect adjacent cells
   e.g. **gastric mucosa/gastrin/gastric pits**

c. **Autocrine** – regulate their own activity by the secretion of hormones
   e.g. **interstitial cells of testis/testosterone**

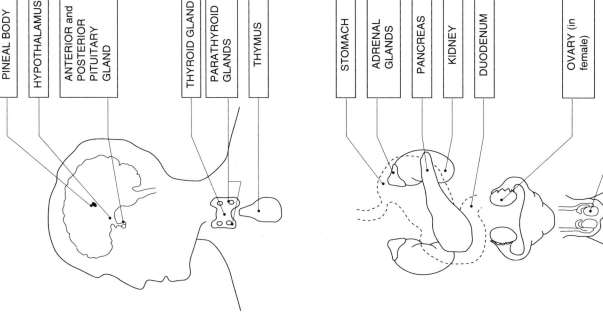

PINEAL BODY

HYPOTHALAMUS

ANTERIOR and POSTERIOR PITUITARY GLAND

THYROID GLAND

PARATHYROID GLANDS

THYMUS

STOMACH

ADRENAL GLANDS

PANCREAS

KIDNEY

DUODENUM

OVARY (in female)

TESTES (in male)

## General principles of hormone activity

1. The specificity of hormone action depends upon *target cells* – these possess *receptor molecules* made of protein in their membranes, cytoplasm or nucleus and can be activated by the *transduction machinery* which can be activated by the *hormone–receptor complex.*

2. Each target cell in the body is regulated only by those hormones to which it has receptor molecules, and not by others.

3. Different cells may respond in different ways to the same hormone – the transduction machinery of different target cell types 'reads' the hormone signal in different ways.

4. Some hormones, such as those which maintain solute concentrations in body fluids (e.g. insulin and calcitonin), are present for much of the time, whereas others, such as adrenaline (stress response) and gastrin (enzyme release), are secreted only when needed.

5. Blood hormone concentrations are usually governed by *negative feedback control* – a reduction in concentration stimulates additional secretion and an increase in concentration inhibits further secretion.

6. Once hormones bind to receptor molecules they are usually degraded rapidly. This 'rapid recovery system' means that target cells can be sensitive to changing levels of the hormones that regulate their activities.

# Endocrine secretions in humans

| ENDOCRINE GLAND AND HORMONE | TARGET | PRINCIPAL ACTION |
|---|---|---|
| **Pineal gland** secretes **melatonin** | Gonads | Seasonal control of reproductive activity in some mammals |
| | Melanocytes | Changes in pigmentation |
| **Hypothalamus** secretes **releasing** and **release-inhibiting factors** | Anterior lobe of pituitary gland (adenohypophysis) | Control secretion of specific hormones, including the trophins |
| **Thymus gland** secretes **thymosin** and **thymopoietin** | Lymphoid tissue | Maturation of T cells during cell-mediated immune response |
| **Stomach** secretes **gastrin** | Gastric glands of stomach | Stimulates secretion of pepsinogen |
| **Adrenal cortex** secretes **aldosterone** and **cortisol** | Kidney tubules | Increase blood levels of sodium and water and decrease potassium level |
| | General - many tissues | Promote resistance to stress; counter inflammatory responses |
| **Adrenal medulla** secretes **adrenaline** | General | Mobilizes glucose, increases blood flow from heart among many responses to danger or stress |
| **Ovary** secretes **Oestrogen** | General | Development of female secondary sexual characteristics |
| | Uterus | Repair of endometrium following menstruation |
| **Progesterone** | Uterus | Preparation for implantation |
| | Breast | Preparation of mammary glands for lactation |
| **Relaxin** | Pubic symphysis | Allows expansion of pelvis |
| | Cervix | Dilation at childbirth |

| ENDOCRINE GLAND AND HORMONE | TARGET | PRINCIPAL ACTION |
|---|---|---|
| **Posterior pituitary gland** secretes **Oxytocin** | Uterus | Stimulates contraction during childbirth |
| | Mammary gland | Stimulates ejection of milk into ducts |
| **Anti-diuretic hormone** | Collecting ducts of kidney | Reabsorption of water from urine |
| **Anterior pituitary gland** secretes many hormones including **trophins** | | Trophins stimulate other endocrine organs |
| **Thyroid gland** secretes **thyroxine** and **triiodothyronine** | Many tissues | Stimulation of metabolic rate |
| **Parathyroid glands** secrete **parathormone** | Bone | Stimulates release of $Ca^{2+}$ |
| | Kidneys | Stimulates $Ca^{2+}$ reabsorption |
| | Gut | Activates vitamin D |
| **Kidney** secretes **erythropoietin** | Bone marrow | Stimulates synthesis and maturation of erythrocytes |
| **Islets of Langerhans** in **pancreas** secrete **insulin** and **glucagon** | General | Lowers blood glucose concentration |
| | Liver, adipose tissue | Raises blood glucose concentration |
| **Testis** secretes **Testosterone** | General | Development of male secondary sexual characteristics |
| | Seminiferous tubules | Promotes spermatogenesis |
| **Inhibin** | Anterior pituitary gland | Controls sperm production by inhibition of FSH secretion |

| ENDOCRINE GLAND AND HORMONE | TARGET | PRINCIPAL ACTION |
|---|---|---|
| **Duodenal mucosa** secretes **secretin** | Pancreas | Stimulates release of $NaHCO_3$ into pancreatic juice |
| **Cholecystokinin** | Pancreas | Stimulates release of digestive enzymes |
| | Gall bladder | Stimulates contraction and emptying |

# Motor (efferent) neurone: the dendrites (antennae), axon (cable), synaptic buttons (contacts) are serviced and maintained by the cell body.

**Nissl's granules** (or 'chromatophilic substance' because they take up stain readily) represent a highly ordered **rough endoplasmic reticulum.** Proteins made here, and passed into the neuronal processes (especially the axon), include structural proteins of the neurone membrane, transport proteins such as the $Na^+/K^+$ pump and enzymes involved in neurotransmitter synthesis.

**Neurofibrils** are formed from microtubules and microfilaments. They offer support to the cell body and may be involved in the transport of materials throughout the neurone.

**Axon collateral** is a side branch of the axon which means that one cell may direct impulses to more than one effector.

**Schwann cell (neurilemmocyte)** is a glial cell which encircles the axon. When the two 'ends' of the Schwann cell meet, overlapping occurs which pushes the nucleus and cytoplasm to the outside layer.

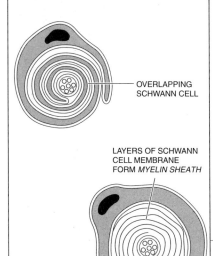

SCHWANN CELL
AXON MEMBRANE
NEUROFIBRIL
AXOPLASM

OVERLAPPING SCHWANN CELL

LAYERS OF SCHWANN CELL MEMBRANE FORM *MYELIN SHEATH*

SCHWANN CELL CYTOPLASM FORMS *NEURILEMMA*

**Dendrites** are extensions of the cell body containing all typical cell body organelles. They provide a large surface area to receive information which they then pass on towards the cell body. The plasma has a high density of **chemically gated ion channels,** important in impulse transmission.

**Cell body** contains a well-developed nucleus and nucleolus and many organelles such as lysosomes and mitochondria. Many neurones also contain yellowish-brown granules of **lipofuscin pigment,** which may be a by-product of lysosomal activity and which increases in concentration as the neurone ages. There is **no mitotic apparatus** (centriole/spindle) in neurones more than six months old, which means that damaged neurones can never be replaced (although they may regenerate – see below).

**Axon hillock** is the point on the neuronal membrane at which a **threshold stimulus** may lead to the initiation of an **action potential.**

**Nodes of Ranvier** are unmyelinated segments of the neurone. Since these are uninsulated, ion movements may take place which effectively lead to action potentials 'leaping' from one node to another during **saltatory conduction.**

**Axon** is the communication route between the cell body and the axon terminals. There are two intracellular transport systems: **axoplasmic flow** is slow, unidirectional protoplasmic streaming which supplies new axoplasm for new or regenerating neurones; **axonal transport** is faster, bi-directional and via microtubules and microfilaments. Axonal transport returns materials to the cell body for degradation/recycling *but* is the route taken by the **herpes virus** and the **rabies virus** to the cell body, where they multiply and cause their damage. The toxin produced by the **tetanus bacterium** uses the same route to reach the central nervous system.

**Axon teminal**

**Neurilemma** is found only around fibres of the peripheral nervous system, i.e. typical sensory and motor neurones. The neurilemma plays a part in the regeneration of damaged nerves by forming a tubular sheath around the damaged area within which regeneration may occur.

**Myelin sheath** is composed of 20–30 layers of Schwann cell membrane. The high phospholipid content of the sheath offers electrical insulation → **salutory impulse conduction.** Not complete until late childhood so infants often have slow responses/poor co-ordination.

**Synaptic end bulb** or *synaptic button* is important in nerve impulse conduction from one neurone to another or from a neurone to an effector. They contain membrane-enclosed sacs (**synaptic vessels**) which store **neurotransmitters** prior to release and diffusion to the post-synaptic membrane.

# Spinal cord and reflex action

**Reflex actions** are rapid responses to internal or external stimuli which allow the body to maintain homeostasis. They may be **somatic** or **autonomic** but all involve the sequence

RECEPTOR → SENSORY NEURONE → CNS → MOTOR NEURONE → EFFECTOR

**Receptor** is the origin of the reflex action. The receptor responds to a **stimulus** (a change in the environment) by producing an amplitude-modulated generator potential which is transmitted along the sensory neurone as a **frequency-modulated action potential.**

**Sensory neurone** transmits information from a receptor towards the CNS. Sensory neurones are myelinated so that transmission is rapid.

**Spinal nerve** is one of 31 pairs and is a **mixed** nerve, i.e. it has both sensory and motor fibres within in.

**Effectors** may be muscles or glands and perform an action (response) when they receive an input from the motor neurone. This response will have a **survival value** to the organism in which it takes place.

**Synapse in the sympathetic ganglion** of the autonomic nervous system has adrenaline or noradrenaline as the major neurotransmitter.

**Dorsal root ganglion** is a swelling in the dorsal root of the spinal nerve caused by an aggregation of cell bodies of the sensory neurones.

**Motor neurone** of somatic nervous system transmits impulses from the CNS to an effector (typically striated muscle fibres). These neurones are myelinated and form the bulk of the ventral root of the spinal nerve.

**Motor neurone** of sympathetic nervous system transmits impulses to a variety of effectors other than striated (skeletal) muscle. Thus one sensory input can bring about a variety of responses.

**Descending fibre** can transmit impulses from higher centres which may modify reflex action by influencing post-synaptic potentials in the outgoing motor neurones. Descending fibres may be **inhibitory** (minimize the reflex action) or **excitatory** (exaggerate the action), and both **temporal** and **spatial summation** of impulses from interneurones and descending fibres may take place. Both ascending and descending fibres are myelinated (medullated) so that they transmit impulses rapidly to and from the brain.

**Ascending fibre** can transmit sensory input to the higher centres of the CNS (medulla, cerebellum and/or cerebral cortex).

**Interneurone (associate or internuncial neurone)** transmits sensory input across the spinal cord. It is not myelinated so that impulse transmission is relatively slow. This is significant in permitting higher centres to modify reflex action via descending fibres. This interneurone may be absent in the most rapid and inflexible reflexes, such as the knee jerk.

**Central canal** contains cerebrospinal fluid (CSF) which nourishes and maintains electrolyte balance in the CNS.

**Grey matter** is largely composed of cell bodies (mainly of motor neurones) and unmyelinated axons of interneurones. There are also many **glial cells** (support and nourish neurones). The absence of myelin is responsible for the grey colour of this region.

**White matter** consists of bundles of motor and sensory neurones, including those of the ascending and descending tracts. These cells are well myelinated – hence the light colour of this region.

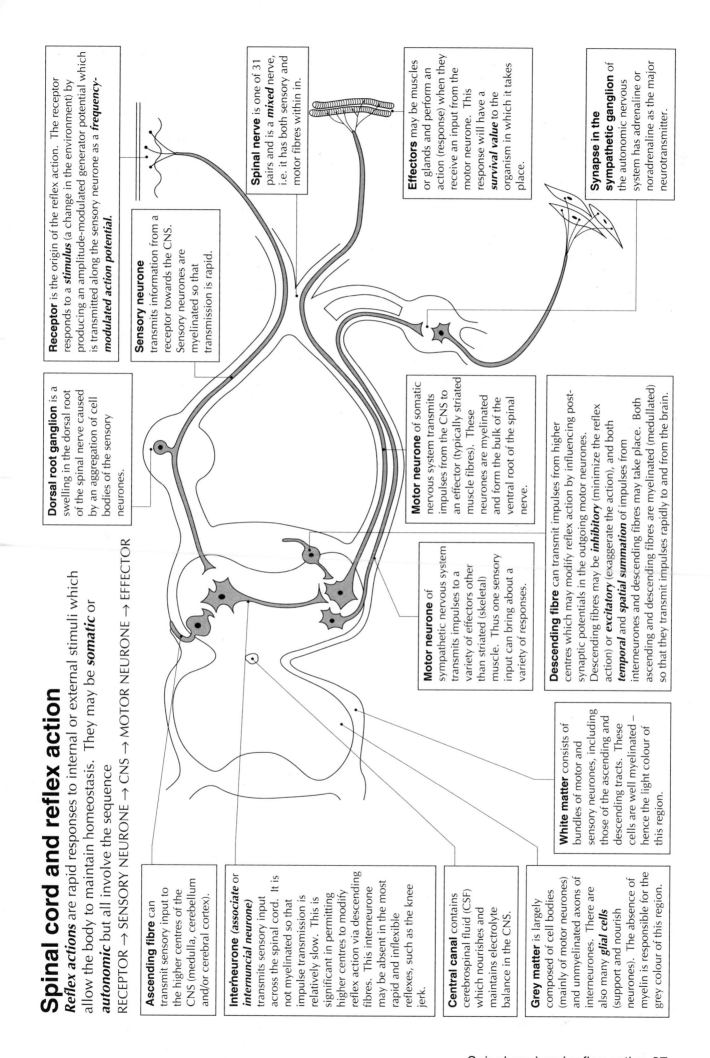

# Action potential: a depolarization of about 110 mV resulting from *an inward flow of Na⁺ ions*

An **action potential** is the depolarization–repolarization cycle at the neurone membrane following the application of a threshold stimulus. Since the depolarization–repolarization depend upon ion concentration gradients and upon time of ion channel opening, both of which are effectively fixed, *all action potentials are of the same size*. Thus a nerve cell obeys the *all-or-nothing principle*: if a stimulus is strong enough to generate an action potential, the impulse is conducted along the entire neurone *at a constant and maximum strength* for the existing conditions.

**Depolarization:** the voltage-gated sodium channels open so that Na⁺ ions can move *into the axon.*

a.　down a *Na⁺ concentration gradient*

b.　down an *outside–inside electrical gradient*

The inward movement of Na⁺ ions during depolarization is an example of a *positive feedback system*. As Na⁺ ions continue to move inward depolarization increases, which opens more sodium channels so more Na⁺ ions enter causing more depolarization and so on.

**Return to resting potential:** although the action potential involves Na⁺ and K⁺ movements, the changes in absolute ion concentrations are very small (probably no more than 1 in $10^7$). Many action potentials could be transmitted before concentration gradients are significantly changed – the sodium–potassium pump can quickly restore resting ion

**Repolarization:** sodium channels are closed but potassium channels are open so that K⁺ ions are able to move *out of the axon.*

a.　down a K⁺ *concentration gradient*

b.　down an *electrochemical gradient*

**Hyperpolarization and refractory period:** Potassium channels close and short term conformational changes in the pore proteins of the sodium channels mean that these voltage-gated sodium channels are **inactivated.** As a result the neuronal membrane becomes *refractory* – unable to respond to a stimulus which would normally trigger an action potential.

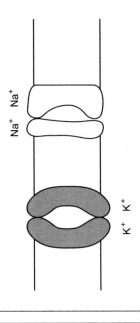

**Threshold value:** any stimulus strong enough to initiate an impulse is called a *threshold* or *liminal stimulus.* The stimulus begins the depolarization of the neuronal membrane – once a sufficient number of voltage-gated sodium channels is opened, positive feedback will ensure a complete depolarization. Any stimulus weaker than a threshold stimulus is called a *sub-threshold* or *subliminal stimulus.* Such a stimulus is incapable of initiating an action potential, but a series of such stimuli *may* exert a cumulative effect which may be sufficient to initiate an impulse. This is the phenomenon of *summation of impulses.*

MEMBRANE POTENTIAL/ mV

+40

0

−70

TIME / ms

0　1　2　3

# Synapse: structure and function

Transmission of an action potential across a chemical synapse involves a uni-directional release of molecules of neurotransmitter from pre-synaptic to post-synaptic membranes

**Drugs and poisons** may interfere with synaptic transmission by

1. *Mimicry of neurotransmitter,* e.g. *nicotine* mimics both acetylcholine and noradrenaline

2. *Reduced degradation,* e.g. *cocaine* inhibits re-uptake of noradrenaline

3. *Blocking receptors,* e.g. *chlorpromazine* acts as an emotional depressant by blocking dopamine receptors

4. *Reduced release of neurotransmitter,* e.g. *alcohol* alters sleeping patterns by reducing release of seratonin.

1. **Increase in local Ca$^{2+}$ concentration:** depolarization of membrane at synaptic button affects 'calcium channels' so that Ca$^{2+}$ ions flow quickly into synaptic button from tissue fluid.

2. **Synaptic vesicles** containing molecules of neuro-transmitter move towards the presynaptic membrane.

**Mitochondria** are abundant in the synaptic button: release energy for refilling of synaptic vesicles and possibly for pumping of Ca$^{2+}$ to re-establish Ca$^{2+}$ concentration gradient across neurone membrane.

**Synaptic cleft** represents a barrier to the direct passage of the wave of depolarization from pre-synaptic to post-synaptic membranes.

6. **Reabsorption of neurotransmitter or products of degradation.** Molecules are resynthesized and reincorporated into synaptic vesicles. *Catecholamines* are often reabsorbed without degradation.

Na$^+$

5. **Enzymes degrade neurotransmitter.** These degradative enzymes, which are released from adjacent glial cells or are located on the post-synaptic membrane, remove neurotransmitter molecules so that their effect on the chemically gated ion channels is only short-lived. They include
*monoamine oxidase* (degrades *catecholamines)*
*acetylcholine esterase* (degrades *acetylcholine)*

4. **Chemically gated ion channels** on post-synaptic membrane – allow influx of Na$^+$ and efflux of K$^+$ → depolarization of post-synaptic membrane. Ion channels are 'opened' when triggered by binding of neurotransmitter.

3. **Neurotransmitter molecules** diffuse across synaptic gap when synaptic vesicles fuse with pre-synaptic membrane. Molecules bind to *stereospecific receptors* in the post-synaptic membrane. *Catecholamines* such as adrenaline are released from *adrenergic nerve endings,* acetylcholine from *cholinergic nerve endings,* and GABA ($\gamma$-aminobutyric acid) and *serotonin* at synapses in the brain.

**Excitatory post-synaptic potentials** result if the neurotransmitter binding to the receptors on the post-synaptic membrane *opens* chemically gated ion channels, making *depolarization more likely.*

**Inhibitory post-synaptic potentials** result if the neurotransmitter binding to the receptors on the post-synaptic membrane *keeps* chemically gated ion channels *closed,* promoting *hyperpolarization* and making *depolarization less likely.*

# Structure and function of the mammalian brain

**Basal ganglia** control gross muscle movements and regulate muscle tone. **Limbic system** controls involuntary elements of behaviour essential to survival, such as hissing and grimacing when threatened, or signs of pleasure during sexual activity.

**Cerebral cortex** has **motor areas** which control voluntary movement, **sensory areas** which interpret sensory information and **association areas** responsible for learning and emotion – connect and integrate sensory and motor regions.

**CEREBRUM** is the centre of intellect, memory, language and consciousness.

**Corpus callosum** is white matter and connects the right and left hemispheres of the brain.

**Thalamus:** main **relay centre** between cerebrum and spinal cord; preliminary sorting of incoming sensory impulses.

**Midbrain** is a **relay centre** but also contains structures – the **colliculi** – which control reflex movements of the head in response to visual and auditory stimuli. The **substantia nigra** secretes dopamine (degeneration → **Parkinson's disease**) and the **red nucleus** integrates information from cerebrum and cerebellum concerning muscle tone and posture.

**Cerebellum** is responsible for smooth, co-ordinated movement via **proprioception** (the body's awareness of the position of one part relative to another). Maintains **posture** and **muscle tone,** and **body equilibrium** (using sensory input from inner ear). May regulate **emotional development,** modulating sensations of anger and pleasure.

**Pituitary body (hypophysis)** has a number of important endocrine functions, especially the secretion of **trophins** which regulate other endocrine organs.

**Central canal:** contains the protective and nutritive **cerebrospinal fluid.** Extends into a series of four CSF-filled chambers, the **ventricles,** within the brain.

**Pons:** acts as a **relay centre** between parts of the brain, and between the brain and the spinal cord– thus important in **integration**. Contains the **pneumotaxic centre** which, together with the respiratory centre, helps to control breathing.

**Hypothalamus:** contains centres for the control of body temperature (**thermoregulation**), hunger (**satiety**) and fluid balance (**osmoregulation**). Secretes **releasing hormones** which regulate the activity of the pituitary body (collectively called the **hypothalamo-hypophysial system**) and two other hormones, **oxytocin** and **antidiuretic hormone.** It controls and integrates the **autonomic nervous system,** thus regulating heart rate, movement of food through the gut and contraction of the urinary bladder. It controls **mind over body** phenomena – it is the centre for many **psychosomatic disorders** and is associated with feelings of **rage and aggression.** It is one of the centres which control waking and sleeping patterns.

**Medulla (medulla oblongata):** acts as a **relay centre** for both sensory and motor impulses between other parts of the brain and the spinal cord. Has part of the **reticular formation** which functions in consciousness and arousal (the most common knockout blow hits the chin, twists and distorts the brain stem and overwhelms the **reticular activating system** by sending a rapid sequence of impulses → unconsciousness). Has **vital reflex centres** which regulate heart beat, breathing and blood vessel diameter, and **nonvital reflex centres** which co-ordinate swallowing, coughing, vomiting and sneezing. Also associated with much of the **vestibular nuclear complex** which is important in helping the body to maintain its sense of equilibrium.

# Synovial joints have a space

between the articulating bones and are freely movable.

## THE MOVEMENTS POSSIBLE AT SYNOVIAL JOINTS ARE:

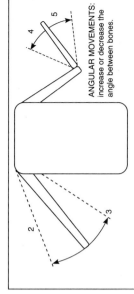

1. **Gliding:** one part slides upon another without any angular or rotary motion, e.g. joints between carpals and between tarsals.

ANGULAR MOVEMENTS: increase or decrease the angle between bones.

2. **Abduction:** moving the part away from the midline of the body.

3. **Adduction:** bringing the part towards the midline.

4. **Flexion:** decreasing the angle between two bones, includes bending the head forward (joint between the occipital bone and the atlas).

5. **Extension:** increasing the angle between two bones, includes returning the head to the anatomical position.

6. and 7. **Rotation:** turning upon an axis.

8. **Circumduction:** moving the extremity of the part around a circle so that the whole part describes a cone.

ROTARY MOVEMENTS

---

**Extracapsular ligament** is one of the possible *accessory ligaments* which offer additional stability to a joint. 'Extracapsular' means outside the articular capsule, although often the ligament is fused with the capsule. An example is the *fibular collateral ligament* of the knee joint.

**Fibrous capsule** is formed of a connective tissue with an abundance of collagen fibres. It is attached to the periosteum of the articulating bones, and may be almost indistinguishable from extracapsular accessory ligament. The flexibility of the fibrous capsule permits movement at a joint and the great tensile strength of the collagen fibres resists dislocation.

**Synovial membrane** is internal to the fibrous capsule and is composed of loose connective tissue with an abundance of elastin fibres and variable amounts of adipose tissue. The membrane secretes *synovial fluid* which lubricates the joint and nourishes the articular cartilage.

**Intracapsular ligament** is located inside the articular capsule, but surrounded by folding of the synovial membrane. Examples are the *cruciate ligaments* of the knee joint.

**Meniscal cartilage (mediscus, articular disc)** is a pad of fibrocartilage which lies between the articular surfaces of the bones. By modifying the shapes of the articulating surfaces they allow two bones of different shapes to fit tightly together. Menisci also help to maintain the stability of the joint, and direct the flow of synovial fluid to areas of greatest friction.

**Synovial fluid** consists of hyaluronic acid and interstitial fluid formed from blood plasma. It is similar in appearance and consistency to egg white – in joints with little or no movement the fluid is viscous, but becomes less so as movement increases. The fluid also contains phagocytic cells which remove microbes and debris that results from wear and tear in the joint.

**Articular cartilage** of synovial joints is hyaline cartilage. It is able to reduce friction in the joint since it is coated by synovial fluid – as the load on the joint increases the spongy nature of the cartilage allows it to absorb water and so increase the proportion of the lubricating hyaluronic acid in the lubricating film. The cartilage may also function as a shock absorber although much of the 'impact loading' on a joint is probably absorbed by the thicker trabecular (honeycombed) bone which lies beneath it.

**Bursae** are sac-like structures with walls of connective tissue lined by synovial membrane, and filled with a fluid similar in composition and function to synovial fluid. They are found between muscle and bone, tendon and bone and ligament and bone, and reduce the friction between one structure and another as movement takes place.

# Movement of the forelimb

**Movement of the forelimb** illustrates the action of *muscle groups.* Skeletal muscles produce movement by exerting forces of contraction on tendons, which in turn pull on bones.

**Trapezius** braces the shoulder, acting as a *fixator* to stabilize the scapula when the upper arm is moved.

**Deltoid** is an abductor of the arm, an action made easier by the partial rotation of the scapula.

**Teres** is an adductor which draws the arm inwards and backwards and rotates it towards the medial line of the body. The teres and pectoralis are *antagonists* of the deltoid.

**Scapula (shoulder blade)**

**Pectoralis** (only the lower part is shown here), which draws the arm forwards and downwards and rotates it inwards. Its origin on the clavicle helps it to stabilize the upper arm during flexion and extension of the forearm: in this case it is acting as a *fixator.*

The pectoralis also helps to depress the shoulder against force and elevation of the body on the arms, when climbing a ladder or rockface for example.

**Sternum**

**Humerus**

**Triceps** is the principal *extensor* of the elbow joint. When the biceps contracts and the elbow flexes, the triceps is the *antagonist* of the biceps.

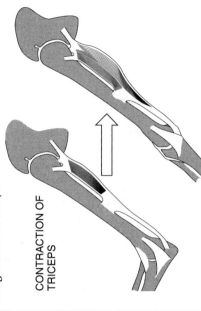

CONTRACTION OF TRICEPS

CONTRACTION OF BICEPS

**Origin:** the attachment of a muscle tendon to the stationary bone.

**Insertion:** the attachment of a muscle tendon to the movable bone.

**Tendon:** inelastic but with some limited flexibility due to parallel arrangements of densely packed collagen fibres. Inelasticity is essential so that contraction of muscle can be transmitted to the moving bone. *Ligaments* are *elastic* to allow movement of bones at joints when muscles contract.

**Radius**

**Ulna**

**Biceps brachii** (commonly 'biceps') is the principal *flexor* of the elbow joint. During flexation of the elbow the biceps is the *prime mover* or *agonist* and the triceps brachii is the *antagonist.* The biceps also supinates the palm and forearm (turns them upward or forward).

An **aponeurosis** is a sheath-like tendon which may extend to become part of the bone covering.

The fleshy part of a muscle (the *belly* or *gaster*) does not generally cover the moving part – instead the inserting tendon extends across the joint which permits the movement.

An individual muscle is composed of hundreds of **muscle fibres.**

TENDON

TENDON

Each muscle fibre is composed of many **myofibrils.**

A myofibril has a distinctive banding pattern due to **microfilaments.**

# Structure and contraction of striated (skeletal) muscle

ACTIN
MICROFILAMENTS

MYOSIN
MICROFILAMENTS

CONTRACTION

I band is reduced as actin slides between myosin.

A band remains the same size: myosin length is unchanged.

H zone is reduced as overlap between actin and myosin increases.

I band or **light** band has only actin microfilaments.

A band or **dark** band has both actin and myosin microfilaments.

H zone has only myosin microfilaments.

Z LINE

M LINE

SARCOMERE is reduced in length

SARCOMERE

**Muscle contraction requires Ca²⁺ ions and ATP**

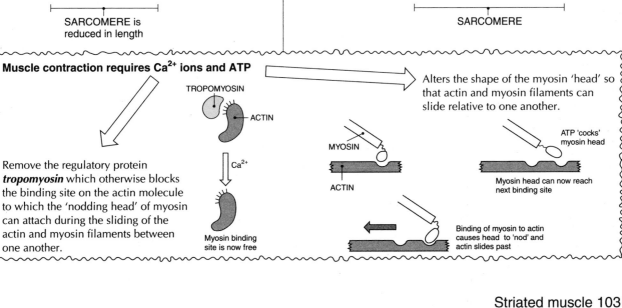

TROPOMYOSIN

ACTIN

$Ca^{2+}$

Myosin binding site is now free

Alters the shape of the myosin 'head' so that actin and myosin filaments can slide relative to one another.

MYOSIN

ACTIN

ATP 'cocks' myosin head

Myosin head can now reach next binding site

Binding of myosin to actin causes head to 'nod' and actin slides past

Remove the regulatory protein **tropomyosin** which otherwise blocks the binding site on the actin molecule to which the 'nodding head' of myosin can attach during the sliding of the actin and myosin filaments between one another.

# Male reproductive system

The **vas deferens** stores sperm for up to several months and then propels them by peristalsis towards the urethra during ejaculation. Cutting and tying of the vas deferens constitutes *vasectomy*, surgical sterilization of the male.

The **prostate gland** secretes an alkaline fluid which makes up about 20% of the volume of the semen – this alkalinity neutralizes the acidic secretions of the vagina, essential since sperm motility is considerably reduced at low pH. Cancer of the prostate is the most common tumour of the male reproductive system.

The **penis** is the intromittant organ, used to deliver sperm to the neck of the cervix, as close to the site of ovulation as possible. The penis is usually limp and flaccid but is erected by dilation of blood vessels allowing large quantities of blood to fill the sinuses in the *corpora cavernosa and spongiosa.* The *glans penis* has a high concentration of sensory cells and plays an important part in initiation of the erection reflex. The *prepuce* or *foreskin* covers the glans – it is sometimes removed by a surgical procedure called *circumcision.*

**Scrotum:** the location of the scrotum and the contraction of specific muscle fibres regulate the temperature of the testes. This regulation is vital since sperm production and survival depend on a temperature about 3°C lower than body temperature, a temperature which is possible in the scrotum since this sac is outside the body cavities. The *cremaster muscle* elevates the testes when they are exposed to cold, moving them closer to the groin where they can absorb body heat. Exposure to a higher temperature reverses this process.

CORPUS SPONGIOSUM

CORPUS CAVERNOSUM

URETHRA

GLANS PENIS

FORESKIN

The **inguinal canal** is a service and supporting structure of the male reproductive system. It carries the vas deferens, testicular artery and vein and branches of the autonomic nervous system. The canal is a weak spot in the abdominal wall and is frequently the site of an inguinal hernia – a rupture of this region of the abdominal wall.

URETER

BLADDER

The **seminal vesicles** secrete an alkaline viscous fluid which makes up about 60% of the volume of the semen. The fluid is rich in fructose (the respiratory substrate for sperm motility) and is an important contributor to sperm viability.

The **Cowper's (bulbourethral) gland** produces an antacid fluid and also a mucus secretion which helps to lubricate the penis during intercourse.

The **epididymis** is the site of *sperm maturation* which begins in the seminiferous tubule, a process which takes between one and ten days. The epididymis also stores spermatozoa for up to four weeks, after which they are reabsorbed. The epididymis is lined with ciliated epithelium and has a smooth muscle layer – together these drive the sperm into the vas deferens.

RECTUM

ANUS

PUBIC BONE

**Semen (seminal fluid)** is the fluid ejaculated from the urethra during sexual excitation. It is a mixture of sperm and the secretions of the prostate gland, Cowper's glands and the seminal vesicles. The sperm number about 250 000 000 per ejaculation, but constitute only about 1% of the total volume of between 2 and 5 cm$^3$ of the semen. The various secretions neutralize the acid environment of the male urethra and the female vagina and contain enzymes which are responsible for the final *capacitation* (activation) of the sperm. The semen also contains an antibiotic – *seminalplasmin* – which destroys some vaginal bacteria, and mucus to minimize friction between the penis and vagina during intercourse.

The **testes** contain tightly coiled *seminiferous tubules* that produce sperm by a process called *spermatogenesis.* The interstitial tissue of the testes produces the hormone testosterone under the influence of LH from the anterior pituitary gland.

# Human spermatozoon and ovum

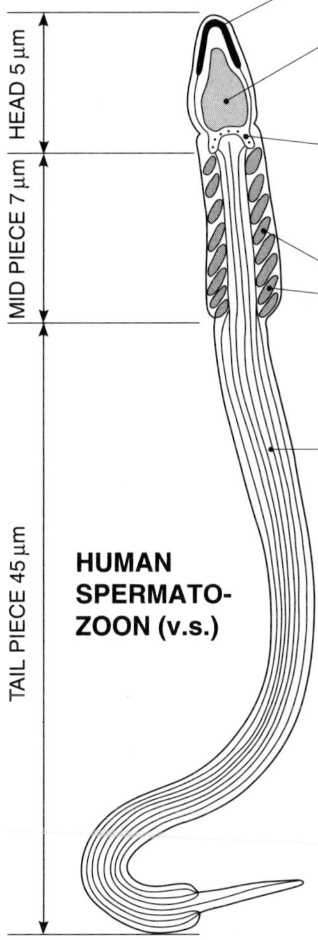

**HEAD 5 μm**

**MID PIECE 7 μm**

**TAIL PIECE 45 μm**

**HUMAN SPERMATO-ZOON (v.s.)**

**Acrosome** is effectively an enclosed lysosome. It develops from the Golgi complex and contains hydrolytic enzymes – a hyaluronidase and several proteinases – which aid in the penetration of the granular layer and plasma membrane of the oocyte immediately prior to fertilization.

**Nucleus** contains the haploid number of chromosomes derived by meiosis from the male germinal cells – thus this genetic complement will be either an X or a Y heterosome plus 22 autosomes. Since the head delivers no cytoplasm, the male contributes no extranuclear genes or organelles.

**Centriole:** one of a pair, which lie at right angles to one another. One of the centrioles produces microtubules which elongate and run the entire length of the rest of the spermatozoon, forming the axial filament of the flagellum.

**Mitochondria** are arranged in a spiral surrounding the flagellum. They complete the aerobic stages of respiration to release the ATP required for contraction of the filaments, leading to 'beating' of the flagellum and movement of the spermatozoon.

**Flagellum** has the 9 + 2 arrangement of microtubules typical of such structures.

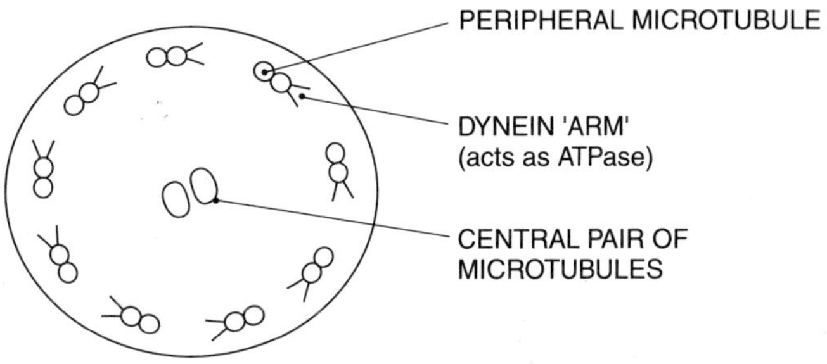

PERIPHERAL MICROTUBULE

DYNEIN 'ARM' (acts as ATPase)

CENTRAL PAIR OF MICROTUBULES

The principal role of the flagella is to allow sperm to move close to the oocyte and to orientate themselves correctly prior to digestion of the oocyte membranes.
The sperm are moved close to the oocyte by muscular contractions of the walls of the uterus and the oviduct.

**First polar body** contains 23 chromosomes from the first meiotic division of the germ wall.

140 μm

**Cumulus cells** which once synthesized proteins and nucleic acids into the egg cytoplasm.

**Zona pellucida** will undergo structural changes at fertilization and form a barrier to the entry of more than one sperm.

**23 chromosomes** will complete second meiotic division on fertilization to provide *female haploid nucleus.*

**Cytoplasm** may contribute extranuclear genes and organelles to the zygote.

**Cortical granules** contain enzymes which are released at fertilization and alter the structure of the zona pellucida, preventing further sperm penetration, which would upset the just restored diploid number.

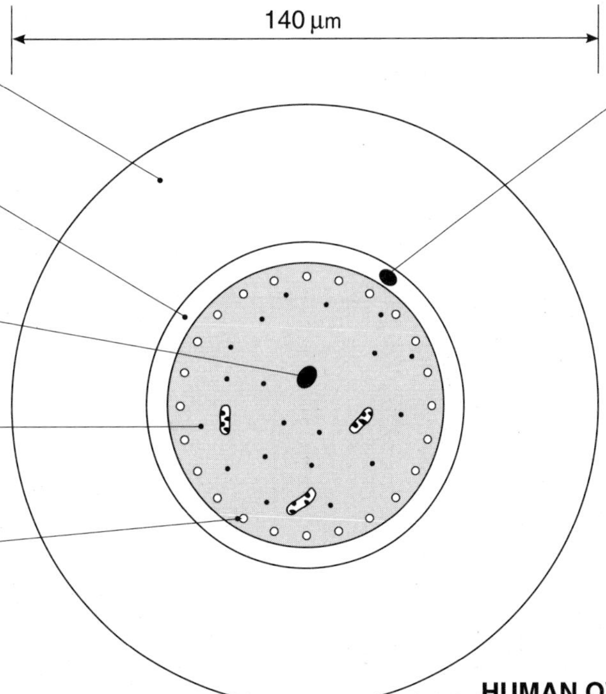

**HUMAN OVUM (v.s.)**

# Female reproductive system

The **oviducts (fallopian tubes)** transport the ova from the ovaries to the uterus – following ovulation fertilization may occur, most typically within 24 hours and in the upper third of the oviduct. The oviduct walls are muscular and lined with ciliated epithelium, and a combination of ciliary action and peristalsis helps to move the ovum or the zygote towards the uterus. The oviduct is the most common site of an ectopic pregnancy.

The **funnel** or **infundibulum** is the open end of the oviduct. It is fringed by fingerlike projections called fimbriae which sweep the released ovum into the oviduct. The infundibulum is the most frequent site of ectopic pregnancy.

The **ovaries** are the sites of ovum production (*oogenesis*) and the production and secretion of the hormones *progesterone* and *oestrogen*. The ovaries are attached to the upper part of the uterus by the *ovarian ligament*, and to the broad ligament by the *mesovarium.*

**URETER**

The **seminal pool** is the site of deposition of sperm following coitus and ejaculation.

The **uterus** is the site of implantation of the fertilized ovum, development of the fetus during pregnancy and the origin of muscular contractions which precede parturition. The bulk of the uterine wall is the **myometrium**, composed of three layers of smooth muscle fibres and responsible for labour contractions. The lining of the uterus is the **endometrium**, a very vascular structure composed of two layers; a permanent one is called the **stratum basalis** and produces the innermost, temporary layer called the **stratum functionalis**, which is shed during menstruation. The *menstrual cycle* is a series of changes in the endometrium in preparation for the possible implantation of a fertilized ovum. In a non-pregnant female the uterus has a volume of about 10 cm³, but during pregnancy this may expand to 5 dm³, an increase of 500 times.

MYOMETRIUM

ENDOMETRIUM

BLADDER

PUBIC BONE

URETHRA

The **clitoris** contains erectile tissue and nerves, and is homologous to the glans penis of the male. Tactile stimulation causes enlargement of the clitoris, and plays an important part in sexual excitation of the female.

The **hymen** is a thin fold of membrane which forms a border around the vaginal orifice, partially closing it. Sometimes the hymen completely covers the orifice and surgery is required to open the orifice to permit the discharge of the menstrual flow.

The **labia minora** and **labia majora** form the major part of the *vulva.* They produce a lubricant mucus secretion during intercourse and protect the clitoris from abrasion. During pregnancy the labiae become bluish owing to venous congestion – this is important in the visual diagnosis of pregnancy.

The **vagina** is a passageway for the menstrual flow, the receptacle for the penis during coitus and the lower part of the birth canal. The lining of the vagina is well supplied with mucus-secreting glands which are important for lubrication during intercourse and during childbirth. This lining undergoes cyclical monthly changes in its degree of keratinization – the appearance of the cells forms the basis of the 'PAP' test for cancer of the uterus. The mucosa of the vagina contains glycogen granules, which are decomposed to organic acids which are responsible for the low pH environment in the vagina. This low pH retards microbial growth, but reduces sperm motility following coitus.

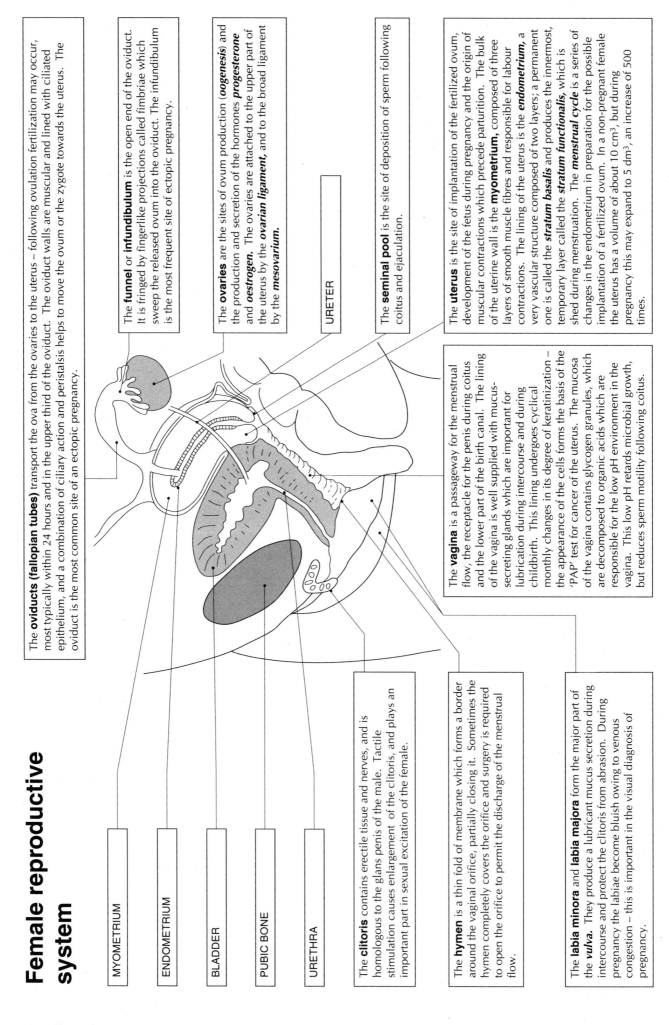

# Events of the menstrual cycle

**Follicle-stimulating hormone (FSH)** initiates the development of several primary follicles (each containing a primary oocyte): one follicle continues to develop but the others degenerate by the process of follicular atresia. FSH also increases the activity of the enzymes responsible for formation of oestrogen.

**Oestrogen** is produced by enzyme modification (in the stroma) of testosterone produced by the thecae of the developing follicle. Oestrogen has several effects:
1. It stimulates further growth of the follicle.
2. It promotes repair of the endometrium.
3. It acts as a feedback inhibitor of the secretion of FSH from the anterior pituitary gland.
4. From about day 11 it has a positive feedback action on the secretion of both LH and FSH.

**Development of the follicle** within the ovary is initiated by FSH but continued by LH. The Graafian follicle Ⓐ is mature by day 10–11 and ovulation occurs at day 14 Ⓑ following a surge of LH. The remains of the follicle become the corpus luteum Ⓒ, which secretes steroid hormones. These steroid hormones inhibit LH secretion so that the corpus luteum degenerates and becomes the corpus albicans Ⓓ.

The **endometrium** begins to thicken and become more vascular under the influence of the ovarian hormone oestrogen. Because of this thickening, to 4–6 mm, the time between menstruation and ovulation is sometimes called the *proliferative phase.*

**Luteinizing hormone (LH)** triggers the secretion of testosterone by the thecae of the follicle, and when its concentration 'surges' it causes release of enzymes which rupture the wall of the ovary, allowing the secondary oocyte to be released at ovulation. After ovulation LH promotes development of the corpus luteum from the remains of the Graafian follicle.

**Progesterone** is secreted by the corpus luteum. It has several effects:
1. It prepares the endometrium for implantation of a fertilized egg by increasing vascularization, thickening and the storage of glycogen.
2. It begins to promote growth of the mammary glands.
3. It acts as a feedback inhibitor of FSH secretion, thus arresting development of any further follicles.

**Body temperature** rises by about 1°C at the time of ovulation. This 'heat' is used to determine the 'safe period' for the rhythm method of contraception.

During the post-ovulatory or luteal phase the **endometrium** becomes thicker with more tortuously coiled glands and greater vascularization of the surface layer, and retains more tissue fluid.

**Menstruation** is initiated by falling concentrations of oestrogen and progesterone as the corpus luteum degenerates.

At **menstruation** the *stratum functionalis* of the endometrium is shed, leaving the *stratum basilis* to begin proliferation of a new *functionalis*.

TIME / days

0    14    28

OVARIAN (FOLLICULAR) PHASE    LUTEAL PHASE

# Functions of the placenta

**Immune protection:** protective molecules (possibly including HCG) cover the surface of the early placenta and 'camouflage' the embryo which, with its complement of paternal genes, might be identified by the maternal immune system and rejected as tissue of 'non-self' origin.

**Site of exchange** of many solutes between maternal and fetal circulations. Oxygen transfer to the fetus is aided by fetal haemoglobin with its high oxygen affinity, and soluble nutrients such as glucose and amino acids are selectively transported by membrane-bound carrier proteins. Carbon dioxide and urea diffuse from fetus to mother along diffusion gradients maintained over larger areas of the placenta by countercurrent flow of fetal and maternal blood. In the later stages of pregnancy antibodies pass from mother to fetus – these confer immunity in the young infant, particularly to some gastro-intestinal infections.

After expulsion of the fetus, further contractions of the uterus cause detachment of the placenta (spontaneous constriction of uterine artery and vein limit blood loss) – the placenta, once delivered, is referred to as the **afterbirth.** The placenta may be used as a source of hormones (e.g. in 'fertility pills'), as tissue for burn grafts and to supply veins for blood vessel grafts.

**Barrier:** the placenta limits the transfer of solutes and blood components from maternal to fetal circulation. Cells of the maternal immune system do not cross – this minimizes the possibility of immune rejection (although antibodies may cross which may cause haemolysis of fetal blood cells if **_Rhesus_** antibodies are present in the maternal circulation). The placenta is **_not_** a barrier to heavy metals such as lead, to nicotine, to HIV and other viruses, to heroin and to toxins such as DDT. Thus the **_Rubella_** (German measles) virus may cross and cause severe damage to eyes, ears, heart and brain of the fetus, the sedative Thalidomide caused severely abnormal limb development, and some children are born already addicted to heroin or HIV positive.

**Endocrine function:** cells of the chorion secrete a number of hormones:
1. **HCG (human chorionic gonadotrophin)** maintains the corpus luteum so that this body may continue to secrete the progesterone necessary to continue the development of the endometrium. HCG is principally effective during the first 3 months of pregnancy and the overflow of this hormone into the urine is used in diagnosis of the pregnant condition.
2. **Oestrogen** and **progesterone** are secreted as the production of these hormones from the degenerating corpus luteum diminishes.
3. **Human placental lactogen** promotes milk production in the mammary glands as birth approaches.
4. **Prostaglandins** are released under the influence of fetal adrenal steroid hormones. These prostaglandins are powerful stimulators of contractions of the smooth muscle of the uterus, the contractions which constitute labour and eventually expel the fetus from the uterus.

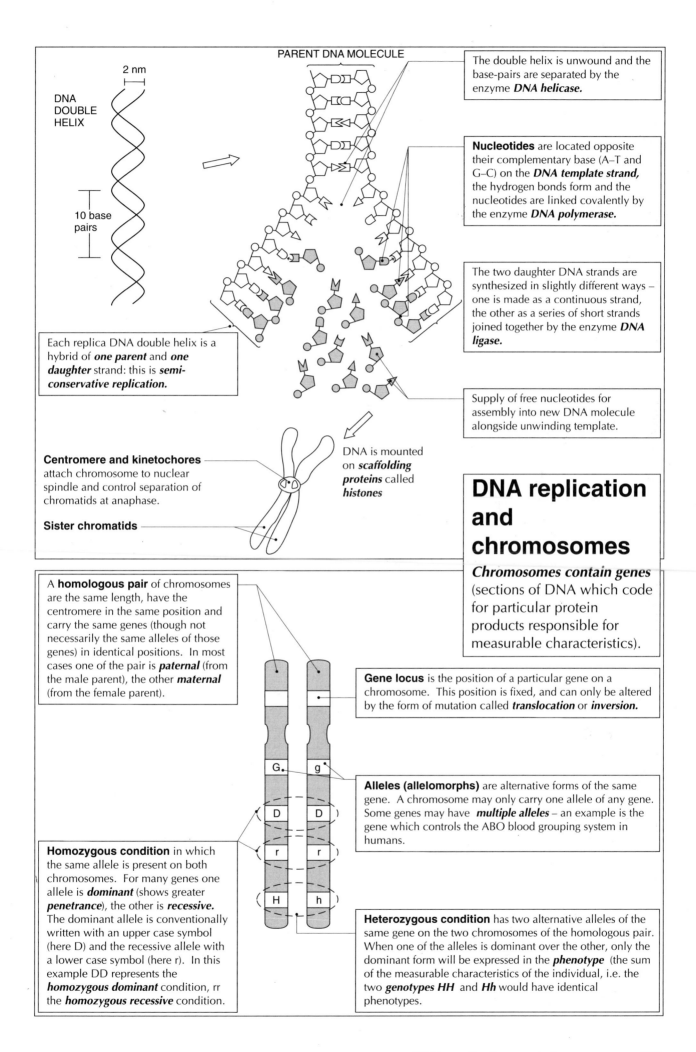

**PARENT DNA MOLECULE**

**2 nm**

DNA DOUBLE HELIX

**10 base pairs**

The double helix is unwound and the base-pairs are separated by the enzyme **DNA helicase.**

**Nucleotides** are located opposite their complementary base (A–T and G–C) on the **DNA template strand,** the hydrogen bonds form and the nucleotides are linked covalently by the enzyme **DNA polymerase.**

The two daughter DNA strands are synthesized in slightly different ways – one is made as a continuous strand, the other as a series of short strands joined together by the enzyme **DNA ligase.**

Each replica DNA double helix is a hybrid of **one parent** and **one daughter** strand: this is **semi-conservative replication.**

Supply of free nucleotides for assembly into new DNA molecule alongside unwinding template.

**Centromere and kinetochores** attach chromosome to nuclear spindle and control separation of chromatids at anaphase.

**Sister chromatids**

DNA is mounted on **scaffolding proteins** called **histones**

# DNA replication and chromosomes

*Chromosomes contain genes* (sections of DNA which code for particular protein products responsible for measurable characteristics).

A **homologous pair** of chromosomes are the same length, have the centromere in the same position and carry the same genes (though not necessarily the same alleles of those genes) in identical positions. In most cases one of the pair is **paternal** (from the male parent), the other **maternal** (from the female parent).

**Gene locus** is the position of a particular gene on a chromosome. This position is fixed, and can only be altered by the form of mutation called **translocation** or **inversion.**

**Alleles (allelomorphs)** are alternative forms of the same gene. A chromosome may only carry one allele of any gene. Some genes may have **multiple alleles** – an example is the gene which controls the ABO blood grouping system in humans.

**Homozygous condition** in which the same allele is present on both chromosomes. For many genes one allele is **dominant** (shows greater **penetrance**), the other is **recessive.** The dominant allele is conventionally written with an upper case symbol (here D) and the recessive allele with a lower case symbol (here r). In this example DD represents the **homozygous dominant** condition, rr the **homozygous recessive** condition.

**Heterozygous condition** has two alternative alleles of the same gene on the two chromosomes of the homologous pair. When one of the alleles is dominant over the other, only the dominant form will be expressed in the **phenotype** (the sum of the measurable characteristics of the individual, i.e. the two **genotypes HH** and **Hh** would have identical phenotypes.

# Genes control cell characteristics

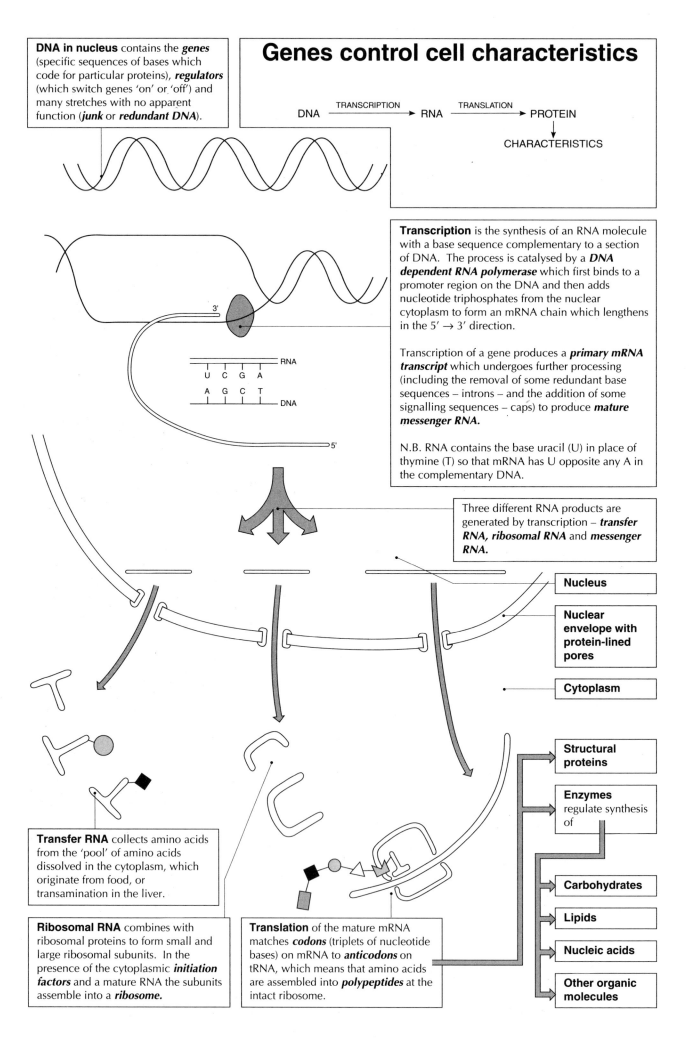

**DNA in nucleus** contains the **genes** (specific sequences of bases which code for particular proteins), **regulators** (which switch genes 'on' or 'off') and many stretches with no apparent function (**junk** or **redundant DNA**).

DNA $\xrightarrow{\text{TRANSCRIPTION}}$ RNA $\xrightarrow{\text{TRANSLATION}}$ PROTEIN $\rightarrow$ CHARACTERISTICS

3'

RNA

U  C  G  A

A  G  C  T

DNA

5'

**Transcription** is the synthesis of an RNA molecule with a base sequence complementary to a section of DNA. The process is catalysed by a **DNA dependent RNA polymerase** which first binds to a promoter region on the DNA and then adds nucleotide triphosphates from the nuclear cytoplasm to form an mRNA chain which lengthens in the 5' → 3' direction.

Transcription of a gene produces a **primary mRNA transcript** which undergoes further processing (including the removal of some redundant base sequences – introns – and the addition of some signalling sequences – caps) to produce **mature messenger RNA.**

N.B. RNA contains the base uracil (U) in place of thymine (T) so that mRNA has U opposite any A in the complementary DNA.

Three different RNA products are generated by transcription – **transfer RNA, ribosomal RNA** and **messenger RNA.**

**Nucleus**

**Nuclear envelope with protein-lined pores**

**Cytoplasm**

**Structural proteins**

**Enzymes** regulate synthesis of

**Carbohydrates**

**Lipids**

**Nucleic acids**

**Other organic molecules**

**Transfer RNA** collects amino acids from the 'pool' of amino acids dissolved in the cytoplasm, which originate from food, or transamination in the liver.

**Ribosomal RNA** combines with ribosomal proteins to form small and large ribosomal subunits. In the presence of the cytoplasmic **initiation factors** and a mature RNA the subunits assemble into a **ribosome.**

**Translation** of the mature mRNA matches **codons** (triplets of nucleotide bases) on mRNA to **anticodons** on tRNA, which means that amino acids are assembled into **polypeptides** at the intact ribosome.

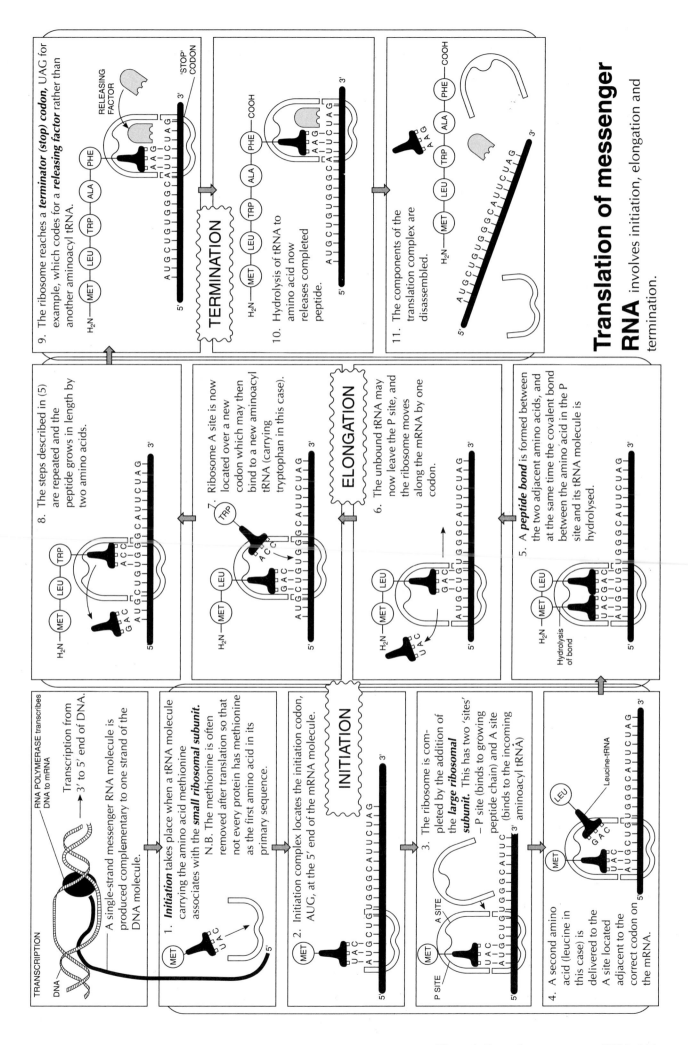

## Translation of messenger RNA involves initiation, elongation and termination.

**TRANSCRIPTION**

RNA POLYMERASE transcribes DNA to mRNA

Transcription from ➔ 3' to 5' end of DNA.

A single-strand messenger RNA molecule is produced complementary to one strand of the DNA molecule.

**INITIATION**

1. *Initiation* takes place when a tRNA molecule carrying the amino acid methionine associates with the *small ribosomal subunit.* N.B. The methionine is often removed after translation so that not every protein has methionine as the first amino acid in its primary sequence.

2. Initiation complex locates the initiation codon, AUG, at the 5' end of the mRNA molecule.

3. The ribosome is completed by the addition of the *large ribosomal subunit.* This has two 'sites' – P site (binds to growing peptide chain) and A site (binds to the incoming aminoacyl tRNA).

4. A second amino acid (leucine in this case) is delivered to the A site located adjacent to the correct codon on the mRNA.

Leucine-tRNA

**ELONGATION**

5. A *peptide bond* is formed between the two adjacent amino acids, and at the same time the covalent bond between the amino acid in the P site and its tRNA molecule is hydrolysed.

Hydrolysis of bond

6. The unbound tRNA may now leave the P site, and the ribosome moves along the mRNA by one codon.

7. Ribosome A site is now located over a new codon which may then bind to a new aminoacyl tRNA (carrying tryptophan in this case).

8. The steps described in (5) are repeated and the peptide grows in length by two amino acids.

**TERMINATION**

9. The ribosome reaches a *terminator (stop) codon,* UAG for example, which codes for a *releasing factor* rather than another aminoacyl tRNA.

RELEASING FACTOR

'STOP' CODON

10. Hydrolysis of tRNA to amino acid now releases completed peptide.

11. The components of the translation complex are disassembled.

# Mitosis and growth

The significance of mitosis is that it involves duplication of the genetic material and its equal distribution to each of two 'daughter' cells: *variation is minimal.*

During *cytokinesis* the tetraploid (4*n*) cell is 'pinched' into two 'daughter cells'. Each product has a *DNA content equal to the other and to the parent cell.* In animal cells the separation is brought about by two contractile proteins which form a *cleavage furrow;* in plant cells a *cell plate* is laid down and covered with cellulose to form a separating *cell wall.*

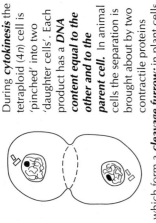

## Interphase
DNA only visible as indistinct mass of *chromatin.* Nucleolus and nuclear membrane still intact. Centrioles lie close to one another.

DNA
CONTENT
OF CELL

4n

2n

## As **interphase** moves to **prophase**

DNA undergoes *spiralization* and *replication.* Each chromosome is now *two identical chromatids,* held together at the centromere. Nucleolus and nuclear membrane disintegrate. *Centrioles* move to opposite poles, forming a *spindle* of *microtubules.*

The rate of replication may be extremely high – in humans 1 x 10$^{11}$m of DNA are produced per day (this is almost 700 miles per second!).

## At **metaphase**

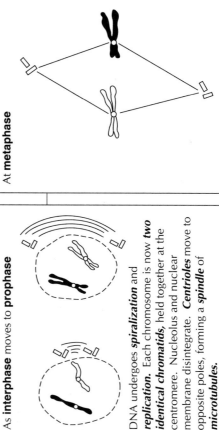

Chromosomes now attached to spindle at *kinetochore* on the centromere. The chromosomes are arranged in such a way that one chromatid from each pair lies on each side of the *equator.*

## Anaphase precedes **telophase**

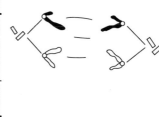

**Centromere** divides and spindle fibres contract to pull *chromatids* to opposite poles. The early separation of the chromatids constitutes *anaphase,* and the separation is complete (so that the chromatids are now *chromosomes*) when the spindle disintegrates and the nuclear membrane reforms at *telophase.*

## Importance of mitosis
1. It is the process which provides the cells required for the *growth* of multicellular organism – this requires an increase in number of cells from one to 6 x 10$^{13}$ in humans.
2. It supplies the cells to *repair* worn-out or damaged tissues. In the human the replacement of skin, gut and lung linings and blood cells requires about 1 x 10$^{11}$ cells per day.
3. It maintains the chromosome number. Daughter cells have identical sets of chromosomes and so function harmoniously as part of the tissue, organ or organism.
4. *Asexual reproduction* provides offspring which are genetically identical to the parent – ideal when rapidly establishing a population. Mitosis provides the cells which make up the fragments of the parent body dispersed during this form of reproduction.

**The cell cycle** typically lasts from 8 to 24 h in humans – the nuclear division (mitosis) occupies about 10% of this time.

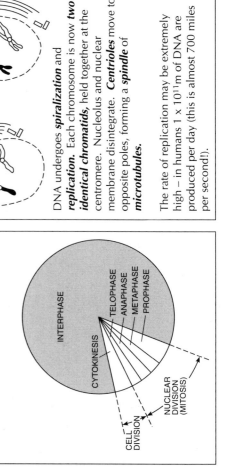

INTERPHASE

TELOPHASE
ANAPHASE
METAPHASE
PROPHASE

CYTOKINESIS

CELL
DIVISION

NUCLEAR
DIVISION
(MITOSIS)

# Meiosis and variation

Meiosis separates chromosomes, halving the diploid number, and introduces variation to the haploid products.

During **prophase I** each replicated chromosome (comprising two chromatids) pairs with its **homologous partner**, i.e. the diploid number of chromosomes produces the haploid number of homologous pairs.

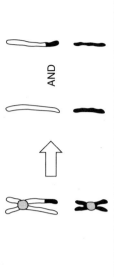

*Crossing over* occurs when all four chromatids are at **synapsis** (exactly aligned) – non-sister chromatids may cross over, break and reassemble so that *parental* gene combinations are replaced by **recombinants**. This is a major source of *genetic variation*.

At **anaphase I** and **telophase I** there is separation of **whole chromosomes** (i.e. of **pairs** of chromatids).

The products of meiosis I now contain the **haploid** (*n*) number of chromosomes, although each chromosome comprises two chromatids.

During the **second meiotic division** (metaphase II, anaphase II and telophase II) there is a modified mitosis which **separates the two sister chromatids of each chromosome.**

AND

At the end of telophase II **cytokinesis** produces daughter nuclei which have **half the number of chromosomes of the parent cell.**

i.e. DIPLOID (2*n*) ⟶ HAPLOID (*n*) GAMETES

In addition, the unpaired chromosomes in the gametes may contain *new gene combinations* as a result of *crossing over* and *independent assortment.*

Further genetic variation results from the **random combination of gametes at fertilization,** i.e. any male gamete may fuse with any female gamete.

DNA CONTENT
OF CELL

4*n*

2*n*

*n*

Following prophase I, **independent assortment** can align the chromosomes in different ways on the **metaphase** plate.

OR

The number of possible combinations of chromosomes is great i.e. $2^n$, where *n* is the number of homologous pairs. This is a second major source of **genetic variation** resulting from meiotic division.

## Importance of meiosis

1. It must occur in sexually reproducing organisms or the chromosome number would be doubled at fertilization.

♂ PARENT ⟶ ♂ GAMETE
(2*n*) MEIOSIS (*n*)

♀ PARENT ⟶ ♀ GAMETE
(2*n*) MEIOSIS (*n*)

ZYGOTE
(2*n*)

NEW INDIVIDUAL
(2*n*)

2. Crossing over, independent assortment and random fertilization promote **genetic variation.** This provides new material for natural selection to work on during evolution.

# Gene mutation and sickle cell anaemia

*Sickle cell anaemia* is the result of a *single gene (point) mutation* and the resulting *error in protein synthesis.*

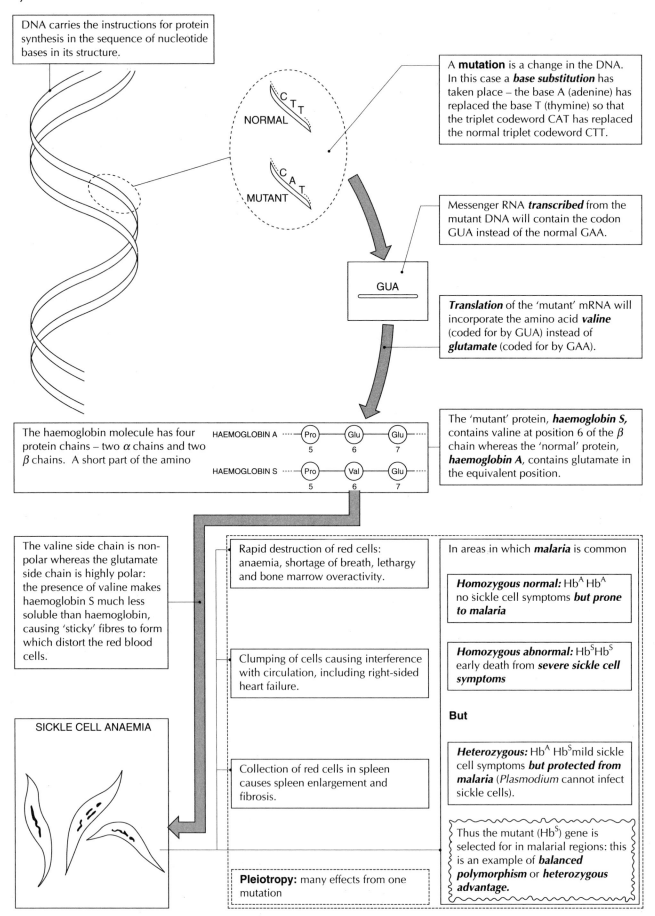

DNA carries the instructions for protein synthesis in the sequence of nucleotide bases in its structure.

A **mutation** is a change in the DNA. In this case a *base substitution* has taken place – the base A (adenine) has replaced the base T (thymine) so that the triplet codeword CAT has replaced the normal triplet codeword CTT.

NORMAL

MUTANT

Messenger RNA *transcribed* from the mutant DNA will contain the codon GUA instead of the normal GAA.

GUA

*Translation* of the 'mutant' mRNA will incorporate the amino acid *valine* (coded for by GUA) instead of *glutamate* (coded for by GAA).

The haemoglobin molecule has four protein chains – two $\alpha$ chains and two $\beta$ chains. A short part of the amino

HAEMOGLOBIN A ---- (Pro) --- (Glu) --- (Glu) ----
                    5        6        7

HAEMOGLOBIN S ---- (Pro) --- (Val) --- (Glu) ----
                    5        6        7

The 'mutant' protein, **haemoglobin S,** contains valine at position 6 of the $\beta$ chain whereas the 'normal' protein, **haemoglobin A**, contains glutamate in the equivalent position.

The valine side chain is non-polar whereas the glutamate side chain is highly polar: the presence of valine makes haemoglobin S much less soluble than haemoglobin, causing 'sticky' fibres to form which distort the red blood cells.

Rapid destruction of red cells: anaemia, shortage of breath, lethargy and bone marrow overactivity.

Clumping of cells causing interference with circulation, including right-sided heart failure.

Collection of red cells in spleen causes spleen enlargement and fibrosis.

In areas in which *malaria* is common

*Homozygous normal:* $Hb^A Hb^A$ no sickle cell symptoms *but prone to malaria*

*Homozygous abnormal:* $Hb^S Hb^S$ early death from *severe sickle cell symptoms*

**But**

*Heterozygous:* $Hb^A Hb^S$ mild sickle cell symptoms *but protected from malaria* (*Plasmodium* cannot infect sickle cells).

Thus the mutant ($Hb^S$) gene is selected for in malarial regions: this is an example of *balanced polymorphism* or *heterozygous advantage.*

SICKLE CELL ANAEMIA

**Pleiotropy:** many effects from one mutation

# Chromosome mutation and Down's Syndrome

Down's syndrome (trisomy-21) is a chromosome mutation caused by **non-disjunction.**

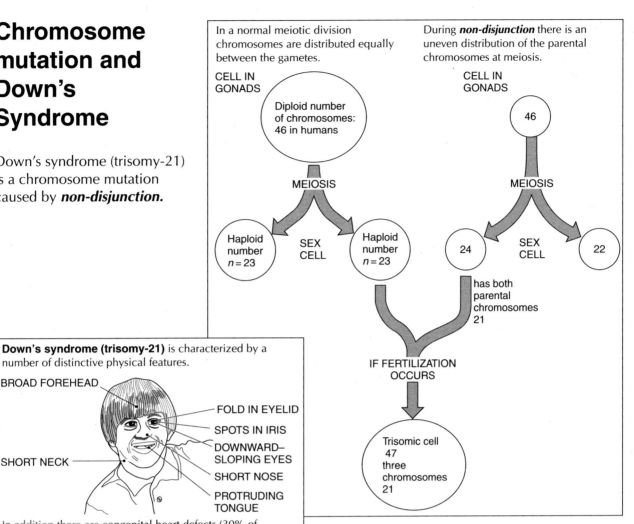

In a normal meiotic division chromosomes are distributed equally between the gametes.

CELL IN GONADS

Diploid number of chromosomes: 46 in humans

MEIOSIS

Haploid number $n = 23$     SEX CELL     Haploid number $n = 23$

During **non-disjunction** there is an uneven distribution of the parental chromosomes at meiosis.

CELL IN GONADS

46

MEIOSIS

24     SEX CELL     22

has both parental chromosomes 21

IF FERTILIZATION OCCURS

Trisomic cell 47 three chromosomes 21

---

**Down's syndrome (trisomy-21)** is characterized by a number of distinctive physical features.

BROAD FOREHEAD

FOLD IN EYELID

SPOTS IN IRIS

DOWNWARD–SLOPING EYES

SHORT NECK

SHORT NOSE

PROTRUDING TONGUE

In addition there are congenital heart defects (30% of sufferers die before the age of 10) and mental retardation.

---

A **karyotype** is obtained by cutting out and rearranging photographic images of chromosomes stained during mitotic metaphase.

KARYOTYPE OF DOWN'S SYNDROME FEMALE

1   2   3    4   5

6   7   8   9   10   11   12

13   14   15    16   17   18    19   20

21   22    X   Y

NOTE THE EXTRA CHROMOSOME 21

---

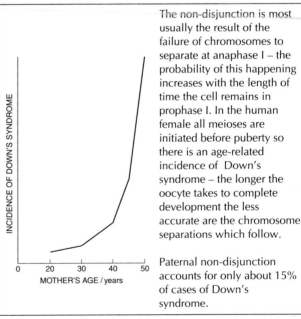

INCIDENCE OF DOWN'S SYNDROME

MOTHER'S AGE / years

0   20   30   40   50

The non-disjunction is most usually the result of the failure of chromosomes to separate at anaphase I – the probability of this happening increases with the length of time the cell remains in prophase I. In the human female all meioses are initiated before puberty so there is an age-related incidence of Down's syndrome – the longer the oocyte takes to complete development the less accurate are the chromosome separations which follow.

Paternal non-disjunction accounts for only about 15% of cases of Down's syndrome.

---

**Two other significant examples of non-disjunction**

**Klinefelter's syndrome** (XXY) caused by an **extra X chromosome** and resulting in a **sterile male** with **some breast development.**

**Turner's syndrome** (XO) caused by a **deleted X chromosome** and resulting in a **female** with **underdeveloped sexual characteristics.**

# Monohybrid inheritance

**Phenylketonuria** results from a lack of the liver enzyme **phenylalanine hydroxylase:** blood phenylalanine levels are raised, causing a number of effects.

PHENYLALANINE in diet

Normal pathway → TYROSINE → MELANIN

Mutant pathway → PHENYLPYRUVATE

**Absence in PKU sufferers causes pale hair, skin and eyes.**

**Accumulation in PKU sufferers causes mental retardation, abnormal muscle tone and body movement.**

Early diagnosis advises a phenylalanine-free diet for children, markedly reducing PKU symptoms.

**Phenylketonuria in humans** is an example of **monohybrid inheritance.**

## If one parent is homozygous normal, the other homozygous mutant

The homozygous normal individual is represented as NN, the mutant individual as nn since in this case normal is dominant to mutant (phenylketonuric).

PARENTAL GENERATION   N N   ×   n n

At meiosis, only one of the two chromosomes (thus only one of the two alleles) can be transmitted to the gamete: **Mendel's First Law.**

1ST FILIAL GENERATION

N        n    GAMETES

At **fertilization,** fusion of gametes to form a zygote restores the diploid number.

•Nn

This individual is **genotypically** heterozygous, but **phenotypically** normal, i.e. a **carrier** of the mutant allele for phenylketonuria.

## If both parents are carriers (i.e. heterozygous)

PARENTAL (P) GENERATION        Nn    ×    Nn

GAMETES        N    n    N    n

A **Punnett square** can be used to predict the possible combinations of alleles in the zygote.

|  | Gametes from father ♂ N | n |
|---|---|---|
| Gametes from mother ♀ N | NN | Nn |
| n | Nn | nn |

1ST FILIAL (F₁) GENERATION    NN    Nn   Nn    nn

**Phenotypically and genotypically normal**

**Phenotypically normal but a carrier**

**Phenotypically and genotypically mutant**

3 NORMAL    :    1 MUTANT

N.B. the 3 : 1 ratio is only approximate unless the number of offspring is very large (unlikely in humans), because

1. Alleles may not be distributed between viable gametes in equal numbers.

2. Fusion of gametes is completely random – it is a matter of chance whether one male gamete fuses with a particular female gamete.

## Other significant examples of monohybrid inheritance in humans

**Albinism:** autosomal recessive

**Cystic fibrosis:** autosomal recessive (the most common lethal allele in Caucasian populations)

**Huntingdon's chorea:** autosomal dominant

**Tay-Sach's disease:** autosomal recessive (prevalent in Jews of Eastern European origin)

# Linkage between genes prevents free recombination of alleles.

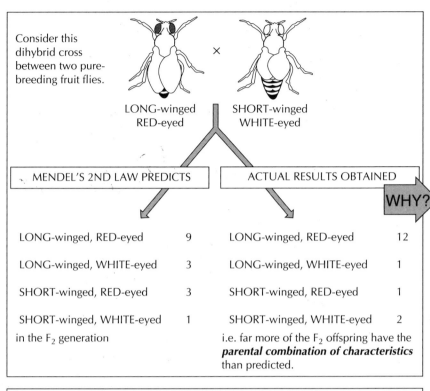

Consider this dihybrid cross between two pure-breeding fruit flies.

LONG-winged RED-eyed × SHORT-winged WHITE-eyed

| MENDEL'S 2ND LAW PREDICTS | | ACTUAL RESULTS OBTAINED | |
|---|---|---|---|
| LONG-winged, RED-eyed | 9 | LONG-winged, RED-eyed | 12 |
| LONG-winged, WHITE-eyed | 3 | LONG-winged, WHITE-eyed | 1 |
| SHORT-winged, RED-eyed | 3 | SHORT-winged, RED-eyed | 1 |
| SHORT-winged, WHITE-eyed | 1 | SHORT-winged, WHITE-eyed | 2 |

in the $F_2$ generation

i.e. far more of the $F_2$ offspring have the **parental combination of characteristics** than predicted.

**How can linked alleles be separated?**

During **meiosis**, homologous chromosomes pair up to form **bivalents** and replicate to form **tetrads** of chromatids.

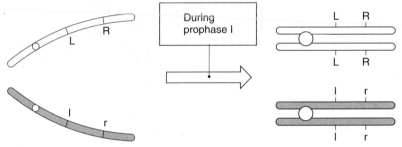

During prophase I

As the chromatids lie alongside one another it is possible for **crossing over** (the exchange of genetic material between adjacent members of a homologous pair) to occur.

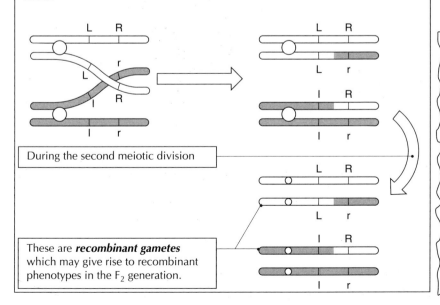

During the second meiotic division

These are **recombinant gametes** which may give rise to recombinant phenotypes in the $F_2$ generation.

---

The genes for **wing length** and **eye colour** are **linked**. This means that **they are located on the same chromosome** and thus tend to **pass into gametes together.**

i.e. **parental** chromosomes can be represented as

producing gametes

which produce $F_1$ individuals with

and since LR are linked, as are lr, the $F_2$ offspring will tend to be

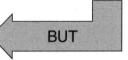

| from ♀ \ from ♂ | LR | lr |
|---|---|---|
| LR | LONG, RED | LONG, RED |
| lr | LONG, RED | SHORT, WHITE |

That is, the alleles tend to remain in the original parental combinations and so parental phenotypes predominate.

**BUT**

One well-known example of **linkage in humans** involves the genes for **ABO blood groups** and the **nail-patella syndrome.**

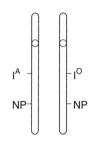

The NP allele is a dominant one: people with this syndrome have small, discoloured nails, and the patella is missing or small and pushed to one side.

Most people with N-P syndrome belong to either A or O blood group.

# Sex linkage and the inheritance of sex

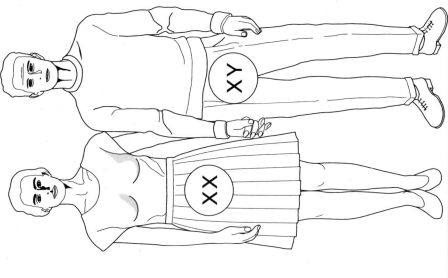

In mammals sex is determined by two chromosomes which are very different to one another. These are the **heterosomes** – the male is **heterogametic** (XY: can produce both X and Y gametes) and the female is **homogametic** (can only produce X gametes).

♀ (XX)    ♂ (XY)

These sections are **homologous** and carry no genes of sex determination.

These **non-homologous** sections carry the genes concerned with sex determination but are of sufficient size to carry other genes. Such genes are **sex-linked.**

---

**Inheritance of sex** is a special form of Mendelian segregation.

♂ XY    ×    ♀ XX

GAMETES    X  Y        X

$F_1$ generation: sex of offspring can be determined from a Punnett square.

|  ♂ GAMETES | X | Y |
|---|---|---|
| **♀ GAMETES** | | |
| X | XX (female) | XY (male) |
| X | XX (female) | XY (male) |

Theoretically there should be a 1 : 1 ratio of male : female offspring. In humans various factors can upset the ratio – the Y sperm tend to have greater mobility; the XY zygote and embryo is more delicate than the XX embryo. The balance is just about maintained.

---

Any genes on the X chromosomes will be inherited by both sexes, but whereas the male can only receive **one** of the alleles (he will be XY, and therefore must be **homozygous** for the X-linked allele) the female will be XX and thus may be either **homozygous** or **heterozygous.** This gives females a tremendous genetic advantage since any recessive lethal allele will not be expressed in the heterozygote.

For example, **haemophilia** is an X-linked condition.

Normal gene = H, mutant gene = h

PARENTS    $X^H X^h$        ×        $X^H Y$
female, carrier        male, normal

i.e. **both parents have normal phenotype ...**

GAMETES    $X^H$  $X^h$        $X^H$  Y

F₁ OFFSPRING

| ♀ GAMETES / ♂ GAMETES | $X^H$ | Y |
|---|---|---|
| $X^H$ | $X^H X^H$ | $X^H Y$ |
| $X^h$ | $X^H X^h$ | $X^h Y$ |

ie.
$X^H X^H$ normal, female
$X^H X^h$ carrier, female
$X^H Y$ normal, male
$X^h Y$ haemophiliac, male

**... but may have a haemophiliac son.**

**Other significant X-linked conditions** include **Duchenne muscular dystrophy, red-green colour blindness** and **coat colour in cats** (where the alleles for ginger (G) and black (g) produce tortoiseshell in the heterozygote $X^G X^g$: thus there should, in theory, be **no male tortoiseshell cats!**

---

Any genes carried on the Y chromosome will be received by **all** the male offspring – there is little space for other than sex genes, but one well-known example concerns **webbed toes.**

$X Y^W$    ×    $X X$
only Y chromosome carries W gene

GAMETES    X  $Y^W$        X  X

OFFSPRING    $X Y^W$    $X Y^W$        X X    X X    X X
<u>males with webbed toes</u>    <u>normal females</u>

# Dihybrid inheritance involves

the transmission of **two pairs of alleles** at the same time but independently of one another.

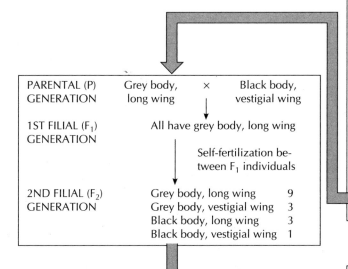

| PARENTAL (P) GENERATION | Grey body, long wing | × | Black body, vestigial wing |
|---|---|---|---|

| 1ST FILIAL (F$_1$) GENERATION | All have grey body, long wing |
|---|---|

Self-fertilization between F$_1$ individuals

| 2ND FILIAL (F$_2$) GENERATION | Grey body, long wing | 9 |
|---|---|---|
| | Grey body, vestigial wing | 3 |
| | Black body, long wing | 3 |
| | Black body, vestigial wing | 1 |

A phenotypic ratio of 9:3:3:1 would seem to be complex, but Mendel explained this as **two separate monohybrid crosses** (i.e. **grey v. black** and **long v. vestigial) occurring at the same time.**

ie.　　GREY v. BLACK　　　= (9+3) : (3+1)
　　　　　　　　　　　　　 = 12 : 4
　　　　　　　　　　　　　 = 3 : 1

　　　　LONG v. VESTIGIAL　= (9+3) : (3+1)
　　　　　　　　　　　　　 = 12 : 4
　　　　　　　　　　　　　 = 3 : 1

i.e. 9 : 3 : 3 : 1 is the same as 3 : 1 x 3 : 1

Thus the inheritance of **body colour** had not influenced the inheritance of **wing shape**.

## Mendel's Second Law (the law of independent assortment)

'Each member of a pair of alleles may combine randomly with either of another pair'

In this example, the allele for **grey** body may combine equally often with the allele for **long** wing or with the allele for **vestigial** wing.

## Using genetic symbols

Let G = grey, g = black, L = long, l = vestigial

P　　　　　　　G G L L　　×　　g g l l

Gametes　　　(GL)　　　　　(gl)

F$_1$　　　　　　　　　　G g L l

Gametes　　　(GL)　(Gl)　(gL)　(gl)

These will be produced in equal numbers, according to Mendel's Second Law.

F$_2$　　　The possible combinations of gametes are most easily derived using a **Punnett square.**

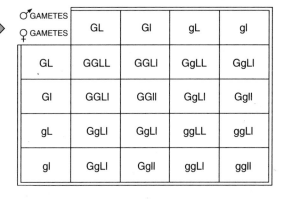

| ♂ GAMETES ＼ ♀ GAMETES | GL | Gl | gL | gl |
|---|---|---|---|---|
| GL | GGLL | GGLl | GgLL | GgLl |
| Gl | GGLl | GGll | GgLl | Ggll |
| gL | GgLL | GgLl | ggLL | ggLl |
| gl | GgLl | Ggll | ggLl | ggll |

or, phenotpically
9 GREY BODY, LONG WING (both G and L in zygote)
3 GREY BODY, VESTIGIAL WING (G and ll in zygote)
3 BLACK BODY, LONG WING (gg and L in zygote)
1 BLACK BODY, VESTIGIAL WING (ggll in zygote)

# Variation is the basis of evolution.

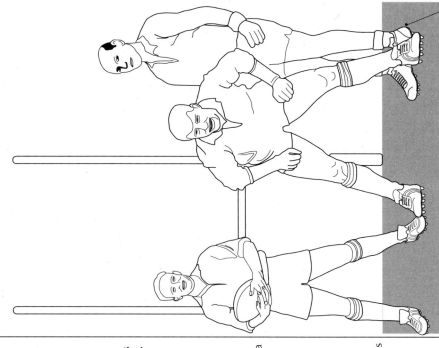

## Discontinuous variation

**Discontinuous variation** occurs when a characteristic is either present or absent (the two extremes) and there are no intermediate forms.

Such variations do not give normal distribution curves but bar charts are often used to illustrate the distribution of a particular characteristic in a population.

Examples are human blood groups in the ABO system (O, A, B or AB), basic fingerprint forms (loop, whorl or arch) and tongue-rolling (can or cannot).

A characteristic which shows discontinuous variation is normally controlled by a single gene – there may be two or more alleles of this gene.

(Bar chart: NUMBER IN GROUP vs BLOOD GROUP — O, A, B, AB)

## Continuous variation

**Continuous variation** occurs when there is a gradation between one extreme and the other of some given characteristic – all individuals exhibit the characteristic but to differing extents.

If a frequency distribution is plotted for such a characteristic a **normal** or **Gaussian distribution** is obtained.

The **mean** is the average number of such a group (i.e. the total number of individuals divided by the number of groups), the **mode** is the most common of the groups and the **median** is the central value of a set of values.

Typical examples are height, mass, handspan, or number of leaves on a plant.

Characteristics which show continuous variation are controlled by the combined effect of a number of genes, called **polygenes**, and are therefore **polygenic characteristics.**

(Histogram: NUMBER IN GROUP vs SIZE/cm — 150, 155, 160, 165, 170, 175, 180, 185)

## Sexual or genetic recombination

**Sexual or genetic recombination** is a most potent force in evolution, since it reshuffles genes into new combinations. It may involve

**free assortment** in gamete formation
**crossing over** during meiosis
**random fusion** during zygote formation.

## Origins of variation

May be **non-heritable** (e.g. sunburn in a light-skinned individual) or **heritable** (e.g. skin colour in different races). The second type, which result from genetic changes, are the most significant in evolution.

**Mutation** is any change in the structure or the amount of DNA in an organism.

A **gene** or **point mutation** occurs at a single locus on a chromosome – most commonly by **deletion, addition** or **substitution** of a nucleotide base. Examples are sickle cell anaemia, phenylketonuria and cystic fibrosis.

A **change in chromosome structure** occurs when a substantial portion of a chromosome is altered. For example, Cri-du-chat syndrome results from **deletion** of a part of human chromosome 5, and a form of white blood cell cancer follows **translocation** of a portion of chromosome 8 to chromosome 14.

**Aneuploidy** (typically the **loss or gain of a single chromosome**) results from **non-disjunction** in which chromosomes fail to separate at anaphase of meiosis. The best known examples are Down's syndrome (extra chromosome 21), Klinefelter's syndrome (male with extra X chromosome) and Turner's syndrome (female with one fewer X chromosome).

**Polyploidy** (the presence of additional **whole sets of chromosomes**) most commonly occurs when one or both gametes is diploid, forming a polyploid on fertilization. Polyploidy is rare in animals, but there are many important examples in plants, e.g. bananas are triploid, and tetraploid tomatoes are larger and richer in vitamin C.

# Natural selection may be a potent force in *evolution.*

Much variation is of the ***continuous type***, i.e. a range of phenotypes exists between two extremes. The range of phenotypes within the environment will typically show a ***normal distribution.***

PHENOTYPIC CLASSES

---

Plants and animals in Nature produce more offspring than can possibly survive, yet the population remains relatively constant. There must be many deaths in Nature.

Overproduction of this type leads to ***competition*** – for food, shelter and breeding sites, for example. There is thus a ***struggle for existence.*** Those factors in the environment for which competition occurs represent ***selection pressures.***

Within a population of individuals there may be considerable ***variation*** in genotype and thus in phenotype.

Variation means that some individuals possess characteristics which would be advantageous in the struggle for existence (and some would be the opposite, of course).

Those possessing the best combination of characteristics would be more competitive in the struggle for existence: they would be more 'fit' to cope with the selection pressures imposed by the environment. This is ***natural selection*** and promotes ***survival of the fittest.***

If variation is ***heritable*** (i.e. caused by an alteration in genotype) new generations will tend to contain a higher proportion of individuals suited to survival.

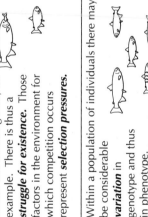

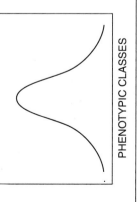

---

The modern ***neo-Darwinian*** theory accepts that:

1. Some harmful alleles may survive, but the reproductive potential of the individual possessing such an allele will be reduced.

2. Selective advantages and disadvantages of an allele relate to one environment at one particular time, i.e. an allele does not always contribute to 'fitness' but only under certain conditions.

---

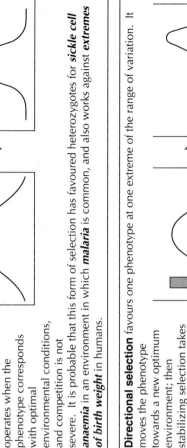

**Stabilizing selection** favours intermediate phenotypic classes and operates against extreme forms – there is thus a **decrease** in the frequency of alleles representing the extreme forms.

Stabilizing selection operates when the phenotype corresponds with optimal environmental conditions, and competition is not severe. It is probable that this form of selection has favoured heterozygotes for ***sickle cell anaemia*** in an environment in which ***malaria*** is common, and also works against ***extremes of birth weight*** in humans.

**Directional selection** favours one phenotype at one extreme of the range of variation. It moves the phenotype towards a new optimum environment; then stabilizing selection takes over. There is a change in the allele frequencies corresponding to the new phenotype.

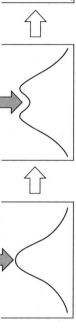

Directional selection has occurred in the case of the peppered moth, *Biston betularia*, where the dark form was favoured in the sooty suburban environments of Britain during the industrial revolution: ***industrial melanism.*** Another significant example is the development of ***antibiotic resistance*** in populations of bacteria – mutant genes confer an advantage in the presence of an antibiotic.

**Disruptive selection** is the rarest form of selection and is associated with a variety of selection pressures operating within one environment.

This form of selection promotes the co-existence of more than one phenotype, the condition of ***polymorphism (balanced*** polymorphism when no one selective agent is more important than any other). Important examples are:
1. ***Colour*** (yellow/brown) and ***banding pattern*** (from 0–5) in *Capaea nemoralis.*
2. ***Three phenotypes*** (corresponding to $HbHb/HbHb^S/Hb^SHb^S$) show an uneven distribution of the sickle-cell allele in different areas of the world.

# Artificial selection occurs when

humans, rather than environmental factors, determine which genotypes will pass to successive generations.

## INBREEDING AND OUTBREEDING

**Outbreeding** occurs when there is selective controlled reproduction between members of genetically distant populations (different strains or even, for plants, closely related but different species).

**Inbreeding** occurs when there is selective reproduction between closely related individuals, e.g. between offspring of same litter or between parent and child.

Tends to **introduce new and superior phenotypes**: the progeny are known as **hybrids** and the development of improved characteristics is called **heterosis** or **hybrid vigour.**

e.g. introduction of disease resistance from wild sheep to domestic strains;
combination of shorter-stemmed 'wild' wheat and heavy yielding 'domestic' wheat.

This may result from increased numbers of dominant alleles or from new opportunities for gene interaction.

Tends to **maintain desirable characteristics**

e.g. uniform height in maize (easier mechanical harvesting);
maximum oil content of linseed (more economical extraction);
milk production by Jersey cows (high cream content).

But it may cause **reduced fertility** and **lowered disease resistance** as genetic variation is reduced.

Thus inbreeding is not favoured by animal breeders.

## TECHNIQUES WITH ANIMALS are less well

advanced than those with plants because:

a animals have a longer generation time and few offspring
b more food will be made available from improved plants
c there are many ethical problems which limit genetic experiments with animals.

Two important animal techniques are:

**Artificial insemination:** allows sperm from a male with desirable characteristics to fertilize a number of female animals.

**Embryo transplantation:** allows the use of **surrogate mothers** (thus increasing number of offspring) and **cloning** (production of many identical animals with the desired characteristics).

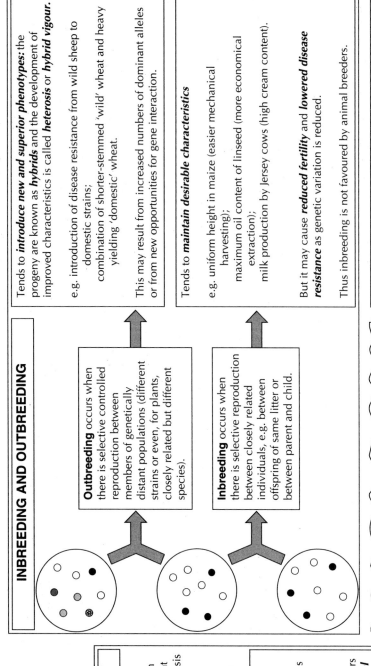

**PROTOPLAST FUSION** is a modern method for production of hybrids in plants.

CELL SUSPENSION OF PLANT A

CELL SUSPENSION OF PLANT B

CELL WALLS REMOVED BY ENZYMES

FUSION OF PROTOPLASTS

HYBRID

e.g. production of virus-resistant tobacco.

## POLYPLOIDY AND PLANT BREEDING

**Polyploids** contain **multiple sets of chromosomes** (chromosome multiplication can be induced by treatment with **colchicine** during mitosis – this inhibits spindle formation and prevents chromatid separation).

**Autopolyploids** (all chromosomes from the **same** species) e.g. all **bananas** are **triploid** – they are infertile and contain no seeds. Most **potatoes** are **tetraploid** – cells are bigger and tubers are larger. Cultivated **strawberries** are **octoploid.**

**Allopolyploidy** (sets of chromosomes from **different** species) is possible if the two species have a chromosome complement similar in number and shape. This might allow plant breeders to **combine the beneficial characteristics of more than one species.**

The evolution of **bread wheat** is an important example.

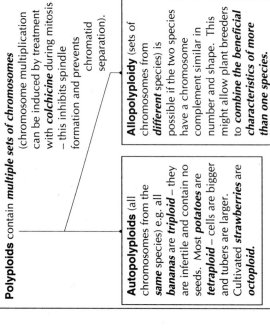

Wild wheat: has brittle ears which fall off on harvesting.

SELECTIVE BREEDING

Einkorn wheat: non-brittle but low yielding.

POLYPLOIDY with *Agropyron* grass

Emmer wheat: high yielding but difficult to separate seed during threshing.

POLYPLOIDY with *Aegilops* grass

Bread wheat: high yielding with easily separated 'naked' seeds.

# Reproductive isolation and speciation

Reproductive isolation is essential for speciation: **allopatric speciation** occurs when populations occupy different environments; **sympatric speciation** occurs when populations are reproductively isolated within the same environment.

**Geographical isolation** takes place when two populations occupy two different environments which are separated by some physical barrier, such as a mountain range, a river or even a road system;
e.g. eastern and western races of the golden-mantled rosella, an Australian parakeet.

**Mechanical isolation** takes place when the reproductive structures are physically incompatible,
e.g. a Great Dane will not mate with a Chihuahua, and some flower species cannot be entered by the same pollinating insect.

**Temporal isolation** takes place when two or more species or populations live within the same area but are reproductively active at different times,
e.g. American frog species.

REPRODUCTIVE ACTIVITY

WOOD FROG   TREE FROG   BULL FROG

APRIL   MAY   JUNE   JULY

TIME

**Behavioural isolation** takes place when two different species or populations evolve courtship displays which are essential for successful mating.
e.g. Peahen is only stimulated to mate by peacock's visual courtship display; fireflies' flight patterns and flash displays prevent interspecific mating.

BLEEP

FLASH

**Ecological isolation** takes place when two species or populations occupy different habitats within the same environment.
e.g. Marbled cat and Asiatic Golden cat may occupy the same forest, but the former is almost completely arboreal, while the latter hunts deer and rodents on the forest floor.

The above **prezygotic isolating mechanisms** will normally prevent the formation of any hybrid zygote. **If** a hybrid zygote is formed (for example when temporal isolation is upset by climatic fluctuation), **post-zygotic isolating systems**, which affect the development or reproductive ability of the hybrid, will come into play.

**Hybrid inviability:** hybrids die before reproduction.
**Hybrid infertility:** hybrids do not produce viable genes.
**Hybrid breakdown:** second or later generations are infertile or inviable.

A species is
'the lowest taxonomic group'
'a group of organisms which can interbreed and produce fertile offspring'
'a group of organisms which share the same ecological niche'

**Allopolyploidy** may produce fertile hybrids **between two different species** – the hybrid species may combine characteristics of both parent species.

## Summary

| | | |
|---|---|---|
| **INTRASPECIFIC SPECIATION:** | Variation within single species | REPRODUCTIVE ISOLATION → Several new species |
| **INTERSPECIFIC SPECIATION:** | Species A ⟍ Species B ⟋ | HYBRIDIZATION → Species C |

# Gene cloning

involves *recombination*, *transformation* and *selection*.

**Donor DNA,** e.g. a human gene. This may have been extracted from a *genome library*, been manufactured from messenger RNA using *reverse transcriptase* or, very rarely, synthesized in an *automatic polynucleotide synthesizer.*

REGULATORY GENE

STRUCTURAL GENE

BACTERIAL REGULATORY GENE

**Human regulatory gene** has been replaced by a *bacterial regulator*. This will ensure a high rate of transcription and of the synthesis of gene product in a bacterial system.

**'Sticky ends'** have been added to the donor DNA. These are short nucleotide sequences (3–6 bases long) which will locate complementary sequences in the recipient plasmid DNA. For example, the 'sticky end' AGCT must be added to locate the complementary 'sticky end' TCGA on the opened recipient plasmid.

GENE FOR ANTIBIOTIC RESISTANCE

**Recipient DNA,** typically a bacterial plasmid, has been 'opened' at the sequence complementary to the donor DNA sticky ends by a specific *restriction endonuclease.* The recipient plasmid also contains a gene which confers resistance to a particular antibiotic. This is vital for the selection process which will occur later.

The donor DNA is now attached to the open plasmid using the enzyme *DNA ligase.*

Complementary 'sticky ends' overlap

The resulting **recombinant DNA** typically carries a human gene within a plasmid: it is then called a *plasmid vector.*

The recipient bacterial cell, typically a non-pathogenic species such as *E. coli,* is treated with $Ca^{2+}$ ions to make it 'leaky'. Such a cell may take up the plasmid vector. The incubation mixture contains few plasmids per cell to encourage uptake of single plasmids, but usually only about 1% of the *E. coli* cells will be *transformed* in this way.

BACTERIAL CHROMOSOME

Growth in culture medium containing antibiotic.

**Transformed cells** are *selected*: these cells must now be cloned and then incubated in conditions which favour synthesis and secretion of the desired human gene product.

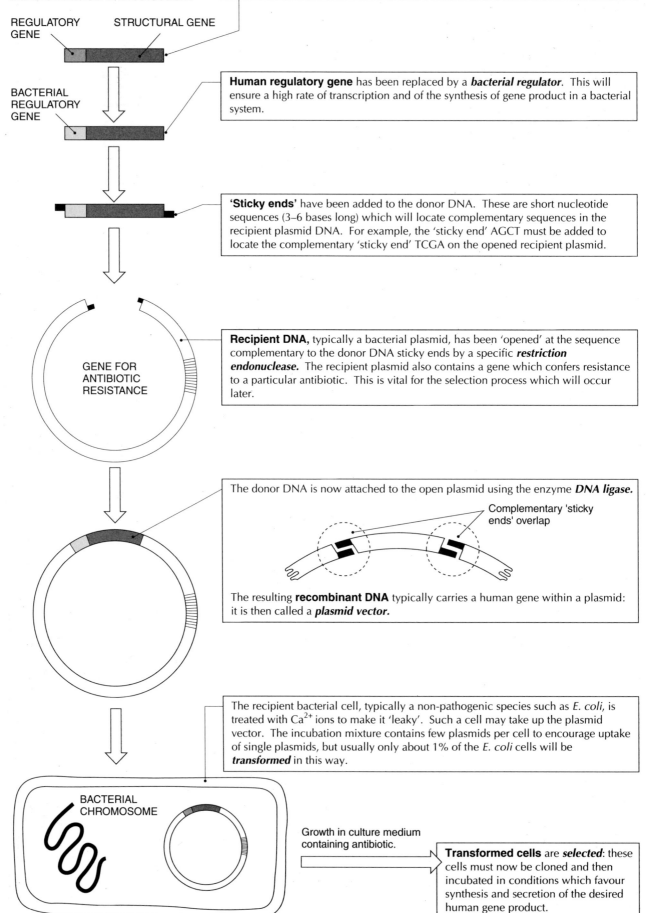

# Enzymes and genetic engineering

**Restriction endonucleases** recognize specific nucleotide sequences in DNA and cut both strands of the double helix at those points. In this example the endonuclease called HindIII recognises the four base sequence AGCT.

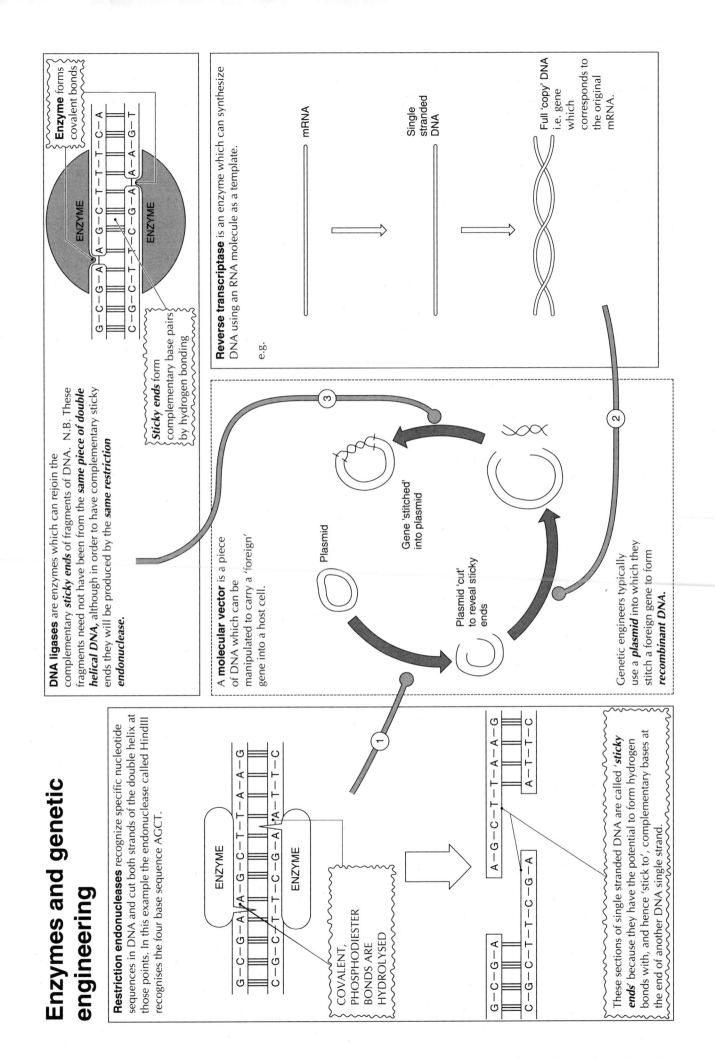

**ENZYME**

```
G – C – G – A │ A – G – C – T – T – A – A – G
C – G – C – T – T – C – G – A │ A – T – T – C
```

**ENZYME**

COVALENT, PHOSPHODIESTER BONDS ARE HYDROLYSED

```
G – C – G – A          A – G – C – T – T – A – A – G
C – G – C – T – T – C – G – A          A – T – T – C
```

These sections of single stranded DNA are called '*sticky ends*' because they have the potential to form hydrogen bonds with, and hence 'stick to', complementary bases at the end of another DNA single strand.

**DNA ligases** are enzymes which can rejoin the complementary *sticky ends* of fragments of DNA. N.B. These fragments need not have been from the *same piece of double helical DNA*, although in order to have complementary sticky ends they will be produced by the *same restriction endonuclease.*

**Enzyme** forms covalent bonds

```
G – C – G – A   A – G – C – T – T – C – A
C – G – C – T   C – G – A – A – G – T
```

**ENZYME**

**ENZYME**

*Sticky ends* form complementary base pairs by hydrogen bonding

**Reverse transcriptase** is an enzyme which can synthesize DNA using an RNA molecule as a template.

e.g.

mRNA

Single stranded DNA

Full 'copy' DNA i.e. gene which corresponds to the original mRNA.

A **molecular vector** is a piece of DNA which can be manipulated to carry a 'foreign' gene into a host cell.

Plasmid

Plasmid 'cut' to reveal sticky ends

Gene 'stitched' into plasmid

Genetic engineers typically use a *plasmid* into which they stitch a foreign gene to form *recombinant DNA.*

① ② ③

# INDEX

Penis   104
Peptide bond   19
Peroxidase   24
Peroxisome   11
Pest   64, 65
Pesticide   64
Petals   48, 49
pH   22, 59
Phagocytosis   90
Phenylketonuria   116
Phloem   32, 34, 39, 40
Photosynthesis   56, 58
Phototropism   32, 47
Phospholipid   10
Phosphate   38, 63
Phosphoglyceraldehyde   25, 36
Phosphoglycerate   25, 36
Phosphorylation, oxidative   25, 27, 29
Photolysis   35
Photosystem   35
Phytochrome   19
Pili   14
Placenta   108
Plasmids   14, 124
Plasmodesmata   12
Plasmolysis   43
Pleated sheet (beta-pleated sheet)   18
Pleural membranes   71, 73
Pollen   48, 49
Polymorphism   114
Polyploidy   120, 122, 123
Population   51, 65
Porphyrin   26
Potassium   44
Potometer   47
Pressure potential   42, 43
Primary production net   52, 53
   gross   52, 53
Producer   52, 53, 54
Progesterone   95, 107
Prophase   112, 113
Prostate gland   104
Protein   66, 68, 94
Proton   28
   gradient   28, 35
Protoplast fusion   122
Pulmonary artery and vein   71, 72
Punnett square   116, 117, 118, 119
Purine   26, 30
Putrefaction   57
Pyramid of biomass, energy, numbers   54
Pyrimidine   26, 30
Pyruvate   25, 26, 27

## R

Receptacle   48
Receptor   83, 92, 93
Resolution   5, 6, 93
Respiration   25, 26, 27, 52, 56, 70
Resting potential   98
Retina   92, 93
Reverse transcriptase   124, 125
Rhodopsin   19, 93
Ribosomal RNA   31, 110, 111

Ribosomes   11, 13, 14, 31
Ribs   71, 73
Ribulose bis phosphate   16, 36
Rod   93
Root hair   39

## S

Sarcomere   103
Sclerenchyma   34
Scrotum   104
Scrubber   59
Schwann cell   96
Seed   50
Selection, artificial   122
   directional, disruptive, natural, stabilizing   121
Semen   104
Seminal vesicles   104
Sensitivity   93
Sepals   48, 49
Sere   55
Sex determination   118
   linkage   118,
   hormones   95, 107,
   organs   104, 106
Sinusoid   87
Skin and temperature control   88
Solute potential   42, 43
Speciation, inter- and intraspecific   123
Species   61, 123
Spectrum, absorption and action   37
Sperm   105
Spinal cord   97
Spirometer   74
Spongy mesophyll   32
Sporophyte   50
Staining   5, 6
Stamen   49
Starch   17, 20, 66, 68
Steroid   15, 26, 94
Stigma   48, 49
Stimulus   83, 84, 97
Stomach   67, 68
Stomata   32, 44
Stratosphere   60
Stroma   37
Style   48, 49
Succession   55
Sucrose   16
Sulphur dioxide   59
Sweating   88
Symplast   46
Synapse   97, 99
Synecology   51
Synovial fluid   8, 101
   joint   101
   membrane   101

## T

Telophase   112, 113
Tendon   102
Tension   46
Termination   111

Testis   94, 95, 104
Testosterone   94, 95
Threshold value   98
Thylakoid   37
Thymine   30, 31
Thyroxine   81, 87, 88, 94, 95
Trachea   71
Tracheole   70
Transamination   33, 57, 87
Transcription   31, 110, 111
Transfer RNA   31, 110, 111
Translation   110, 111
Translocation   40
Transpiration stream   8
Triceps   102
Triglyceraldehyde   15
Trisomy   115
Trophic level   52, 53
Troposphere   60
Turgor pressure   8

## U

Ultraviolet radiation   60
Uracil   31
Urea   29, 87
Urine   85, 86
Uterus   106

## V

Vacuole   12
Vagina   106
Vagus nerve   81
Variation, continuous and discontinuous   120, 121
Vas deferens   104
Vasoconstriction   86, 88
Vasodilation   88
Vesicle   11
Vitamins   66, 87

## W

Water potential   9, 42, 43, 46
Wheat   122
White matter   97

## X

Xanthophyll   37
Xylem   32, 34, 39, 46